WD

Easton

The UK Food and Drink Industry

A sector by sector
economic and
statistical analysis

The UK Food and Drink Industry

A sector by sector economic and statistical analysis

Editors

John Strak and Wyn Morgan

Sponsors

Booker plc

Geest plc

Market Taskforce, MAFF

Northern Foods plc

Safeway plc

*Euro*PA
& Associates

Whilst every care has been taken to ensure that the statistical information in this book is accurate the publishers accept no responsibility for any errors or omissions and readers are recommended to check the information against current published accounts and sources.

Foreword

The food and drink industry is of special interest because it is part of the manufacturing sector, but is also closely connected with agriculture, on the one hand, and retailing, on the other. As such it is of special importance to the consumer, but it is also significant because of the employment it provides, both directly and indirectly. Despite its value to the economy, and the large number of interesting problems that it introduces, economists have perhaps paid less attention to it than it deserves. Even within academic courses concerned with applied economics it plays only a peripheral part. Almost certainly, one reason for this is a paucity of research literature which would make it accessible to students, and, for that matter to the interested lay reader and academic too.

The purpose of this excellent volume is to fill that gap. It provides a broad ranging and up-to-date view of the industry within a serious economics context. The chapters are noteworthy for their completeness and clarity and the combination of academic and industry expert views. Chapters One and Two, offering, respectively, an overview of the industry and an exposition of the economic theory which is most relevant to it, are particularly helpful. The individual sector Chapters (Three to Nine) are complete in themselves, and are based on comprehensive and current data. Taking all of the contributions together the book provides a first class perspective on the UK food and drink industry for students, analysts, practitioners and policy makers.

The Lord Peston and The Lord Carter
House of Lords

Contents

Foreword

Glossary

Preface

Glossary of Terms

ABU	Alcohol by Volume
ACP	African, Caribbean, Pacific
AGB	Auditors of Great Britain
BSE	Bovine Spongiform Encephalopathy
CAP	Common Agricultural Policy
CBEA	Caribbean Bananas Exporters Association
CATFI	Common Approach to Financial Information
CEEC	Central and Eastern European Countries
CSO	Central Statistical Office
cif	cost, insurance, freight
DAFS	Department of Agriculture and Fisheries, Scotland
DANI	Department of Agriculture Northern Ireland
dcw	dead carcase weight
DG VI	Directorate General for Agriculture (EC)
DTF	Dairy Trade Federation
DTI	Department of Trade and Industry (UK)
ECU	European Currency Unit
EEC	European Economic Community
EU	European Union
FAO	(UN) Food and Agriculture Organisation
FDF	Food and Drink Federation
fob	free on board
FP	Food Processing Industries
GAP	Gross Agricultural Product
GATT	General Agreement on Tariffs and Trade
GDP	Gross Domestic Product
HGCA	Home Grown Cereals Authority
HL	Hectolitres
HLCA	Hill Livestock Compensatory Allowance
HoC	House of Commons
HoL	House of Lords
LPA	Litres of Pure Alcohol
MAFF	Ministry of Agriculture Fisheries and Food (UK)
MCA	Monetary Compensatory Amount
MLC	Meat and Livestock Commission
MMB	Milk Marketing Board
MMC	Monopolies and Mergers Commission
NABIM	National Association of British and Irish Millers
NFS	National Food Survey
NPQH	Non-producing Quota Holders
OECD	Organisation for Economic Co-operation and Development
OFT	Office of Fair Trading (UK)
PA	Pure Alcohol
PC	Personal Computer
PMB	Potato Marketing Board
R&D	Research and Development
ROCE	Return on Capital Employed
SIC	Standard Industrial Classification
SMP	Skimmed Milk Powder
SWA	Scotch Whisky Association
USDA	United States Department of Agriculture
USTR	United States Trade Representative
UK	United Kingdom
WMP	Whole Milk Powder
WSE	White Sugar Equivalent
WTO	World Trade Organisation

Preface

This book aims to provide a comprehensive description, and some preliminary analysis, of the links between raw material production and the sectoral components of the food and drink manufacturing sector. These links are described by the general term, "the UK food chain". Chapter Two is mainly concerned with a presentation of economic theory that is relevant to the food industry but also presents some general analysis of the UK food and drink sector. The subsequent sector chapters include up-to-date descriptions of; supply and demand at raw material and product level, the institutions involved in the UK food and drink industry, and analyses of the structure, conduct and performance of food and drink companies. Thus, the book covers the availability of raw materials and food processing capacity and the economics of the food industry which, in turn, should reflect the demands of the modern consumer.

These aims are ambitious because the food chain in a modern society is complex, dynamic, and poorly described by publicly available data. With these constraints in mind we have drawn on the skills of a number of industry experts and academics who, in turn, have used their trade sources for information and made extensive reference to industry studies produced by trade associations or market research companies. The brief for this team has assumed that the food and drink processing industry is the focal point of food production and food demand decisions. This seems axiomatic. Food processors have farmers and retailers as their customers, therefore they must look up and down the food chain and, if they are to remain in business, they should accurately reflect and transmit the demands of the marketplace.

In order to perform this task of market linkage successfully the food and drink industry must be able to deal with several elements. It needs to be innovative and able to adopt technological change. It takes raw material produced by the farmer (often from widely distributed sources and varying qualities) and transforms it using sophisticated technology and packaging facilities into the final food product which the consumer recognises and purchases. It is the key link in the market system by which consumer preferences for food and resource allocation decisions of investors are dealt with. It is also a medium for the regulations that Governments wish to impose on farmers, processors and retailers. Finally, as in most countries, the food and drink industry in the UK is a source of significant employment and it contains some very large, global scale, companies. Hence, labour and capital use are important dimensions.

With this list of attributes a book on the UK food and drink industry might seem to be an impossible task. The framework of analysis apparently has to embrace - technology, logistics, raw materials, consumer demand and lifestyles, regulatory effects, market structure and power, etc. Any one of these various areas could provide enough material for a book. Our decision has been to focus on two key aspects of the industry and to use a commodity-based structure for the chapters. The first aspect is relatively straightforward in that we wished to provide an economic and statistical "snapshot" of the whole sector as it stands in 1995. Too often researchers, analysts, students and industry specialists are left with little data or partial information on which to make decisions, or try and solve problems with inadequate sources with resulting inconsistencies in data. Hence, this books seeks not only to provide a statistical update of what is happening in the food manufacturing sector and also aims to give a comprehensive coverage of all the major sub-sectors within one book.

Our second aim is to give a structure to the material in a form that lends itself to further analysis. We have tried to deal with the "economics" of the food and drink manufacturing sector in the structure-conduct-performance paradigm used in most analyses of industrial organisation. This gives a context for the data shown and gives an indication of the manner in which the various sub-sectors have evolved over time. At times, we readily admit, this has led the book's content in the direction of financial analysis rather than economic analysis. Both methodologies, and the structure-conduct-performance paradigm, have their limitations. Nevertheless, we believe the book provides an informed view of the individual sectors to those who are interested in getting a clear picture of the overall structure of the food manufacturing sector, and secondly it stands as a useful precursor or catalyst for further work.

In attempting to cover all food and drink categories in the industry there are bound to be several omissions and these must be admitted here. In the first-stage sectoral classifications, the fish processing sector is omitted, as is the egg sector. Lack of time and data precluded close examination of the catering sector, bread and cakes, and food ingredients. Dealing comprehensively with the further-processed and branded goods sector has generally been difficult because it changes rapidly and data sources are the weakest for second and third stage transformed products. Regulatory influences are also important for the food and drink industry. The book mentions a number of these but really deals in depth only with the agricultural and trade policy aspects. Thus, we list the regulatory areas e.g. health and nutrition, labelling, residues and additives, competition policy, branding and look-a-likes, packaging and the environment, and so forth, but do not present analyses of their effects. These will have to wait for another day.

Our intention when editing and producing the book has been that it could be read from start to finish or used as a reference tool with selective reading throughout. We hope that our footnotes and Indexes assist readers whichever style of use is chosen. Our overview in Chapter One is a reference point from which readers can dip into the chapters on food sectors they are interested in and it sets the scene for the theory in Chapter Two. In Chapters Three to Nine, with the major food groups, we have mixed two ingredients - the industry specialist and the academic. The former provides the insight into a particular sector whilst the latter contributes the theoretician's view of the development of the sectors and the policy background. We feel that this is a productive combination as it meshes commercial experience with the rigor of the academic. Nevertheless, it has not been an easy task for the Editors to achieve the right blend and any remaining inconsistencies of style or approach are regrettable but perhaps inevitable. The final chapter presents the Editors' views on the important dimensions that will affect the food and drink industry in the future.

Finally but very importantly, our list of thanks and acknowledgements for help in producing this book is a long one. The financial sponsorship of Booker plc, Geest plc, Northern Foods plc, Market Task Force in the MAFF, and Safeway plc is very gratefully acknowledged. Without their underwriting of some of the costs of the book's production it would probably never have been written. British Sugar plc, the Meat and Livestock Commission and the Potato Marketing Board also provided staff time and help with relevant parts of the book. The Food and Drink Federation helped with a large number of queries, as did several market research companies and many trade associations who allowed generous use of their statistics and analyses. In all cases we have attributed the sources we have used and, chapter by chapter we have cited individuals, companies or organisations who have given assistance. We are very grateful to all these individuals and organisations and if any are inadvertently missing from this list or the book's contents we apologise and ask for understanding.

On the production side we would single out for special thanks; Laura Black, Mark Gunthorpe, Nicolas Heslop, Tara Moxham, Emma Ridley, Rosie Simpson, and Fiona Stewart Sandeman for their help and assistance at various key stages in the research and production phases of the book. Thanks are also due to our families for their tolerance and support. Lastly, we must make it clear that any omissions or errors that remain in the text are ours alone, and that no comment or opinion expressed in this book should be viewed as an indicator of the effective or ineffective handling of a business situation in the UK food and drink industry. This last caveat should be borne in mind throughout the book.

John Strak and Wyn Morgan

Chapter 1: Overview of the UK Food and Drink Industry

Christine Ennew, Scott McDonald, Wyn Morgan and John Strak[1]

Introduction

The food industry in the UK plays a vital role in linking the farmer to the food consumer. It is a dynamic and vigorous industry and the development and adoption of new technology and the provision of new products to satisfy consumer demands have played an essential part in its success.......I recognise the valuable contribution that the food industry makes to employment and economic activity in the UK. Overall the farm and food sector in the UK contributes around 9 per cent to GDP and employs around 14 per cent of total jobs. We have some of the largest food companies in Europe and lead the way in chilled food distribution, new product development and the size and scope of our retailing outlets.

Rt Hon Gillian Shephard MP, Minister for Agriculture, Fisheries and Food 1993 - 94

This opening statement by a former Minister for Agriculture in the UK is taken from the Foreword in Hughes (1994) and it neatly summarises the accepted wisdom on the UK food industry. But it is not at all straightforward to demonstrate this wisdom analytically, or to reach conclusions about different hypotheses on the food industry's structure, conduct or performance. Indeed, just presenting the data in a consistent format in one book is a significant task. Nevertheless, this book sets out to provide some clues, from economic theory and up-to-date data, of how the UK food and drink industry is operating in its economic and business environment. This objective requires the reader to give some time to a discussion of definitions and limitations of the statistical data. It also requires the recognition that the method chosen to construct a book on the food and drink industry is one that involves a combination of public and private data, and commercial and academic interests. Importantly, the perspective of the analyses here is an economic and

---

1   Dr Christine Ennew is a Reader in the School of Management and Finance at the University of Nottingham, Dr Scott McDonald is a Lecturer at the Department of Economics, University of Sheffield, Dr Wyn Morgan is a Lecturer in the Department of Economics at the University of Nottingham, Dr John Strak is the Principal at Euro PA & Associates, Cambs.

statistical one. Whilst new product development, technological change, and the logistics of food distribution, for example, are crucial aspects of the food industry they are not dealt with in this book to any degree. Rather this chapter is an introduction to a process of examination which is slanted towards economists, business analysts and policy makers rather than technologists and food scientists and, accordingly, it sets the scene for the rest of the book.

The chapter begins with a brief review of food consumption and consumer lifestyles as they affect demand for the food manufacturing sector's products, and moves on to a discussion of the statistical categorisation of the UK food industry. It then proceeds to give an overview, and some general analyses of the economic components of the sector, in macroeconomic terms. Wherever possible the points made and questions raised are supplemented by appropriate market data that provide a commercial perspective. Theoretical and empirical issues are dealt with more fully in the following chapters but after reading this initial overview, the reader should have an insight into the book's structure, and the background and key aspects of the food and drink industry that need analysis in the subsequent chapters.

Chapter Two deals almost exclusively with the type of theoretical models that are relevant to a study of a modern food manufacturing sector. Chapters Three to Eight deal, respectively, with; cereals and oilseeds, sugar, potato products, dairy products, the meat industry, and fruit and vegetables. This breakdown is, effectively, one that follows an approximate view of first-stage transformation of raw material into food. The second-stage transformation, of intermediate products into "further processed" food products, is covered in Chapter Nine along with branded products and alcoholic drinks. This separation and classification is not perfect by any means but it generally accords with a lay reader's view of the food and drink industry and this familiarity is helpful. In any event, the book's Indexes are intended to help the reader through the structure of the analysis and the various cross references to theoretical and practical issues including different food products and food companies. The final chapter of the book describes the pressures for change that may be on the food industry in the future and presents some ideas for research in a format that goes beyond the traditional "food chain" conceptualisation.

A key impression that the reader should take from this chapter is the possibility of using the food and drink industry as an example of the "frontier" for pure and applied economics. It abounds with potential case study material and difficult data and theory problems for the analyst. The food manufacturing sector is a dynamic and rich economic and business environment for theorists and empiricists alike. When one remembers that regulatory changes are a significant part of the day-today experience of food and drink companies, the interest of institutional or political economists should also be assured. With these declarations made it is left to the reader to appraise the economics and statistics of the UK food and drink industry, sector by sector, in the following pages and chapters.

Food Consumption and Lifestyles

Figures 1.1, 1.2a and 1.2b indicate how consumption patterns and food consumption expenditures are changing in the UK. Detailed and comprehensive analyses of household food consumption and expenditure are presented in the National Food Survey (HMSO, various).

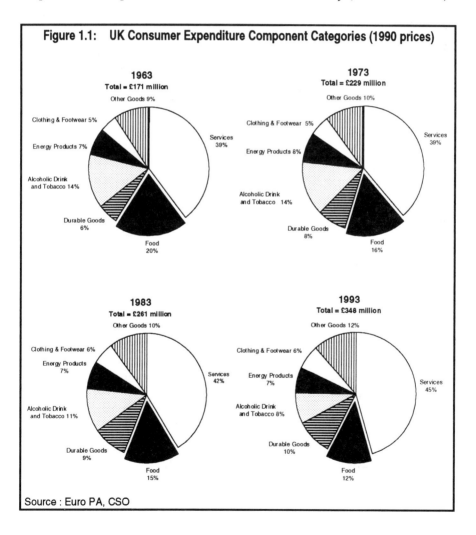

Figure 1.1: UK Consumer Expenditure Component Categories (1990 prices)

Source : Euro PA, CSO

These figures reflect, first, the changing proportion of food expenditure as part of consumers' total expenditure, second, the distribution of expenditure on different product categories, and third, consumers' changing lifestyles and increased demand for "prepared" and "convenience" foods and away-from-home eating. The share of household expenditure on food has fallen from 20% in 1963 to 12% in 1993. Within this total, Figure 1.2a illustrates those categories of food with a declining trend in expenditure since 1980; meat and bacon, milk, dairy products and eggs, oils and fats, tea and coffee. Figure 1.2b shows the winners over the same period i.e. those food categories where consumer expenditure has generally been increasing in real terms; fruit, vegetables, sugar and confectionery, bread and cereals, fish, and other goods.

Figure 1.2a: Growth In Consumers' Expenditure on Food by Sector. Constant (1990) Prices, (Index 1990=100)

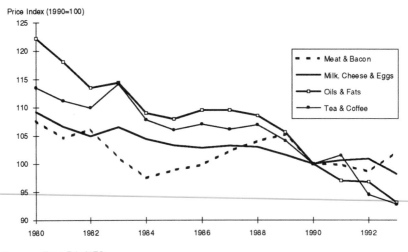

Source : Euro PA, NFS

These general observations must not be taken too far and there are many examples of products within the declining group of foods and food products which have grown in total sales and/or per capita consumption (for instance poultrymeat consumption has increased within the total meat category) Amongst the winners, there are examples of products that have behaved perversely and lost market size. These different patterns of purchase behaviour reflect changes in consumer demand and tastes.

**Figure 1.2b: Growth in Consumers' Expenditure on Food by Sector
Constant (1990) Prices, Index 1990=100**

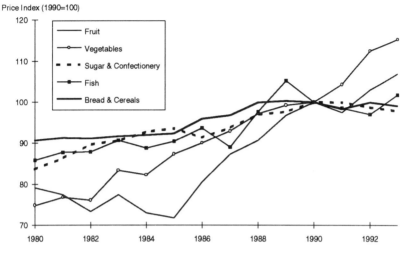

Source : Euro PA, NFS

As social and economic trends have altered - for example the rise in numbers of working women (shown in Figure 1.3) and single parent families, the increasing proportion of elderly people in the population, the rise in per capita disposable income, the decline of "traditional" meal situations in the home, and the recognition of "healthy" foods - so consumption habits have changed. For the food industry these changes have shown themselves through increased demand for fresh and prepared foods, more snack products, increased consumption of food outside the home in catering and take-away outlets (see Figure 1.4), and a general demand for "convenience". This last observation is very important. The food industry's ability to produce and distribute new products that fit consumers' modern lifestyles is a key test of its productivity and competitiveness.

The product development process in the food and drink industry seems to be a never-ending one. In the US 8,000 new food products were introduced in 1993 (Rudolph, 1995). Of these around 80-90% are estimated to have failed within one year of introduction. The implied cost of research, development, sales promotion, etc. of this new product development process is huge.

Figure 1.3:   Female Employment in the UK 1959-1994

Females in Employment (million)

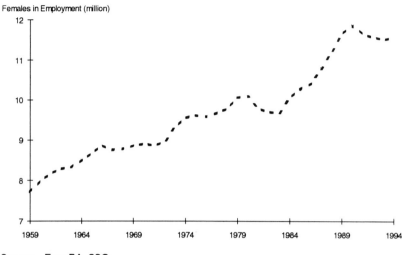

Source: Euro PA, CSO
Note: Figures before 1978 are annual averages, figures after 1978 are for June of each year

Figure 1.4:   Meals Consumed Outside the Home*

Meals Sold (millions)

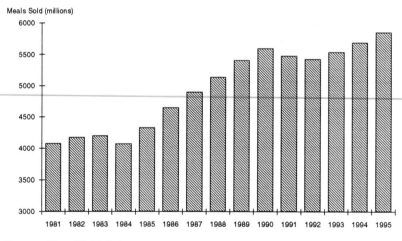

Source :   Euro PA, Marketpower
* Note :   These are meals sold in the private sector: restaurants, pubs, fast food, cafes, travel,
               leisure, etc. Figure for 1994 is an estimate, 1995 is a forecast

The Food and Drink Industry in the UK Economy

Definitions

The food and drink industry is essentially engaged in activities which transform basic agricultural raw materials into a form which is more acceptable or convenient for consumption. This can cover a tremendously wide range of activities which stretch from the very simple e.g. grading, trimming and packing of vegetables, grain milling to produce flour, to the very complicated e.g. combining a range of ingredients to produce chilled microwaveable ready-to-eat meals. Statistically, the food processing industry is typically defined with reference to the Standard Industrial Classification (SIC) system, although five different SICs have been used in the UK since 1945: SIC (1948), (1958), (1968), (1980) and (1992) which can create problems when extended time series of industry specific data are sought.

The basis of a SIC is that enterprises are allocated to industry groups by reference to their 'principal product': thus tables are published in the Censuses of Production (in PA1002 - Summary Tables) which identify the average 'degree of specialisation' for enterprises in that industry group. While for some revisions to the SIC, and for some industries, the changes were not substantial, the revision for SIC (1980) introduced a major change as far as food processing was concerned: 'slaughtering' and associated activities were transferred from a Distribution Service category to a Census of Production category. This, and other substantive SIC changes, are the principal constraints upon using industry specific data prior to 1980.

The Food Processing (FP) industries are part of 'Other Manufacturing Industries' - Division 4, Class 41/42 of SIC (1980). Specifically, the 'Groups' are

- 411 Organic oils and fats
- 412 Slaughtering of animals and production of meat and by-products
- 413 Preparation of milk and milk products
- 414 Processing of fruit and vegetables
- 415 Fish Processing
- 416 Grain milling
- 419 Bread, biscuits and flour confectionery
- 420 Sugar and sugar by-products
- 421 Ice cream, cocoa, chocolate and sugar confectionery
- 422 Animal feeding stuffs
- 423 Starch and miscellaneous foods

A feature of this classification is the inclusion of animal feeding stuffs (422) within the category of food processors. The inclusion of an industry whose output is primarily an intermediate input to agriculture, in a SIC class otherwise composed of industries the destinations of whose outputs are downstream in the food chain is less than ideal. But, since the overwhelming majority of the published aggregate data under the heading of 'Food' includes animal feeding stuffs, it is important to be aware of the animal feeding stuffs industry when considering published aggregate data[2].

A further distinction among food processors (following Grieg, 1971) is arguably useful. It has been suggested that food processors can be categorised on the basis of the characteristics and/or the destinations of their products: thus first-stage processors produce undifferentiated products, with the majority of their output being sold to intermediate demand, whereas second-stage processors produce differentiated products, the majority of which are sold to final demand. This categorisation is imprecise, at the level of aggregation in the published data in the UK, but three food processing groups can be identified that fit this definition of first-stage processors: grain milling (416), sugar and sugar by-products (419), and animal feeding stuffs (422), and a fourth is, a priori, a potential first-stage processor - organic oils & fats (411). This initial breakdown of statistics and the operations of transformation in food manufacturing suggest a structure for this book. Wherever possible, the first-stage processing classification is used to allow easy (recognisable) access to data. Thus a sector by sector approach to the analysis in the book follows from this.

This first-stage/second-stage categorisation of food processors raises a theoretical hypothesis based on the implications of the nature of products for the competitive strategies adopted by first- and second-stage food processors: namely first-stage food processors are more likely to emphasise process innovation, rather than product innovation, in their competitive strategies, whereas second-stage food processors are more likely to emphasise product innovations. This hypothesis may be simplistic through its implicit down grading of the implications of the impact of competition within the food industry, and in particular, the effects of the high degree of apparent market power in the food retailing sector. For instance, the extensive development of own-label branding by the major retail chains may induce large second-stage processors to emphasise process and partnership rather than product or marketing innovations. (McGoldrick, 1984) explores some aspects of this.

The role of the food industry within the UK economy can be examined in a number of different ways. The sector's share in GDP, along with its labour and capital use provide an indicator of the overall importance of the food sector, while an examination of value-added, research, and links

---

2   See Mark and Strange (1993) for a detailed review of Food industry statistical sources.

with other sectors (including its regulatory environment) provides an indication of the extent to which the activities of the food sector will impact upon other related sectors. Each of these areas is examined in turn in the following sections, along with appropriate references to the business environment, in order to provide an overview of the position of the food sector.

Share of GDP

Figure 1.5 : The Food and Drink Industry in Relation to UK Industry in 1993

NATIONAL LEVEL

		Visible Balance of Payments	
Population	58 million	Imports	£134.62 bn
Employees	28 million	Exports	£121.41bn
		Net Visible Balance	-£13.21 bn
GDP	£546 bn	Invisibles Balance	£2.90 bn
		Current Account	-£10.30 bn

INDUSTRY LEVEL

Construction		**Electricity**		**Mining**		**Financial Services**	
GDP	£29.2 bn	GDP	£14.0 bn	GDP	£12.1 bn	GDP	£134.0 bn
Employees	0.83 million	Employees	0.24 million	Employees	0.13 million	Employees	2.79 million

Transport & Communications		**Manufacturing**		**Wholesale and Retail Trade & Catering**		**Other Services**	
GDP	£46.3 bn	GDP	£118.3 bn	GDP	£78.3 bn	GDP	£127.0 bn
Employees	1.36 million	Employees	4.36 million	Employees	4.62 million	Employees	7.05 million

Agriculture, Hunting Forestry & Fishing

GDP	£10.37bn
Employees	0.28 million

AGRICULTURE		**FOOD & DRINK MANUFACTURING**		**TRADE IN FOOD & DRINK**	
Farm Output	£15.0bn	Gross Output	£52.5bn	Food Imports	£14.1bn
Farm Input	£7.4bn	Gross Value Added	£13.7bn	Food Exports	£8.2bn
GAP (GDP)	£7.6bn	Employees	0.48 million	Food Balance	£5.9bn

Consumer Food Expenditure

Total Consumer Expenditure	Household	£70.1bn
£382.2bn	Catering	£34.7bn
	Total	£105.4bn

Source : CSO, Euro PA

Figure 1.5 presents a simplified macroeconomic overview of the food manufacturing sector in the UK economy in 1993. The figures shown for agriculture and food and drink manufacturing in the final section of Figure 1.5 have been extracted from the agriculture and manufacturing categories at the industry level. GAP (in the case of agriculture) and Gross Value-Added (in the case of food and drink manufacturing) are roughly equivalent to contribution to GDP. Thus, food and drink manufacturing constitutes around 12% of all manufacturing contributions to GDP.

Table 1.1 shows that, as might be expected, the share of 'food' processing in GDP has tended to decline, but the share of 'food' in all manufacturing has not declined, which is, arguably, contrary to expectations. However, this perception may be a product of two factors: first, changes in relative prices, and second the relatively poor performance of UK manufacturing in general over recent decades.

Table 1.1:   Contributions to GDP (£m)*3

		1972	1980	1984	1988	1990
1	GDP @ factor cost	55,672	200,517	280,758	401,127	479,452
2	Manufacturing	17,876	52,872	65,975	92,368	105,808
3	Food	1,510	4,696	6,281	8,127	10,114
5	2 as % of 1	32.1	26.4	23.5	23.0	22.1
6	3 as % of 1	2.7	2.3	2.2	2.0	2.1
8	3 as % of 2	8.4	8.9	9.5	8.8	9.6

Source: National Income and Expenditure (various years).
*Contribution before providing for depreciation but after stock appreciation.

The published output volume indices do suggest different patterns of development (Figure 1.6). Food output has expanded less rapidly than GDP, hence the declining importance of food in the economy has been a real change. Manufacturing output and GDP have tended to follow similar paths, but manufacturing output has been subject to greater variations, and declined sharply in the late 1970's and early 1980's.

---

3   Since 1993 the sectoral breakdown published in the National Income and Expenditure has been on the basis of Standard Industrial Classification (SIC) (1992) rather than SIC (1980).

Figure 1.6   Output Volume Indices for GDP, Food and Manufacturing

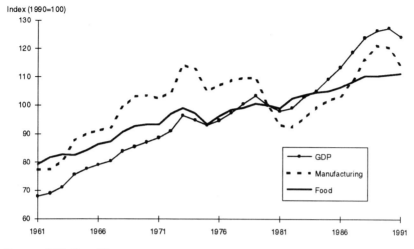

Source : CSO, Euro PA

The decline in the importance of manufacturing in the economy appears to have been a one-off change, and the apparent increase in the importance of food in manufacturing seems to owe more to circumstances impacting upon other manufacturing rather than an enduring structural change.   Furthermore, the output indices suggest that the aggregate demand conditions facing food are appreciably more stable than those facing manufacturing in general, and less prone to variation than the economy as a whole - as would be expected given Engels Law.   This evidence might support the suggestion that *ceteris paribus* profit rates for food processors would be less than those for manufacturing industries in general because of the lower degree of risk associated with a higher degree of demand stability.

Value-Added

The ratio of value-added to gross output for food processors has typically been some two-thirds of the average for manufacturing (Table 1.2).   This implies that per unit of output (in value terms) the services provided by food processors are relatively less than those provided by manufacturing as a whole.   Such an implication would be consistent with a characterisation of food processing, relative to manufacturing in general, as being dominated by bulk processing activities and the hypothesis that food processors are geared more towards processes than products.

Table 1.2 :   Value-Added as a Percentage of Gross Output

		1980	1984	1988	1991
411	Organic oils and fats	12.7	12.3	15.6	13.7
412	Slaughtering of animals and production of meat and by-products	20.7	19.1	20.8	22.2
413	Preparation of milk and milk products	17.9	18.6	17.5	19.3
414	Processing of fruit and vegetables	23.4	22.7	25.4	29.1
415	Fish Processing	23.9	26.7	22.0	21.7
416	Grain milling	13.8	13.0	15.1	20.4
419	Bread, biscuits and flour confectionery	36.9	37.2	38.5	40.9
420	Sugar and sugar by-products	24.4	18.9	21.1	21.6
421	Ice cream, cocoa, chocolate and sugar confectionery	29.5	28.8	32.7	32.9
422	Animal feeding stuffs	14.4	13.9	17.0	15.5
423	Starch and miscellaneous foods	30.6	28.9	32.5	33.3
	Food Processors	23.0	22.5	24.7	26.3
	All Manufacturing*	34.9	33.9	35.3	34.2

Source: Census of Production (various years).
* All Manufacturing includes Food Processors

This image of the food industry would suggest that the rate of value-added to gross output should be lower for first-stage than second-stage food processors, since the former would be even more process orientated. The ratios of value-added for each of the three first-stage processors are, with the exception of sugar in 1980, constantly below the average for food processing as a whole. If this was the sole criterion for distinguishing between first and second-stage processors the evidence would indicate that Oils & Fats and Milk should be categorised as first-stage processors.

Considered from the perspective of value-added per employee, food processors have had a mixed performance. Some sectors appear to have been as productive as general manufacturing during the 1980's whilst other have been less productive (Table 1.3). But the figures and averages probably conceal great variation as individual products and product groups have changed at widely differing rates. Note also that in the recent UK Government report on UK Competitiveness (p 33, DTI, 1995) the UK food and drink industry is reported to have higher productivity (on an output per hour worked basis) than the German food and drink industry, and was the only UK manufacturing sector to have this positive differential.

It would appear that the rate of value-added per employee has been lower for second-stage than first-stage food processors. As it would be reasonable to expect, industries with the greatest scope for product differentiation, *ceteris paribus*, to be more productive. This result runs counter to the principles underlying the distinction. However, there is a negative correlation between an industry's ratio of value-added to gross output and its value-added per employee, i.e., the lower its rate of value-added in gross output (the more it uses purchased intermediates) the higher its value-added per employee. This is confirmed by a (Pearson) correlation coefficient of -0.527 between the ratios of value-added to gross output and the ratio of value-added per employee relative to the average value-added per employee in all food processing industries.

Table 1.3:   Value-Added per Employee (£)

		1980	1984	1988	1991
411	Organic oils and fats	14,110	24,994	31,677	37,396
412	Slaughtering of animals and production of meat and by-products	6,601	11,670	13,382	17,065
413	Preparation of milk and milk products	14,120	20,159	22,344	30,014
414	Processing of fruit and vegetables	7,266	13,079	15,546	20,004
415	Fish Processing	6,762	9,446	12,732	13,396
416	Grain milling	16,694	24,564	32,089	41,771
419	Bread, biscuits and flour confectionery	6,015	8,493	11,807	15,628
420	Sugar and sugar by-products	18,221	23,986	34,534	55,209
421	Ice cream, cocoa, chocolate and sugar confectionery	8,523	12,758	19,872	25,549
422	Animal feeding stuffs	14,994	20,301	29,454	29,567
423	Starch and miscellaneous foods	12,802	19,659	26,546	33,012
	Food Processors	9,093	13,361	17,362	21,876
	All Manufacturing	8,796	14,052	20,261	23,274

Source: Census of Production (various years).

Labour

During the 1980's employment in UK food processing fell, as Table 1.4 shows. With the exception of slaughtering, employment declined for every food processing group although the rate was relatively slow for Bread etc. (possibly due to a growth of in-house baking activities) and Starch etc. (which is the catch-all group to which a disproportionate share of new product firms are likely to be allocated). However, despite the appreciable decline in employment, food processing activities accounted for a greater share of manufacturing employment in 1992 than it did in 1980. This change will have resulted partly from the very sharp decline in manufacturing employment during the 1980s, and partly from the food sector's intrinsic productivity growth.

Table 1.4   Labour Employed in Food and Drink Processing

		1980	1992	% Change
411	Organic oils and fats	8,836	5,197	-41.2
412	Slaughtering of animals and production of meat and by-products	96,237	117,031	21.6
413	Preparation of milk and milk products	52,088	39,045	-25.0
414	Processing of fruit and vegetables	26,755	20,297	-24.1
415	Fish Processing	28,453	19,700	-30.8
416	Grain milling	8,957	5,941	-33.7
419	Bread, biscuits and flour confectionery	161,248	151,365	-6.1
420	Sugar and sugar by-products	11,463	5,208	-54.6
421	Ice cream, cocoa, chocolate and sugar confectionery	67,632	50,727	-25.0
422	Animal feeding stuffs	27,967	20,090	-28.2
423	Starch and miscellaneous foods	66,217	61,312	-7.4
	Food Processing	555,853	495,913	-10.8
	All Manufacturing	6,494,957	4,537,512	-30.1
	Food Processing as percentage of All Manufacturing	8.56	10.93	

Source: Census of Production (various years).

There is some evidence to suggest that employment in first-stage processing declined more rapidly than employment in second-stage processing. First-stage processing recorded three of the five fastest rates of employment decline first (420), third (416) and fifth (422), while Organic Oils & fats reported the second fastest rate of employment decline. This would be consistent with the first/second-stage hypothesis noted earlier. First, an emphasis on process innovation is more likely to produce input-reducing technical change, and second, the rate of growth of demand for first-stage products is likely to be slower.

The low ratios of value-added to gross output in food processing relative to those in manufacturing on average, do not necessarily imply that earnings in food processing are relatively low. The data on incomes in the Censuses of Production are reported by occupation - 'operatives' and 'administrative, technical and clerical staff', although this does not provide information on the length of the working week or the relative rates of pay by gender.

Table 1.5 reports incomes by occupation and industry for 1984 and 1992 and includes data for the drink and tobacco industries. These data indicate the appreciable range of incomes within food processing, and are consistent with average incomes in food processing being somewhat lower than average incomes in manufacturing. Incomes in first-stage food processors produce a contradictory image: operative incomes are above the food, drink & tobacco average while administrative, technical and clerical incomes are not. Furthermore, it is notable that incomes in food processing are on average lower than incomes in drink and tobacco industries.

Table 1.5:   Annual Earnings in Food, Drink and Tobacco Processing (£)

		Operatives		Administrative, Technical and Clerical	
		1984	1992	1984	1992
411	Organic oils and fats	8,392	17,588	10,303	18,093
412	Slaughtering of animals and production of meat and by-products	5,694	9,872	7,795	16,818
413	Preparation of milk and milk products	7,461	13,371	8,311	16,901
414	Processing of fruit and vegetables	6,114	10,090	9,070	16,291
415	Fish Processing	4,983	8,405	8,895	15,959
416	Grain milling	8,941	15,912	8,607	18,482
419	Bread, biscuits and flour confectionery	5,066	8,751	7,226	15,343
420	Sugar and sugar by-products	9,791	18,206	11,771	26,299
421	Ice cream, cocoa, chocolate and sugar confectionery	6,245	11,337	9,502	18,912
422	Animal feeding stuffs	8,567	15,323	9,287	18,137
423	Starch and miscellaneous foods	6,864	12,864	9,819	20,032
41/42	Food, Drink & Tobacco	6,360	10,933	9,284	18,430
424	Spirit distilling &compounding	6,686	13,806	10,271	21,365
426	Wines, cider & perry	7,408	13,024	10,055	19,430
427	Brewing & malting	9,163	14,479	10,441	18,681
428	Soft drinks	6,467	12,633	8,707	19,307
429	Tobacco	10,150	19,168	13,537	29,481

Source: Censuses of Production

The data in the Censuses of Production are complemented by those in the Employment Gazette, except for the fact that the Employment Gazette reports neither industry specific data nor aggregated data for food processing only. However, the Employment Gazette does report earnings, hours of work and earning rates for both male and female employees (see Table 1.6). The most obvious feature is that male (average) earnings are below those for manufacturing while (average) hours of work by males are greater, indicating a lower (average) earning rates. The reverse applies to women. The figures also indicate that earnings in food, drink & tobacco are below the manufacturing average whereas the length of the working week is above average with the result that earning rates are appreciably below average. The apparently perverse result that earnings and earnings per hour for all food, drink & tobacco employees are lower, relative to manufacturing, than earnings and earnings per hour for male and female employees derives from the larger proportion of female employees in food, drink & tobacco.

Table 1.6:   Earnings and Working Hours in Food, Drink and Tobacco by Employee Gender Relative to those in All Manufacturing - (Average % 1985 to 1992)

	Earnings/wk (%)	Hours/wk (%)	Earnings/hr (%)
Men	99.0	102.6	96.5
Women	101.9	101.7	100.5
All	**97.6**	**101.9**	**95.7**

Source: Employment Gazette

Capital

A partial explanation for the relatively lower incomes in food processing might derive from food processing having a lower capital/labour ratio than the average for manufacturing (Table 1.7). On the other hand, the output/capital ratios produce a slightly different picture. In 1980 manufacturing and food processing had similar output/capital ratios; by 1984 food processing's ratio appreciably exceeded that of manufacturing, but by 1988 manufacturing's ratio exceeded that for food processing. No explanation for this is obvious, although it may be a consequence of the perpetual inventory method with accelerated scrapping of capital, (which is reported to have happened during the early 1980's) and which may be under-recorded. Because the degree of under-recording was possibly greater for manufacturing than food processing in the 1980's, manufacturing's output/capital ratio may have been underestimated during the early 1980's.

Table 1.7:   Gross Capital Stocks (£ '000m @ 1985 prices)[4]

		1980	1984	1988
1	All Industry & Services	927.1	1,000.1	1,103.1
2	All Manufacturing Industry	250.3	254.6	263
3	Food Industries*	21.57	22.8	24.29
4	2) as % of 1)	27.00	25.46	23.84
5	3) as % of 1)	2.33	2.28	2.20
6	3) as % of 2)	8.62	8.96	9.24
	Capital/Labour Ratios: ('000 of Gross capital stock per employee) All Manufacturing Industry.	38.54	50.32	53.32
	Food Processing*.	38.81	44.98	48.27
	Output/Capital Ratios: (Output per £'000 of Gross capital stock) All Manufacturing Industry.	211	259	351
	Food Processing*.	218	275	335

Source: UK National Accounts (1990)
* Includes Animal feeding stuffs (420)

---

4   Detailed data have not been published for the years after 1988.

Research and Development (R&D) Expenditure

Data on Research and Development activity by food processing is limited: for example it appears that the Central Statistical Office (CSO) has not produced a report on 'Industrial Research and Development Expenditure and Employment' since 1988 (Business Monitor MO14), and that only provided data up to 1985. Moreover, the Business Monitor MO14 reports neither separately identify expenditure by industries nor have they always separated food processing industries from drink and tobacco industries.

However, the information in the MO14 Business Monitors indicates that the differences in the patterns of expenditure between food, drink & tobacco and manufacturing are sufficiently great as to indicate appreciable differences in research and development activities. Specifically, capital expenditure accounts for a far greater proportion of total research and development expenditure by food, drink and tobacco and a far greater proportion of food, drink and tobacco's expenditure is directed towards basic and applied research, whereas manufacturing directs the overwhelming majority of its research and development funds towards development (see Table 1.8).

Table 1.8:   Research and Development Expenditure (£m)

		Food, drink & tobacco		Manufacturing	
		1981	1985	1981	1985
1	Total Expenditure	91.5	123.2	3,511.7	4,697.3
2	Private industry	88.2	119	2,084.9	3,535.7
3	Public corporations & Government	3.3	4.1	1,426.8	1,161.6
4	Capital Expenditure	14.2	20	283.7	444.2
5	Current Expenditure	77.3	103.2	3,228	4,253.1
6	Basic	6.1	10	78	116.4
7	Applied	32	43.1	543.5	906.1
8	Development	39.2	50.1	2,606.4	3,230.7
	4 as % of 1	15.5	16.2	8.1	9.5
	5 as % of 1	84.5	83.8	91.9	90.5
	6 as % of 5	7.9	9.7	2.4	2.7
	7 as % of 5	41.4	41.8	16.8	21.3
	8 as % of 5	50.7	48.5	80.7	76.0

Source: Business Monitor M014 (1981 & 1985)

Given the definition of development,[5] this suggests that food, drink and tobacco companies direct less of their efforts towards process and/or product innovation than manufacturing. This probably reflects the

---

5   "The use of the results of basic and applied research directed to the introduction of useful materials, processes, products, devices and systems, or the improvement of existing ones" (Business Monitor MO14, 1988, p 2).

relatively low rate of research and development expenditure by food, drink and tobacco compared to its share of GDP: specifically manufacturing spends some forty times the amount on R & D that food, drink and tobacco spends while producing only some ten times the amount of GDP.

Nevertheless, product and packaging innovation in the food industry is very important and the effort to gain a technological lead must be a part of the overall effort to gain and maintain market share. This is sometimes driven by environmental and food safety factors. Table 1.9 shows the leading spenders on research in the UK food and drink sector. These figures should be interpreted with care and with reference to the activities of each company. The relatively high position of Booker, for example, probably reflects its poultry breeding and genetics activities.

Table 1.9:   The UK's Top Food and Drink Companies by R&D Expenditure 1993

	Company	Current R&D Spend	R&D as % of Sales
1	Unilever	518.0	1.86
2	Grand Metropolitan	51.0	0.51
3	Tate & Lyle	22.2	0.61
4	United Biscuits	19.5	0.57
5	Booker	13.4	0.38
6	Cadbury Schweppes	12.9	0.35
7	Dalgety	10.8	0.24
8	Hillsdown	10.5	0.23
9	Allied Domecq	8.0	0.15

Source : Financial Times Top 100 Companies by R&D Expenditure

Links with Other Sectors

The relatively low ratios of value-added to gross output indicate relatively high rates of intermediate input use by food industries, and therefore suggest that inter industry relations may be important. Input-output tables identify these interdependency effects. Recent UK input-output tables are a particularly rich source of information on the food industries because of the disproportionate degree of disaggregation of food processing reported in the tables.

The most immediately noticeable feature is the limited extent to which the food industries interrelate with other manufacturing industries. From the perspective of input use in 1990, Table 1.12 shows the high proportions of inputs sourced from either agriculture or other food industries, and the relatively heavy dependence of the food industries upon imported intermediates. Given the relatively low rate of value-added in gross output, the low rates of 'income from employment' and 'gross profit etc.' would be expected. However, it is notable that whereas for the economy the proportion of gross output accounted for by 'income from employment' was approximately twice that of 'gross profit etc.', for the food industries it was less than one and a half times the rate.[6] Since a similar pattern of income distribution can be found in previous years, this suggests several causes: the food industries are on average more capital intensive than other industries, or that they use less skilled (lower wage rate) labour, or they are earning appreciable rents, or some combination of these factors.

Given the first-stage/second-stage distinction it would be reasonable to expect to find that second-stage processors were more dependent upon inputs from other food industries, and that first-stage processors were more reliant upon inputs from agriculture. The information in Tables 1.11 and 1.12 is consistent with the distinction, with the exception of animal feeding stuffs, although it would be reasonable to argue that this exception is not surprising given the use of by-products in animal feed.

Table 1.10   Distribution of Food Industry Output (1990) Shares of Total Output

	Delivered to Food Industries	Delivered to Intermediate Demand	Delivered to Final Demand
Oils and fats	0.34	0.52	0.48
Slaughtering and meat processing	0.06	0.22	0.78
Milk and milk products	0.16	0.34	0.66
Fruit, vegetables and fish processing	0.10	0.35	0.65
Grain milling and starch	0.75	0.86	0.14
Bread, biscuits and flour confectionery	0.00	0.44	0.56
Sugar	0.50	0.74	0.26
Confectionery	0.06	0.25	0.75
Animal feeding stuffs	0.05	0.72	0.28
Miscellaneous foods	0.06	0.22	0.78
Economy Average	**n/a**	**0.41**	**0.59**

Source : CSO 'Input Output Tables for the United Kingdom 1990'

It is also of interest to consider the distribution of food industry outputs (Table 1.10). Again, looking at the proportions of outputs delivered to other food industries, the first-stage/second-stage distinction appears to be justified, with the exception of animal feeding stuffs[7]. The distinction is further confirmed by the distribution of output between (total) intermediate and final demands, a facet highlighted by comparing the food industries with the economy average.

---

6   The (weighted) average proportions across all food industries were 0.17 for 'income from employment' and 0.11 for 'gross profit etc.' in 1990.

7   Animal feeding stuffs delivers a large proportion of its output to agriculture rather than food processors.

Table 1.11 Input-output Relations (1990)

	Oils and fats (411)	Slaughtering and meat processing (412)	Milk and milk products (413)	Fruit, vegetables and fish processing (414 & 415)	Grain milling and starch (416 & pt 423)	Bread, biscuits and flour confectionery (419)	Sugar (420 & pt 421)	Confectionery (pt 421)	Animal feeding stuffs (422)	Misc. foods (pt 423)	Average for the Economy
Agriculture, Fishing & Forestry	0.31	0.45	0.46	0.18	0.55	0.01	0.21	0.07	0.24	0.13	0.02
Utilities	0.02	0.02	0.02	0.02	0.02	0.02	0.02	0.01	0.02	0.01	0.05
Other	0.11	0.09	0.10	0.15	0.03	0.12	0.04	0.16	0.13	0.18	0.15
Manufacturing Food Industry	0.33	0.11	0.13	0.19	0.05	0.29	0.31	0.19	0.27	0.14	0.02
Construction	0.00	0.00	0.00	0.00	0.00	0.00	0.00	0.00	0.00	0.00	0.03
Distribution & Communications	0.12	0.06	0.05	0.09	0.08	0.04	0.07	0.08	0.07	0.07	0.08
Other Services	0.11	0.06	0.05	0.09	0.04	0.09	0.06	0.13	0.10	0.14	0.14
Imports of goods and services	(0.27)	(0.09)	(0.10)	(0.16)	(0.14)	(0.12)	(0.15)	(0.11)	(0.13)	(0.16)	(0.07)
Taxes on expenditure less subsidies	-0.05	-0.03	-0.04	-0.03	0.01	0.01	-0.04	0.01	-0.04	0.01	0.02
Income from employment	0.10	0.16	0.11	0.19	0.10	0.32	0.10	0.21	0.11	0.18	0.32
Gross profits etc	-0.05	0.09	0.12	0.11	0.12	0.10	0.21	0.13	0.11	0.15	0.17

Source : CSO 'Input Output Tables for the United Kingdom 1990'

Table 1.12 Intra-Food Industry Relations (1990)

	Oils and fats (411)	Slaughtering and meat processing (412)	Milk and milk products (413)	Fruit, vegetables and fish processing (414 & 415)	Grain milling and starch (416 & pt 423)	Bread, biscuits and flour confectionery (419)	Sugar (420 & pt 421)	Confectionery (pt 421)	Animal feeding stuffs (422)	Misc. foods (pt 423)
Oils and fats	0.269	0.006	0.003	0.006	0.000	0.016	0.000	0.010	0.055	0.015
Slaughtering and meat processing	0.021	0.028	0.000	0.024	0.000	0.008	0.000	0.001	0.051	0.010
Milk and milk products	0.028	0.011	0.101	0.018	0.006	0.029	0.000	0.047	0.025	0.021
Fruit, vegetables and fish processing	0.000	0.007	0.005	0.065	0.000	0.027	0.000	0.004	0.055	0.016
Grain milling and starch	0.001	0.023	0.002	0.019	0.029	0.124	0.001	0.017	0.053	0.041
Bread, biscuits and flour confectionery	0.000	0.000	0.000	0.000	0.000	0.001	0.000	0.000	0.000	0.000
Sugar	0.005	0.002	0.010	0.025	0.000	0.030	0.312	0.058	0.016	0.015
Confectionery	0.000	0.002	0.000	0.006	0.000	0.016	0.000	0.054	0.000	0.001
Animal feeding stuffs	0.000	0.017	0.000	0.000	0.000	0.000	0.000	0.000	0.007	0.000
Miscellaneous foods	0.005	0.018	0.005	0.027	0.013	0.035	0.000	0.002	0.008	0.016
Total	**0.330**	**0.113**	**0.127**	**0.191**	**0.047**	**0.285**	**0.313**	**0.192**	**0.270**	**0.136**

Source : CSO 'Input Output Tables for the United Kingdom 1990'

Trade in Food and Drink

In evidence given to the Agriculture Committee enquiry into the food trade gap in 1992, the size of the food trade gap was estimated at £6 billion by Food From Britain (p2, HoC, 1992). The external trade gap in food and drink is considered here because this type of calculation and the concept of a "food trade gap" is often part of a general analytical approach to the food industry. However, that general approach, exemplified by the quoted £6 billion estimate from Food from Britain, can be misleading. Trade data is probably most useful as a guide to the potential productivity of the UK food and drink industry rather than as a source of prescriptive policy. Certainly, the relevant trade gap figure is very much less than £6 billion[8].

Table 1.13 presents a summary of food sectors broken down into raw materials and processed products. When various policy and physical factors are considered it is possible to say that the total realisable[9] food and drink trade gap is nearer £2 billion. This must immediately be qualified by noting that there are particular sectors where imports are relatively high, and that the overall net figure is greatly influenced by one major sector - whisky exports are very significant to the aggregate food trade gap calculation. Net trade in whisky in 1993 accounts for approximately £2.1 billion on its own.

Table 1.14 presents the food trade gap in processed products. This was £2.3 billion in 1991 with meat the largest deficit processing sector. In 1993 the figure was £2.4 billion with meat still the largest deficit sector[10]. These two tables and the concept of a "realisable" gap are important to the understanding of the aggregate trade position in food and drink for analysts, policy makers and commercial operators in the food and drink sector.

---

8   See pp 139-141 in Volume II of the House of Commons Agriculture Committee report on the Trade Gap in Food and Drink (*op cit*) for a similar view and analysis expressed by J Sainsbury plc in its evidence to the Select Committee.

9   The concept of a "realisable" gap is defined as;
     that part of the trade deficit that can be altered by the allocation or reallocation of resources within the physical and policy constraints that agriculture and food and drink manufacturing operate under. No value judgement is implied in this concept. It is a measurement concept rather than a policy objective and its purpose is simply to draw attention to the distinctions between indigenous and non-indigenous foods, and the trade policy framework.

10   See footnotes to Table 1.12

Table 1.13:   The Food and Drink Trade Gap (£m)

	1991	1993
Overall Food Trade Gap	-5,435	-5,890
Constraints on reducing the GAP include:		
i) Commodities covered by Lomé IV		
1. Sugar	-433	-463
2. Bananas	-217	-262
Sub-Total	**-639**	**-725**
ii) Non-indigenous commodities i.e. those that cannot be grown or processed in the UK, or production is very limited		
Raw Materials		
Rice	-111	-100
Citrus Fruit	-226	-144
Maize	-223	-220
Coffee	-170	-180
Cocoa	-157	-150
Stone Fruit	-97	-128
Tea	-51	-90
Oilseeds and Oleaginous fruit	-171	-242
Sub-Total	**-1,206**	**-1,254**
Processed		
Wine	-869	-980
Preserved/Frozen Fruit and Fruit Juice	-397	-407
Animal Oils and Fats	-292	-355
Sub-Total	**-1,658**	**-1,742**
'Realisable' Food and Drink Trade Gap	**-1,832**	**-2,169**

Source :   MAFF, Business Monitors MM20 and MQ20, Authors
Notes: The figures shown above are net trade figures - i.e. imports - exports
             In 1993 the total visble balance of payments deficit in was £13.4 billion.
The 'Realisable' Food Trade Gap depends upon a definition of indigenous and non-indigenous products, different definitions would yield a different 'realisable' gap. It is possible to reduce the gap for 1993 to under £1 bn, essentially by classifying out-of-season fruit and vegetables as non-indigenous. Figures for 1993 have not been 'raised', apart from the overall food trade gap figure. The figures for 1991 have all been raised. This 'raising' of figures is undertaken to account for all trades that are under the threshold limit for inclusion in the Intrastat system of the EC. The overall figure for 1993 of £5.89 bn has been raised by £100m. If the other 1993 figures were also raised, the 'Realisable' Food Trade Gap would fall below £2.1 bn

Table 1.13 illustrates that the realisable food trade gap in 1993 was around £2 billion[11]. In Table 1.14 the deficit in processed products is shown to be around £2.4 billion in 1993.

With a total food gap of £5.9 billion and a £2.4 billion deficit in processed products, this implies a £3.5 billion raw material trade gap. Around £2 billion of this raw material is "non-substitutable" i.e. unlikely to be

11   See footnotes to Table 1.12 regarding the 'raising' of trade figures.

grown or produced in the UK. Hence about £1.5 billion of (net[12]) raw material is being imported that could potentially be grown in the UK[13].

Table 1.14 : UK Trade Gap in Processed Food Products (£m)

	1991	1993
Domestically substitutable		
Meat (processed)	-933	-855
Dairy (Cheese and Butter/Skimmed Milk Powder, etc.)	-347	-366
Fish	-462	-419
Vegetables	-329	-349
Animal Feed	-316	-499
Beer	-113	-150
Pasta	-7	-18
Misc. Products (excl. Pasta)	-181	-337**
Subtotal	**-2,688**	**-2,993**
Non-substitutable		
Wine	-869	-980
Preserved and Frozen Fruit and Fruit Juice	-397	-407
Animal Oils and Fats	-292	-355
Subtotal	**-1,558**	**-1,742**
Exported Products		
Whisky	+1,831	+2,091
Malt, Bakery Products	+95	+204
Sugar Confectionery	+46	+59
Subtotal	**+1,972**	**+2,354**
"Realisable" Processed Food and Drink Trade Gap	**-2,274**	**-2,381**

Source : MAFF, Business Monitors MM20 and MQ20, Authors
* This figure is not strictly comparable to the 1991 figure as the definitions of several extra categories are different
Note : The 'Realisable' Gap is calculated using certain definitions of products. Different definitions may lead to different results. Figures for 1991 are from MAFF. Figures from 1993 are by the authors who have attempted to follow these MAFF definitions as closely as possible, though interpretation may not be precise.

The preceding discussions and tables may usefully be supplemented by reference to the discussions in Lund *et al* (1994) in which the overseas trade statistics of the UK are broken down in great detail. The concepts of indigenous and non-indigenous food are examined and a further breakdown of food trade into highly processed, lightly processed, and unprocessed trade is given. Table 6 from Lund *et al's* paper is

---

12 'Net' indicates that raw material exports are included in this figure.
13 This calculation relies on assumptions made about the indigenous nature of commodities and products traded. Different indigenous nature assumptions may yield different results.

reproduced here as Table 1.15. One of the conclusions from this analysis is reported in Lund *et al* as, "..in a numerical sense, the UK's food trade gap may be (largely or wholly) attributed to trade in non-indigenous items or to trade in unprocessed or lightly-processed items." This underlines the need to use trade data very specifically to identify where domestic food manufacturing opportunities exist and to consider these opportunities in relation to specific raw material availability, processing capacity, etc.: and not to use trade statistics as a general indicator of an economic or commercial problem.

Table 1.15: UK Overseas Trade in Food, Feed and Drink in 1993 - Classified by Degree of Processing and Indigeneity

Overseas Trade Statistics basis

Exports (£ million)

		Indigenous	Non-Indigenous	Total
	Highly Processed	3,714	590	4,304
	Lightly Processed	2,397	626	3,023
	Unprocessed	827	61	889
	Total	6,398	1,277	8,215

Imports (£ million)

		Indigenous	Non-indigenous	Total
	Highly Processed	2,024	2,153	4,177
	Lightly Processed	4,754	2,230	6,984
	Unprocessed	1,109	1,836	2,944
	Total	7,887	6,218	14,106

Trade Gap (£ million)

		Indigenous	Non-indigenous	Total
	Highly Processed	+1,690	-1,593	+127
	Lightly Processed	-2,357	-1,604	-3,961
	Unprocessed	-282	-1,774	-2,056
	Total	-949	-4,941	-5,890

Exports as % of Imports

		Indigenous	Non-indigenous	Total
	Highly Processed	183.5	27.4	103.0
	Lightly Processed	50.4	28.1	43.8
	Unprocessed	74.6	3.3	30.2
	Total	88.0	20.5	58.2

Source :   Reproduced from Lund *et al* (*op cit*)
Note :   Figures may not sum to total due to rounding.
           The calculations above are based upon a more detailed breakdown of raw materials and food products. They are also derived from a set of judgements about degree of processing, unlike Tables 1.13 and 1.14

Food Industry Structure and Performance

The merger activity in UK manufacturing, including food processing, in the 1980's occurred for several reasons. First, there was probably a belief that large scale production would be necessary to ensure global competitiveness as markets opened up. The much-vaunted European

"Single Market" was probably part of this perception[14]. Second, the global financial sector was willing and able (because of capital market liberalisation) to fund growth by acquisition by loans of one type or another. The liberalisation of the UK financial sector in the mid 1980's via the Financial Services Act (1986) would have been part of this. It is likely to have helped make capital available and therefore to support mergers and aquistions within manufacturing generally. The parallel consumer-led boom in the UK and the enthusiasm for increased market shares encouraged firms to expand and restructure.

Table 1.16:   The Top 20 Food and Drink Manufacturers in Europe, 1994

	Company	Country Base	Sales (US$m)	Profit (US$m)	Profit Margin	Main Market	Main Product
1	Unilever	UK/Neth	42,217	2,944	6.97	Europe	Oils, dairy
2	Nestlé	Switz.	40,770	2,048	5.02	US	Dairy,dietics
3	Danone (BSN)	France	12,343	602	4.88	France	Dairy
4	Grand Metropolitan	UK	12,303	955	7.76	US	Drinks
5	Eridania/ Beghin-Say	UK	8,757	401	4.58	France	Oils
6	Allied Domecq	UK	7,979	765	9.59	UK	Wine, spirits
7	Guinness	UK	7,065	1,064	15.06	UK	Spirits
8	Hillsdown	UK	6,962	245	3.52	UK	Meat & produce
9	Dalgety	UK	6,773	170	2.51	US	Distribution
10	Bass	UK	6,744	770	11.37	UK	Brewing
11	ABF	UK	6,645	512	7.71	Europe	Milling
12	Saint Louis	France	6,210	126	2.03	France	Sugar
13	Tate and Lyle	UK	5,783	338	5.84	US	Sugar, starch
14	Cadbury Schweppes	UK	5,644	630	11.16	UK	Bevergaes
15	Booker	UK	5,408	145	2.68	UK	Wholesaling
16	United Biscuits	UK	5,220	177	3.39	UK/Eire	Biscuits
17	Procordia	Sweden	5,088	616	12.11	Sweden	Beverages
18	Heineken	Neth.	4,839	435	8.99	Neth.	Beer
19	Sara Lee/DE	Neth.	4,014	320	7.97	Neth.	Coffee
20	LVMH	France	3,813	529	13.87	France	Cognac, spirits

Source : Seymour Cooke, Euro PA
Note: These figures relate to each company's last financial year

Table 1.16 illustrates that UK food companies and the UK market have a significant presence and scale amongst European food companies operating in Europe. 13 of the Top 20 European food and drink companies are based in the UK.

The merger and acquisition activity of the 1980's encouraged and supported a trend to concentration in the UK food sector. The trend

---

14   See for example Dudley (1989).

towards bigger companies reflects the recognition of the European and global marketplace in which many food and drink brands operate in. Table 1.17 illustrates, for selected companies, that operating margins for food companies in the UK have, generally, been growing and that companies have obtained a reasonable return on investment in recent years. Of course, this point and Table 1.17 emphasise the difficulties of presenting a general conclusion about the food and drink industry. Sector by sector it would be expected that the market structure and profit margins experienced by food and drink companies will vary. Hence the need to follow these points through to the individual sector chapters. In these later chapters industry structure and performance is often considered with reference to financial information and analyses derived from the annual reports of the relevant sector's major companies. For reference, explanations and definitions of the terms used in these financial analyses are presented in the Appendix to this Chapter.

Table 1.17:   Food Company Operating Margins

	1986	1987	1988	1989	1990	1991	1992	1993
ABF	4.2	4.9	5.6	5.7	5.7	6.0	7.8	7.6
Cadbury	7.6	8.9	9.6	9.8	10.6	11.5	11.0	11.7
Hazlewood	10.5	11.1	10.1	10.7	11.8	10.6	9.5	8.7
Hillsdown			3.6	4.8	5.8	4.8	4.5	4.4
Northern Foods	4.9	5.9	7.6	8.5	8.6	9.4	9.5	8.9
RHM	6.9	8.4	10.5	11.6	10.4	-	-	-
Tate and Lyle	4.4	5.3	6.2	7.8	8.1	8.6	7.1	7.0
Unigate	4.7	5.2	4.2	4.2	4.0	3.9	5.1	5.1
Unilever	7.2	8.6	9.0	9.1	9.1	8.9	8.5	8.7
United Biscuits	7.1	8.1	8.1	7.8	8.1	8.2	6.8	6.4

Source :   Reports and Accounts
Note :   Figures are for food margins only

Capacity

Lack of data and poor definition are not good auspices for economists and analysts interested in the structure of the food and drink industry. But a brief note here on the "capacity" issue is necessary to place the capacity figures given later in the book into context.   Typically, investment decisions and capacity/utilisation information are held back from the marketplace as long as possible to maximise competitive advantage Furthermore, there is little in the way of agreed definition about the term "capacity".   Nevertheless, capacity information is often part of the analysis of industry structure and, difficult though it may be, the definition of capacity requires some comment. The planning process for the UK's Processing and Marketing Grant scheme (under Regulation 866/90) and specifically aimed at food processing companies, involved denotations of capacity created by the European Commission. These provide a useful framework for discussion here[15].

The capacity categories the Commission used were;

Storage capacity -

This concept probably relates to the storage of raw material or semi-processed material at factory. Estimates given of storage requirements at factory (farm) depend upon climate influences on harvest, length of harvesting season and specifics of the factory process. Different raw materials and food stuffs will have a different reliance on storage so an industry standard is often not possible or sensible. An important qualifier to storage capacity at factory is the delivery capacity at factory i.e. the maximum amount of delivery tonnage that can be received per day through the local transport network.

Processing capacity -

This probably symbolises the typical "capacity" definition and most easily fits a view of processing at first stage and at the factory. Estimated utilisation rates are possible for this type of capacity estimate but processing definitions will vary according to product and need to be carefully related to the actual process being undertaken.

Storage capacity of finished product -

This assumes storage at the factory of product after first stage of processing. However, it may not always be appropriate to measure storage capacity for a finished product as modern transport and distribution structures and "just in time" ordering procedures would reduce such storage requirements to a bare minimum or compensate for their absence. Also, there has been a marked growth in external distibution and warehousing functions which service food processors, and large retailers have increasingly tended to provide their own centralised storage facilities.

---

15   The commentary here reflects only the views of the Editors and it is not intended as a critique of the European Commission.

Marketing capacity of finished product -

Marketing capacity is a very important subject in a modern food industry. In practice, much marketing capacity relates to (novel) ways of packaging and storing the food product for use in the home and this "adds value" in some way to the modern food product e.g. microwaveable containers, Tetrapaks, etc.. In the processed food market new technology in this area and new ways of distributing the product are critical "drivers" for change.

Physical measures of marketing capacity are perhaps best represented in terms of storing/packaging throughput at the point in the manufacturing process after the first stage of transformation and before distribution to a wholesale or retail outlet. These marketing functions in a food factory are usually distinct from the technical processes required to transform the raw material into an edible product. Hence, food companies talk about investment in bagging/packaging lines independently of their investment in the transformation process: although often they are closely linked in operational terms. These areas are very important in understanding the food industry's ability to market a product and are frequently a locus of technical change.

It is clear from the preceding discussion that any measure of processing capacity that just details the physical units of processing capacity available is not particularly useful. Such a measure does not allow the reader/analyst to understand what the qualitative condition of processing capacity is. Nor does it capture the important time dimension that is relevant to many processing operations. For example, the processing capacity of a plant can be increased by adding more labour and time and running the plant on a 2 or 3 shift system. Also, a new factory which contains the latest technology for processing/packaging etc. may be smaller than an older one but it may also put new and "better" characteristics into the finished product i.e. it is better related to current market demands. It may also operate consistently and be less affected by factors such as input quality, variability, climate etc.

These different aspects of "capacity" may be thought of as being "time related", "demand driven" or "cost reducing". The ideal examination of capacity in the food industry should therefore distinguish between these aspects and identify them wherever possible. The sectoral chapters that follow have not, in general, been able to meet this ideal. Nevertheless, wherever possible capacity figures (usually relating to the first-stage transformation process in the factory) are given for each industry or food sector. Imperfect though these may be, they give the reader an estimate of current and recent industry structure.

Marketing Expenditures and Own-Label

Consumer demand and lifestyle statistics touched upon briefly at the beginning of this chapter disguise many changes in growth rates and market shares for specific brands in different product categories. Most significantly for the business environment of the food and drink industry, the prevailing trend in branding has been towards a dichotomy where major brands and the own-label products[16] of multiple retailers occupy the supermarket shelves. The marketing aspects of the food and drink industry and the growth of own-label are worthy of an examination here. They will certainly reappear in later chapters as individual food product sectors demonstrate more or less experience of them.

Figure 1.7 and Table 1.18 illustrate how own-label penetration varies across product categories and how some major food brands have increased their market share despite increasing competition from retailers' own-brand labels: this is explained largely by the decline of secondary and tertiary brands. Table 1.18 also suggests that one of the reactions of food companies to the own-label issue is to fight back against the threat of own-labels by "growing the brand" at the expense of secondary brands. Marketing expenditures on food brands are an important element of this increased competition for brand image in the consumer's mindset.

Figure 1.7 : Own Label Penetration by Broad Product Groups (UK) - 1993

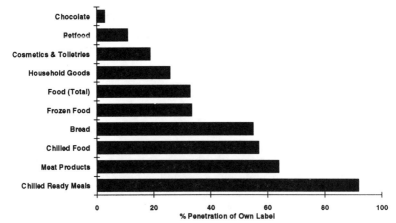

Source : Kleinwort Benson Research

---

16   Own-label is sometimes termed private-label.

Table 1.18 : Growth in Market Share of Major Brands

	Brands	1983 (%)	1992 (%)
Tinned Fruit	Del Monte	30.9	33.7
	Own Labels	20.3	29.8
	Others	48.8	36.5
Nuts	KP	51.0	57.1
	Own Labels	20.0	31.2
	Others	29.0	11.7
Baked Beans	Heinz	54.9	60.7
	Own Labels	16.1	19.5
	Others	29.0	1.8

Source : UBS

In the UK the growth of own-label products is far ahead of most of Europe as Figure 1.8 shows. This fact is probably not unconnected with the growth of market share by food retailers in the UK. Table 1.19 illustrates this trend for these retailers.

Table 1.19: Trends in UK Food Retailers Market Share (%)

	1987/88	1991/92	% Change
Top 5 Multiples	35.3	38.9	+3.6
Next 4 + M&S	8.7	11.0	+2.3
Co-ops	7.4	7.2	-0.2
Other Grocers	9.6	7.2	-2.4
Food Specialists	14.8	12.0	-2.8
CTNs/Chemists etc.	24.2	23.7	-0.5
Total	**100.0**	**100.0**	

Source : UBS

The majority (80%) of UK food brands that make up the top 100 ad spenders, spent at least £1 million each on advertising in the UK and many spent much more than this. Food brands that cannot compete with this scale and level of marketing expenditures in their particular part of the marketplace in the 1990s will be in danger. If the marketplace is global this implies huge marketing expenditures and increasing pressure on the number of surviving food brands.

Most commentators argue that the growth of the retail chains in the UK and the outlawing of many restrictive practices have altered the balance of market power[17]. Recent cases whereby retailers' own brands have been set in direct competition with some leading brand names illustrate this point (Sainsbury's cola versus Coca-Cola is the clearest example of this "look-a-like" controversy[18]) although it must be noted that the

---

17 See, pp 147-148, Volume II, House of Commons report on the Trade Gap in Food and Drink (op cit) for a UK retailer's view on this.

18 See the report in Supermarketing pp 21-22, Septermber 1994, on this subject for a useful discussion of the "look-a-likes" issue. Also, The Times 19.04.94, London , The Financial Times, 23.04.94, London, and Harvard Business Review (1993, 1994).

major brand names, such as Kelloggs, Nestle, PepsiCo etc. still enjoy huge brand loyalty and perhaps it is the medium sized manufacturer who suffers most in such "brand wars".

Figure 1.8 : Retailers' Own-label Trends in Europe - % Share of the Retail Market

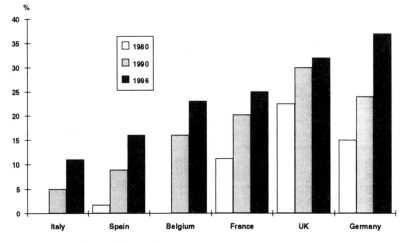

Source : Kleinwort Benson Research

Figure 1.9 illustrates the scale of total food advertising expenditures in the UK. Table 1.20 shows another aspect of this in its listing of the 15 largest advertising expenditures on specific food brands in the UK.

Figure 1.9:   Total Food Advertising Expenditure 1980-1993 (constant 1990 prices)

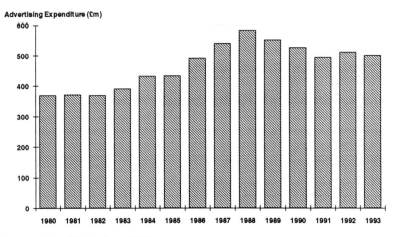

Source : Euro PA, Register-MEAL

Table 1.20: Top 15 Generic Brands By Advertising Expenditure, 1993

	Brand	Expenditure (£m)
1	Kellogg	56.90
2	Mars	25.58
3	Cadbury	24.73
4	Birds Eye	20.85
5	Nestlé	15.70
6	Nescafé	15.53
7	Brooke Bond	13.70
8	Heinz	13.56
9	Walls	13.46
10	Kraft	13.21
11	Rowntree	10.08
12	Weetabix	9.37
13	Tetley	8.55
14	McCain	8.47
15	Wrigley	8.18

Source :   Register-MEAL
Note :   Register-MEAL data have been adjusted to allow for discounting to estimate what
           advertisers actually spent rather than what they would have spent if their time and
           space was bought at rate card levels.

Food retailers in the UK are now very active in promoting their brand image and therefore their own-label products. Table 1.21 shows that these retailer brand advertising expenditures are equivalent to those of many major food brands. And food retailers have the added advantages of;

• having direct contact with consumers,

• using scanning and barcoding technology to obtain rapid and comprehensive market information systems,

• being able to present products in new and innovative forms,

• using systems of centralised distribution and storage.

The first two points in particular must provide modern retailers with very real opportunities to react to consumer purchasing behaviour and to influence it on a mass scale. It is interesting to speculate to what extent these aspects of the modern retail operation will be supported or undermined by changes in consumer lifestyles and technology in the future.

Table 1.21:   Top 10 Supermarkets & Grocery Stores by Advertising Expenditure, 1993

	Outlet	Expenditure £m
1	Tesco	26.90
2	Sainsbury	23.50
3	Safeway	18.40
4	Asda	17.42
5	Co-op	8.16
6	Gateway	7.72
7	Iceland	6.36
8	Kwik Save	5.42
9	Thorntons	1.62
10	Farmfoods	1.31

Source : Register-MEAL

There is an argument that suggests that the use of own branding by retailers has provided some brake on the movement towards an ever increasing concentration amongst food processors.   The retailers maintain that they use medium and small sized manufacturers to supply their own brand product as it enables them, the retailers, to keep close control over production and supply thus ensuring quality and availability.   This issue of retailer and manufacturer power is not one addressed in detail in this book, but it does play an implicit part in any description of the current structure, conduct and performance of the UK food processing sector.   The food manufacturing/food retailer relationship in the UK may be undergoing structural change - partly driven by the quality and production assurance conditions that food manufacturers have had to meet to satisfy retailers' demands.

Regulation

The potential for Governments to interfere with the food and drink industry through legislation and regulation is enormous. In the UK this legislative potential is usually two-tiered in that there is a national component based on UK government legislation and an EC component which has become more dominant since the target date for the implementation of the Single Market was agreed[19]. The European Single Market came into effect in 1993 and prompted a major increase in regulatory actions aimed at harmonising the legislation affecting businesses (in all sectors) across the European Community. The food and drink industry was particularly affected by this.   In the UK a suggested structure for considering the regulatory impact of Government

19   See for example Euro Analysis (1992) for a review of the preparations for the Single Market for Food Products.

on the food industry is given below. Regulatory actions can show themselves through several general areas;

- agricultural and trade policy e.g. the CAP[20], GATT, WTO[21], etc.

- food policy concerned with health and nutrition, hygiene and food safety, residues, additives, labelling, packaging, product standards and definitions, etc[22].

- competition policy affecting pricing, company behaviour and industry structure, state aids, etc[23].

- intellectual property rights affecting trade descriptions and copyright on product design, brands, etc[24].

- taxation policy and Government aids to investment in capital or labour e.g. excise duties on spirits and alcoholic drinks, grant schemes or capital allowances for investment, subsidised training or employment schemes[25].

These categories are not definitive and could easily be redrawn but they indicate the potential scope of Government interference in the food industry. When policies on animal welfare, pollution, transport, and recycling, etc. are included in the list it would seem that there is hardly an area of public policy that does not have an implication for the food and drink industry. The following chapters focus, almost entirely, on the agricultural and trade policy aspects of the regulatory environment for the food and drink industry. This is not to imply that the other areas are not significant. Indeed, without question, they are vitally important but the farm and trade policy aspects of food and drink provide a natural boundary for the book's coverage of the regulatory scene. Other aspects of legislation and Government interference can, for the purposes of this book, be put to one side.

---

20   See DG VI CAP Working Notes annual.
21   See DTI (1994) Cm 2579 and GATT (1994).
22   See MAFF (1994) Food Safety Directorate, Painter (1992)., and Euro Analysis (1993).
23. See DTI (undated), Merger Control in Europe, which presents a summary of the areas covered by the Merger Control Regulation (EC 4064/89) and Articles 85 and 86 of the Treaty of Rome.
24   See ESC Opinion 849/94 and Council Regulation No 40/94.
25   See OECD (1993).

Summary

This chapter has attempted to give an introduction to the examination of the food and drink industry which follows in detail in Chapters Two to Nine. In doing so, it has established general and specific definitions of the "food industry" and to what extent it plays an important role in the UK economy. The statistical breakdown suggests that the terms "food industry", "food and drink industry" and "food manufacturing sector" may be used interchangeably sometimes and at others may be quite specific. Undoubtedly, the economic activities undertaken in the food industry are worthy of research and analysis. There are some issues that will be common to all manufacturing but, in this chapter and later, the emphasis is on exploring those that are most pertinent to "the food chain".

By way of a summary and to leave the reader with a general picture of the food industry Figure 1.10 approximates the main economic parameters of the food chain. It provides a schematic interpretation of the various component parts, of the food and drink sector. This gives the reader a simplified overview of the economic and business environment of the food chain[26]. In particular, the value of the food chain is illustrated in terms of output and employment.

The food and drink industry is a vital part of the economy even though its nature and performance have been changing over time. It is important at this stage to emphasise the role of the consumer in shaping food company behaviour. On the demand side, satisfying consumers is a necessary condition for food companies to survive and prosper. On the supply side the most profitable food companies will meet these consumer demands by least cost methods. For regulators this should occur in an industry structure that is competitive in nature. Competition will express itself through the actions of firms, domestic and foreign, in production, distribution, marketing, and in the acquisition of assets (including brands). These aspects of individual company behaviour are, sector by sector, explored in the following chapters.

The changing structure of the food retailing industry in the UK and the use of own-labels to counter the power of the established brands is important to any understanding of structure, conduct and performance in food manufacturing. The UK is leading the way in own-label penetration of markets and the effects of this trend needs to be interpreted carefully. Own-label can be a threat and an opportunity to the food industry. In many respects, this is the key issue facing the food industry in the 1990's.

---

26   In Chapter Ten discussion of the food chain concept is developed to consider the idea of a "food web" rather than a simple chain.

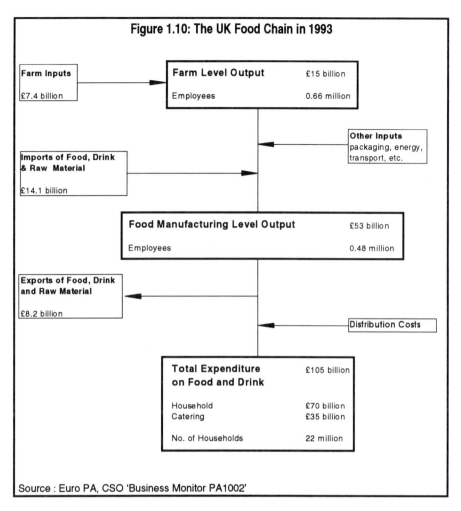

Figure 1.10: The UK Food Chain in 1993

Farm Inputs	**Farm Level Output** £15 billion
£7.4 billion	Employees 0.66 million

Other Inputs packaging, energy, transport, etc.

Imports of Food, Drink & Raw Material

£14.1 billion

Food Manufacturing Level Output   £53 billion

Employees   0.48 million

Exports of Food, Drink and Raw Material

£8.2 billion

Distribution Costs

Total Expenditure on Food and Drink   £105 billion

Household   £70 billion
Catering   £35 billion

No. of Households   22 million

Source : Euro PA, CSO 'Business Monitor PA1002'

Finally and appropriately a further note on data should be given. Changes in the SIC classification have not helped the construction of a consistent and long series of data. Also, the aggregation within categories may mask important dynamic and specific effects. In the chapters that follow, data are used and presented that represent the best that are available at the moment. Much of this information is derived from market research or private trade sources and it should complement publicly available data. The Editors have tried to ensure that data used are up-to-date and generally consistent. However, the reader is asked to bear the caveat in mind that inconsistencies may still be apparent and thus caution should be exercised when using the text and numerical tables.

Appendix

The book chapters contain tables which describe the average performance of companies in each sector of the food and drink industry over a three year period. The parameters and indices used in the financial tables are defined as:

Turnover: Sales Revenue in the accounting period, less VAT, in £m

Profits: Are shown before tax, in £m

Return on Capital Employed (ROCE): Capital employed includes all the long-term funds in the balance sheet: shareholders' funds, plus long-term loans, and other miscellaneous long-term funds. Profit before tax is then expressed as a percentage of this to give return on capital employed.

Current Ratio: A ratio of current assets to current liabilities. A value in excess of 1.0 indicates current assets exceed current liabilities.

Debt Ratio: A ratio of total (current plus fixed) liabilities to total assets. A value greater than 1.0 indicates total liabilities exceeds total assets.

Caveat Whilst the tables offer a guide to the performance of companies they do not attempt to represent the current position at the date of going to print and nor do they distinguish between immediate liabilities and contingent and deferred liabilities. The publishers accept no liability for any errors or omissions in the statistical information presented and the reader is recommended to check the latest set of published accounts or sources in respect of any company in which he is interested.

The data used has been sourced from four publications, The Kompass directory, McMillans unquoted companies, the Hambro Company Guide and Company annual reports. The aim has been to produce three year average indices in the tables. Ideally, this three year average would be over the same period for each company. The reader should be wary of making comparisons between companies whose averages have been derived from different periods. With a UK recession in the late 1980's/early 1990's and the start of a recovery in the mid 1990's companies will generally have better results in recent years.

In the case of large companies, the focus is on the relevant subsidiaries rather than the whole group. Subsidiaries with large parent companies are in a different financial situation to smaller independent companies, and this can feed through into the averages calculated. Every attempt has been made to display data in a balanced and accurate manner, in order to give an unbiased view of company operation in the UK food and drink industry but the reader is advised to check current sources of data and annual accounts and form his own opinion.

The Editors wish to make it clear that the data and opinions expressed in the text and financial tables of the chapters of this book are not intended to imply or describe effective or ineffective handling of any business situation nor should they be used as the basis for an investment decision.

References

(EC) (Jan 14, 1994), Council Regulation No 40/94 on the Community trade mark, European Commission, Brussels, Belgium.

CSO (1995). Annual Abstract of Statistics, HMSO, London.

CSO (1994). Business Monitors MM20 and MQ20 - Overseas Trade Statistics of the United Kingdom, HMSO, London.

CSO (1994). Input-Output Tables for the United Kingdom 1990, HMSO, London.

CSO (1994). United Kingdom National Accounts, HMSO, London.

CSO (1981 and 1985). Business Monitor M014, HMSO, London.

CSO Business Monitor PA1002 (selected years) - Summary Volume - Report on the Census of Production, HMSO, London.

CSO (selected years). National Income and Expenditure, HMSO, London.

Department of Employment (1992). *Employment Gazette*, HMSO, London

DG VI (annual). *CAP Working Notes*. European Commission, Brussels, Belgium.

DTI (1995). *Competitiveness: Forging Ahead*, Cm. 2867, HMSO, London

DTI (1994). *The Uruguay Round of Multilateral Trade Negotiations 1986-94*, Cm. 2579, HMSO, London.

DTI (Undated). *Merger Control in Europe*. HMSO, London.

Dudley, J.W. (1989). *1992 - Strategies for the Single Market*. The Spartan Press Ltd, Lymington.

ESC (July 6, 1994) Opinion 849/94 on the Proposal for a European Parliament and Council regulation on the Community design and on the legal protection of designs, ESC, Brussel, Belgium.

Euro Analysis (1993) unpublished report R58. *A Review of Health and Nutrition Policy*, Euro PA & Associates, 11 Church Street, Northborough, Cambs, PE6 9BN, UK.

Euro Analysis (1992) unpublished report, R41. *CEPS seminar on Preparing the Internal Market in Food*. Euro PA & Associates, 11 Church Street, Northborough, Cambs, PE6 9BN, UK.

Financial Times (1994 and 1995). *FT500*, Financial Times, London

GATT (1994). *Agreement Establishing the World Trade Organisation Agreement on Agriculture*, Cm 2559, Misc No 17, HMSO, London.

Grieg, W.S. (1971). *The Economics of Food Processing.* Westport: AVI.

Hambros (various). *The Hambro Company Guide.* Hemington Scott Publishing Limited, London.

Harvard Business School (1994). *Cott Corporation: The European Entry,* Harvard Business School Publishing, Boston, Massachussetts, USA.

Harvard Business School (1993). *Cott Corporation: Private Label in the 1990s,* Harvard Business School Publishing, Boston, Massachussetts, USA

HoC (1992). Agricultural Committee Second Report, *The Trade Gap in Food and Drink,* Volume II, HMSO, London.

Kleinwort Benson Research (1995). *The Rise and Rise of Private Label,* Kleinwort Benson, 20 Fenchurch St, London EC3P 3DB.

Lund P.J, Hamilton C.B.J., and Price R.D.S. (1994). *UK Overseas Trade Statistics: Food, Feed and Drink,* Paper presented to Agricultural Economics Society Conference, MAFF, London.

MAFF (1994). *Food Safety Directorate Legislation Governing Labelling, Advertising & Composition of Food.* HMSO, London.

Mark, J. and Strange, R. (1993). The Food Industries, *Reviews of United Kingdom Statistical Sources* Ed Fleming, M.C., **(28)**, Chapman & Hall, London.

McGoldrick, P.J. (1984). *Grocery Generics - An Extension of the Private Label Concept,* European Journal of Marketing, **18**, pp 5-24.

McMillans (various). *McMillans Unquoted Companies.* McMillans Press Ltd, Basingstoke.

Newman Books (1995). *European Food Trades Directory 1995. Volume One - United Kingdom.* Newman Books Limited, London.

NFS (various). *Household Consumption and Expenditure.* Annual Report of the National Food Survey Committee. HMSO, London.

OECD (1993). *Taxation in OECD Countries,* OECD, Paris, France.

Painter, A.A, (1992). *Butterworth's Food Law,* (first edition) Butterworths.

Read Information (various). *Kompass,* Read Information Services, East Grinstead.

Rudolph, M.J. (1994). *The Food Product Development Process,* MCB British Food Journal, **97 (3)**, 3-11, University Press Limited, London

UBS (1993). Communication from UBS to the Chairman, Booker plc.

Chapter 2: Economic Theory and the Food and Drink Industry

Christine Ennew and Scott McDonald[1]

Introduction

Despite its importance to the economy as a whole, the food industry is relatively under-researched. Agricultural economists have devoted considerable effort and expertise to understanding the factors determining the production and consumption of agricultural products. Policy analysts have considerably enhanced our understanding of the effects of government intervention and, especially, the transfers of resources between different categories of society e.g. consumers, producers and taxpayers. Agricultural marketeers have analysed the processes and institutions associated with the movement of food products beyond the farm gate and provided useful information on the transmission of prices along the food chain. However, the other stages in the overall food system - food processing and food retailing have received rather less attention. In order to understand the production and consumption of food requires analyses of the behaviour of firms within the food processing and retailing sectors, particularly as the value-added in these sectors accounts for a substantial proportion of the total expenditure on food. Indeed, given the overall limits on the volume of food consumed, value-added in processing and retailing is set to increase thus reinforcing the importance of understanding the behaviour of these sectors.

The current chapter takes as its focus the economic analysis of the behaviour of food processing firms. This is not to understate the increasingly important role of the retailers, but for the purposes of this analysis, the retailers will be examined not as a sector themselves but rather as customers of the food processing industry. The chapter presents an economic analysis of the behaviour of firms and the nature of competition in the food processing sectors. Empirical evidence on the structure and performance of food processing is presented in general, but a more specific examination is reserved for the individual sector

---

1   Dr Christine Ennew is a Reader at the School of Management and Finance, Nottingham University; Dr Scott McDonald is a Lecturer at the Department of Economics, University of Sheffield. The Editors have made several additions and amendments to this chapter, but it remains largely the work of the authors.

chapters. The main objective of this chapter is to highlight the range of different economic issues which are relevant to the food industry and to provide a broad overview of their application.

The Economics of Competition in Food Processing

An understanding of the workings of the food and drink industry, as with any other industry, requires an understanding of the competitive process. The nature of the markets and the competitive environment within which food processors operate will affect their behaviour (pricing, production and marketing decisions) and their performance (profitability, sales growth etc.). However, this competitive environment is not stable; it undergoes continuous change and development. Firms must react to these changes and recognise that their behaviour may be constrained by the environment without losing sight of the potential to alter the environment in which they operate through their own strategic choices.

Given the complexity surrounding the workings of markets and the range and diversity of environmental influences on organisations, the process of simplification which characterises the economic analysis of competition can be a useful starting point. The standard economic analysis of the competitive process proceeds by simplifying the characteristics of a particular market environment and then examining the way in which price and output are determined in that environment. The economic description of a market is based on the number and size of buyers and sellers, the characteristics of the product, the height of barriers to entry and exit and the nature of information flows. These characteristics of the market condition the way in which firms behave, the prices and quantities which are realised and the overall level of economic welfare. Basic economic analysis identifies two extreme forms of market structure (perfect competition and monopoly) and two intermediate forms (monopolistic competition and oligopoly), with the two extreme forms providing the benchmarks against which the performance of other market structures can be assessed.

Perfect competition effectively describes a market in which there is no competition in the generally accepted sense of the word. The market is characterised by a large number of small producers, all of whom are price takers and thus face a perfectly elastic demand curve; there are no barriers to entry or exit, no product differentiation and there is perfect information. In long run equilibrium, the profit maximising rule of marginal revenue equals marginal costs means that price equals marginal and average total costs; there are no supernormal profits and producer and consumer surpluses are jointly maximised. In the opposite case, that of monopoly, there is a single producer (and many buyers); there are barriers to entry, perfect information and the product is undifferentiated. In order to profit maximise, the monopolist will still select the level of output at which marginal cost and marginal revenue are equal, but in this case, price (average revenue) is greater than marginal revenue and supernormal profits can be earned based on the difference between average revenue and average costs. The result is a lower level of output and a higher price than would occur under perfect competition. This price-output configuration results in a loss of consumer surplus and additional inefficiencies because the monopolist does not produce at lowest average cost.

Monopolistic competition and oligopoly represent intermediate stages between perfect competition and monopoly. In the case of monopolistic competition, the market continues to be characterised by a relatively large number of producers, but each produces a differentiated product. There are no major information problems and no barriers to entry or exit. In the case of perfect competition the buyer has no reason to prefer any one supplier over another; this is not the case in monopolistic competition. The products offered in the market are substitutes but not perfect substitutes; there are discernible differences between the products offered by different manufacturers and there is some element of brand loyalty. Consequently, producers are no longer price takers, they have some discretion in pricing and can expand their sales by reducing their prices (i.e. they face a downward sloping demand curve). In the short run, the firm in a monopolistically competitive industry will select the level of output at which marginal revenue and marginal cost are equal (as would the monopolist) and the result will be a lower level of output and a higher price than that which would have prevailed under conditions of perfect competition. However, short term supernormal profits attract new entrants and in the long term no supernormal profit is earned although there are inefficiencies because price does not equal marginal cost and firms do not produce at their lowest average cost.

While monopolistic competition relies on a large number of small scale producers, oligopoly is characterised by a small number of large scale producers and is a market structure in which there are typically barriers to entry and exit, in which information is not perfect and in which products may or may not be differentiated. The key feature of oligopoly is the high degree of interdependence between firms; whether any individual producer's decision results in the desired outcome depends upon the decisions taken by other producers. Thus industry level outcomes depend on what each individual firm does and how other firms react (the conjectural variations). Accordingly, there are many different oligopoly models based on different specifications for the conjectural variations and these include simple models in which one producer 'leads' the market and others follow; collusive models and more complex game theoretic models. Some aspects of oligopoly will be discussed in greater detail later in this chapter.

The extreme cases of perfect competition and monopoly provide benchmarks for the economic analysis of the competitive process but their direct relevance to real world markets is limited; in particular they are of little value when considering food processing. The dominance, in some markets, of a relatively small number of large scale producers suggests that models of oligopoly are perhaps more appropriate, while in other markets, the extent of product differentiation may indicate that models of monopolistic competition are required. Other markets may be a combination of the two, with a dominant, oligopolistic 'core' producing branded products while a more monopolistically competitive but 'peripheral' sector concentrates on the production of own-label products. In each case, it is apparent that we are dealing with imperfectly competitive markets, in which the degree of interdependence between firms is such that price and quantity outcomes are no longer uniquely determined by simple structural conditions such as number of producers and the degree of product differentiation.

Even recognising that the understanding of competition in food processing must be built around an understanding of imperfect competition may not be enough to capture fully the behaviour of the industry. Raw material costs are such that spatial issues have much greater significance for the food industries than for many other manufacturing sectors. The location of food processing factories bears witness to the importance of spatial factors, but these factors may then necessitate modifications to the analysis of competition which may need to be examined at a local rather than a national level. The significance of locational issues is developed later in this chapter.

From the above discussion it is apparent that once we move away from the simple microeconomic models of perfect competition and monopoly, understanding the process of competition becomes increasingly complex. Models of imperfect competition are rather more relevant to food processing, although they too are still problematic. In particular, the tendency to 'side step' issues of downstream market power (e.g. among retailers) is a significant weakness. Although the various economic models of competition are easily criticised, they do provide an organising framework for a more general analysis of competition based on the principle of linkages between market structure, the conduct of business and overall performance. These relationships are not uniquely determined, nor are they deterministic or one way, but the recognition of such linkages between structure, conduct and performance provides a useful analytic framework for understanding the food and drink industry.

Structure, Conduct and Performance

Underlying the economic analysis of the previous section is the concept of a link between the structure of a market, the conduct of firms in the market and the various performance outcomes. This is the well known Structure-Conduct-Performance model developed in industrial economics (Bain, 1958; Sawyer, 1981; Hay and Morris, 1991) which has provided one of the most widely used frameworks for the analysis of imperfectly competitive industries. An interesting variant of this model is found in the strategy literature and particularly in the work of Michael Porter (1980, 1985). Porter argues that the underlying attractiveness of a market depends on five forces - namely; the buying power of suppliers, the buying power of buyers, the threat of entry, the threat of substitutes and competitive rivalry. The performance of any individual firm will be partly determined by the structure of the market in which it operates but will also be influenced by the strategic decisions taken by the firm (conduct). As we shall see later, one of the advantages of the Porter perspective may be its rather greater generality when compared to traditional S-C-P, although this greater generality is achieved with the loss of some of the analytic rigour associated with S-C-P.

Market structure

In the context of S-C-P, the term 'market structure' covers those characteristics of a market which determine the inter-relationships between buyers and sellers; as such it includes the number and size of firms, the conditions of entry and exit and the degree of product differentiation. The number and size distribution of buyers and sellers is important because it affects market power - i.e. the ability of a firm to set price and output without reference to the competition. Generally, concentration measures are used as measures of market structure and market power (Pickering, 1974). Disparities in market power between buyers and sellers are likely to alter conduct and performance. For example, if the market power of sellers is much greater than that of buyers, it becomes possible for the sellers to maintain higher price levels and produce lower quantities than in a market with no disparities in market power - i.e., market power can enable a firm or group of firms to earn supernormal profits.

The presence of market power and the opportunity to implement such power are partially dependent on the presence of barriers to entry to the market. The term 'barriers to entry' covers all those factors which result in a potential new entrant being at a disadvantage in comparison with firms currently producing for the market in question. In addition, there are barriers to exit which include all those factors which make it difficult for firms to leave the industry. Barriers to entry are commonly of five types;

1. Where substantial economies of scale exist (in either production, distribution or marketing), a new entrant will need to make substantial and costly investments in order to be able to compete with firms currently involved with the product.

2. Firms currently producing the product concerned may possess absolute cost advantages - for example, the cost of production may have been reduced by a learning process, or firms may have preferential access to raw materials.

3. The existence of patents or intellectual property rights may prevent new firms from adopting the most economically efficient production or sales techniques.

4. The size of the market may be restricted by demand conditions.

5. The existence of product differentiation and consumer loyalty may create a situation in which a new entrant has to exert considerable effort and undertake substantial expenditure (e.g. advertising) in order to gain a foothold in the market. However, product differentiation may also serve to encourage new entrants who may be able to overcome existing barriers to entry by offering a slightly different product to the market.

The presence of any or all of these factors can create barriers to entry, protecting firms already in the industry and allowing those firms to earn somewhat higher profits than would have been allowed in the absence of such barriers. Generally, the higher the barrier to entry, the greater the scope for firms in the industry to depart from a competitive price level and thus earn higher profits. This effect is not created by the presence of barriers to entry; their presence simply serves to provide some degree of isolation from the effects of competition for firms in an industry. This in turn allows those firms to exercise greater discretion in their output and pricing decisions.

At the other extreme, the structure of a market may be affected by the presence of barriers to exit. These can be defined as economic or institutional conditions which increase the opportunity cost of leaving the industry and in so doing, make it preferable for inefficient or even loss-making firms to remain in production. Barriers to exit can be of many sorts, but perhaps the most commonly encountered are factors such as poor resource mobility or low salvage value for assets. The presence of such barriers would tend to result in excess capacity within the industry and a misallocation of resources as competition would not force all the inefficient firms to cease production. One consequence of this may be that the degree of competitive rivalry in the industry increases as firms which cannot exit engage in greater price competition.

Market Conduct

When the particular structural characteristics of a market have been defined - the level of concentration, the nature and height of barriers to entry - they can be seen as directing firms in the industry towards certain types of behaviour. This behaviour in turn results in a particular performance outcome for the market.

Market conduct refers to the strategy or form of behaviour chosen by the firm in pursuit of its specified objectives. Of particular importance, from an economist's perspective, is pricing policy and patterns of reaction on the part of firms to changes in the conduct of other firms. The existence of an objective function is implicit in any definition of conduct. In the traditional S-C-P framework, the firm's objective was always taken to be profit maximisation. In a sense, there could be no debate about the choice of such an objective for the perfectly competitive firm; profit maximisation was a condition of survival in the long run. For the monopolist, profit maximisation was seen as a rational objective and its use gave consistency across the two models. When the perfectly competitive market ceases to be a normative ideal, the need to rely on profit maximisation as the appropriate objective function no longer exists. It becomes possible to consider firms as acting according to a greater variety of objectives with profit maximisation just one possibility. The implication is that conduct is not uniquely pre-determined by structure as in the traditional model, but rather that firms may act according to any one of a number of objective functions (sales maximisation, managerial perks, etc.) and may take a satisficing rather than a maximising approach. Some degree of insulation from competition as a result of market imperfections means that profit maximisation is no longer essential for survival. Consequently, firms may exercise a degree of discretion as regards conduct.

Given the specification of the appropriate objective function, the purpose of examining conduct is to identify the methods employed by a firm in pursuit of that objective. There are numerous dimensions of conduct, though certain areas warrant particular interest because of their obvious implications for performance. Price and output decisions are of obvious

importance because of their welfare implications, but these are accompanied by variables such as advertising, sales promotion, product design and quality, the practice of predatory or exclusionary tactics, product branding and own-label products. A given market structure will permit firms to engage in such activities to a greater or lesser extent and the nature of the tactics adopted will in turn have implications for performance. While it is admitted that the postulated relationships between structure, conduct and performance are too deterministic, in the sense that structural and behavioural variables are necessary but not sufficient for a particular performance outcome (Sosnick, 1958), these factors are taken to be the systematic determinants of performance with any other influences being primarily random effects.

Market Performance

Definitions of market structure and market conduct are fairly clear cut. The definition of performance is rather more complex. There is the problem of specifying the appropriate dimension of performance, for example, does it refer to market performance or firm performance. The two are quite different and the distinction is important. The notion of market performance is concerned primarily with notions of economic efficiency in terms of the benefits accruing within the economy as a result of the specific operation of that market, and the cost it imposes. Firm performance is more concerned with the extent to which a firm has satisfied its own objectives. There is no guarantee that the two will be the same, except in the case of a perfectly competitive market. Hence, there is no universally accepted set of performance criteria although some of the more important ones are listed below:

1. The level of price relative to costs of production, bearing in mind the extent to which any economies of size or scale exist, the ideal being a price which just covers production costs and provides an adequate return on capital.

2. Capacity utilisation is important as a way of identifying whether competition has weeded out the inefficient producers. The presence of excess capacity may be indicative of market imperfections which prevent the efficient reallocation of under-utilised resources.

3. The level of advertising costs and sales promotion expenditure relative to the overall costs of production is an indicator of product suitability. Excess expenditure on advertising is a welfare loss and suggests that there is not an adequate market for the product

concerned. The notion of product suitability is important in general because of its effects on consumer welfare.

4. The degree of progressiveness of the industry must also be considered - particularly its willingness to adopt and adapt to new technologies. Again the implication is that adaptivity and progressiveness are representative of competition, i.e. technical progress is a condition of survival.

There are obvious parallels in the specification of decision variables for firm conduct and the outcome variables for market performance. These parallels arise because the decision variables specified for firm conduct will define firm performance, and the sum of firm performances defines market performance. This implicit link is generally shortened such that the measurement of market performance is based on the decisions taken by firms in pursuit of their own objectives.

Much of the analysis of market structure and its implications for conduct and performance has been based on the analysis and modelling of oligopoly, since this is arguably the most widespread form of market structure. Given the significance of oligopoly in the economic analysis of modern industry and business, it is appropriate to explore the economics of oligopoly in a little more detail.

Models of Oligopoly

As explained in the previous sections, the key feature of oligopoly is interdependence. Thus, while perfect competition is characterised by an absence of rivalry and monopoly is characterised by an absence of rivals, this is not the situation for firms in markets where the structure is oligopolistic. This places an emphasis upon how a firm reacts to its rivals' conduct and how it expects its rivals to react to its own conduct - the so-called conjectural variations. Since it is possible to conceive of a vast array of conjectures about conduct, it is possible to develop an almost endless array of different oligopolistic models. Hence the arguably simplistic conclusions derivable from perfect competition and monopoly are not repeated in the realm of oligopoly models. Moreover, the strong preference among economists towards models that yield deterministic solutions for prices and quantities, typically requires the adoption of restrictive assumptions. The critical point that derives from these features of oligopoly models is that models tend to be case specific rather than general.

The role of conjectural variations can be seen most easily in simple models that derive from a classic representation of structure-conduct-performance model. Interdependence within an industry means that actions by one firm have implications for all other firms in that industry. This can be seen most starkly in a model where the only variable at a firm's discretion is output, thus the number of firms remains constant at N, with each firm producing an identical product sold to price-takers using inputs purchased at fixed prices. Hence the price received by a firm is dependent upon the total output of the industry, and the firm's profit (Π_i) function can be written as

$$\Pi_i = p(Q)q_i - C_i(q_i) \tag{1}$$

where q_i = the output of the ith firm;
        Q = the output of the industry;
        $$= \sum_i^N q_i$$
        $C_i(q_i)$ = the cost function of the ith firm;

and the first order condition for profit maximisation is given by differentiation with respect to the firm's output,

$$\frac{d\Pi_i}{dq_i} = p + q_i \frac{dp}{dQ} \cdot \frac{dQ}{dq_i} - C_i' = 0 \tag{2}$$

that is where marginal revenue is equal to marginal cost C_i' .

The critical component of (2), in the context of interdependence, is the relationship between the change in the firm's output and the change in the industry's output, dQ/dq_i, since the change in the industry's output determines the price received by the firm. This can be expanded to give

$$\frac{dQ}{dq_i} = \frac{dq_i}{dq_i} + \frac{d(Q-q_i)}{dq_i} \equiv 1 + \lambda_i \tag{3}$$

which simply identifies the need for the firm to make a conjecture about how other firms will change their output in response to changes in its own output $d(Q-q_i)/dq_i$. Thus it can be argued   that "[D]ifferent oligopoly theories ..... can be viewed as assuming different conjectures about λ_i " (Waterson, 1984, p19).

An important general result was derived by Cowling and Waterson (1976). Assuming that all firms have the same cost functions and the same conjectural variations, then from (1), and noting that all firms will be the same size, the Lerner index of monopoly power for the industry is

$$\frac{p - C'}{p} = \frac{(1 + \lambda)}{N|\eta|}.$$

(4)

Thus the industry's performance, its price-cost margin, is a product of its structure, i.e. the number of firms and demand conditions, and its conduct, captured by the conjectural variations term.

A more general result can be achieved by allowing costs and conjectural variations to differ across firms. Assuming marginal cost is equal to average variable cost for each firm, the ratio of an industry's profit plus fixed cost to total revenue, profit-revenue ratio, can be written as

$$\frac{\Pi + F}{R} = \frac{\sum_i^N s_i^2 (1 + \lambda_i)}{|\eta|} = \frac{H}{|\eta|} \cdot \left(1 + \frac{\sum_i^N s_i^2 \lambda_i}{\sum_i^N s_i^2} \right) = \frac{H}{|\eta|} \cdot (1 + \mu)$$

(5)

Again the industry's performance is a product of its structure, as defined by the Herfindahl index of structure (H) and demand conditions, and its 'average' conduct defined as the share weighted sum of the firm specific conjectural variations. Expressions (4) and (5) can be used to summarise a range of competitive conditions. For monopoly $H = 1$ and $\lambda_i = 0$, an absence of rivals, and thus they simplify to

$$\frac{\Pi + F}{R} = \frac{p - C'}{p} = \frac{1}{|\eta|}$$

(6)

which is the well-known condition for profit maximisation by a monopolist, whereas for perfect competition, H tends to zero, as do λ and μ,[2] and hence price equals marginal cost.

The presence of demand conditions in (4) and (5) are of potentially important interest with respect to the food industry. Since the price

---

2   There is an absence of rivalry.

elasticities of demand for the vast majority of food products are low relative to the majority of manufactured products, this model suggests that for any given industry structure and conduct it would be reasonable to expect performance, as measured by price-cost margins or profit-revenue ratios, to be relatively 'better' in the food industry.[3]

Among the appealing features of the Cournot model, also captured by the Cowling and Waterson model, is the fact that if the number of firms equals one the model reduces to that of monopoly and as the number of firms increases so the model tends to the perfect competition case, provided average costs are non-decreasing. This type of model is particularly suited to strategic interactions that are conducted in terms of variations in the outputs of the firms in the industry. Commonly, industrial organisation models that use this type of formulation assume firms adopt Cournot strategies, and a large number of models have been developed that examine the properties of such models, with particular reference to their Nash equilibria and welfare implications. For the food industry it would appear that the most fruitful application of conjectural variations in quantities may relate to those food processors who produce largely undifferentiated products, or so-called first-stage food processors.

Typically non-collusive Bertrand (price adjusting) strategies are inconsistent with the realisation of profits when products are homogeneous because firms face incentives to bid prices down to marginal costs. If price is the firm's decision variable then the firm's profit function can be written as

$$\Pi_i = p_i q_i - C_i(q_i) \tag{7}$$

where $\quad p_i = f_i(q_1, q_2, \ldots, q_N)$

but the first-order condition with respect to quantities does not yield a conjectural variation term. An alternative is to maximise with respect to price, see Waterson (1984, pp 26-28) or Cubbin (1983), in which case the first-order condition for a profit maximum with respect to (own) price is

$$\frac{d\Pi_i}{dp_i} = q_i + p_i \frac{dq_i}{dp_i} - \frac{dC_i}{dq_i}\frac{dq_i}{dp_i} = 0 \tag{8}$$

---

3   This presumes that the elasticity of substitution between the characteristic commodities of different industry groups is the same. For the food industry many obvious substitutes are allocated to different industry groups, e.g. butter, part of 'preparation of milk and milk products' and margarine, part of 'organic oils and fats'.

and a conjectural variations term can be identified by the expansion of dq_i/dp_i to

$$\frac{dq_i}{dp_i} = \frac{\partial q_i}{\partial p_i} + \sum_{j \neq i}^{N} \frac{\partial q_i}{\partial p_j} \frac{dp_j}{dp_i} \tag{9}$$

and the conjectures of firm i about the response of firm j to the effect of changes in its price is given by dp_j/dp_i.

Cubbin demonstrates that by rearranging (8) to yield a price-cost margin and manipulating (9) it is possible to derive an expression relating the price-cost margin to demand conditions and conjectural variations, i.e.,

$$\frac{p_i - C_i'}{p_i} = \frac{1}{\alpha |\eta_I| + (1-\alpha)|\eta_i|} \tag{10}$$

where $\quad \alpha = \dfrac{\displaystyle\sum_{j \neq i}^{N} \frac{\partial q_i}{\partial p_j} \cdot \frac{dp_j}{dp_i}}{\displaystyle\sum_{j \neq i}^{N} \frac{\partial q_i}{\partial p_j}}$;

η_I = industry elasticity of demand;

η_i = firm elasticity of demand, if other firms hold their prices constant;

but (10) contains no expression for the number of firms in the industry. Waterson demonstrates (1984, p 28) that, "if the cross-elasticity between products does not fall as their number increase" (p 28) then the price-cost margin falls as the number of firms increases, i.e. structure does matter.

This type of model appears particularly suited to circumstances characterised by product differentiation, hence unsurprisingly, it can be related to models of monopolistic competition. A standard representation of Chamberlin's large numbers monopolistic competition model presumes that firms do not recognise interdependence, because of the large number of firms, and hence implicitly assumes that $\alpha = 0$ in (10), which amounts to presuming that their demand curve is independent of the industry's demand curve. On the other hand, if it is assumed that $\alpha = 1$ in (10), then firms act in a manner equivalent to full collusion, whether this happens explicitly or not, and thus the industry realises maximum (monopoly) profits and the issue of stability of the model becomes a prime concern.

In practice it is probably reasonable to argue that firms within a concentrated industry are aware of interdependence and hence that α is greater than zero although it may be less than one. Thus, where monopolistic competition models are appropriate, it may be realistic to expect models that are intermediate to the standard monopolistic competition examples, to be the most appropriate for an understanding of competitive interactions. Indeed, the extent of product branding by food industries, from premium private labelled products through own-labelled products to generic products, indicates the existence of an awareness of interdependence. This suggests that conjectural variations terms in price may be most appropriate in the context of second-stage food processors.

A classical variant on the Cournot model is the price-leadership model developed by von Stackelberg whereby firms recognise the reactions of their competitors. This has led to a class of conjectural variations known as consistent, or rational, conjectures. Kamien and Schwartz (1983) argued that conventional Cournot conjectures, which presume an absence of reaction by rivals, so-called zero conjectural variations, are unacceptable for five key reasons:

i)   in the case of sequential reactions firms "are bound to observe that rivals do in fact react to their actions" (p 193);

ii)   zero conjectural variations lead to a logical inconsistency, specifically "the firm is in the position of believing that it is optimal to respond to its rivals' actions while also believing that its rivals will not react to its choices" (p 193);

iii)   because zero conjectural variations do not maximise joint profits incentives exist for firms to seek additional profits, i.e., the basis for the von Stackelberg (price leadership) and Chamberlin (tacit collusion) criticisms;

iv)   the criticism that price, not quantity, is the most probable decision variable for a firm has been developed to show that the equilibrium is a consequence not only of the decision variable (price or quantity) but also the assumption about conjectural variations, specifically "[Z]ero conjectural variation in quantity (price) does not correspond to zero conjectural variation in price (quantity)" (p 194);

v)   empirical evidence is not consistent with zero conjectural variations.

In light of these criticisms Kamien and Schwartz argue that zero conjectural variations are logically inconsistent and therefore they focus on non-zero conjectural variations. Kamien and Schwartz argue that in a homogenous good market "that a harmonic sum of the conjectural variation ... contains all the relevant information about market structure ... and conduct ... for determining market performance ....", and that "the more homogeneous beliefs are, the smaller is industry output" (Kamien and Schwartz, 1983, p 209). Arguably it would be reasonable to expect that the more stable the demand conditions facing an industry the more likely are the beliefs of firms in that industry to converge. Given that the food industry faces relatively stable demand conditions this would suggest the possibility that the output of food processing industries producing largely undifferentiated products may be reduced by the presence of consistent conjectures. For differentiated product markets conjectural variations in price and quantities "are equivalent in the sense of yielding the same price and output .... in symmetric equilibrium", and that if demand is linear and conjectures are consistent "the same equilibrium price and quantity will be attained if either conjectural variation is constant" (Kamien and Schwartz, 1983, p 210).

Structure-Performance and the Food Processing Industry

Although the idea of relating structure to conduct and performance provides a useful framework within which any industry can be analysed, it is important to recognise that it has a number of limitations. The conventional S-C-P approach has a tendency to presume that an industry's competitive relationships can be analysed with scant reference to the nature of its input and output markets. An implication of this appears to be the presumption that input and output markets are competitive. This weakness is addressed to some degree in the Porter framework which explicitly recognises the bargaining power of suppliers and customers as determinants of market structure. In the food processing sector, there is a particular need explicitly to recognise the significance of supply and demand side conditions. Specifically, while price-taking may be a reasonable presumption when referring to food processors' interactions in some input markets, it is notable that a large proportion of input costs are accounted for by purchases from agricultural markets where prices are predominantly administered. Similarly, on the output side, food processors overwhelmingly sell to food retailers/food distributors who would appear to have very substantial scope for the exercise of market power (McDonald, Rayner and Bates, 1989).

Thus, the simple S-C-P framework by itself may not cover all the facets of the food industry. Furthermore, there is a need to consider some of the broader aspects of structure and to recognise the dynamics of structural change. In addition to influencing the behaviour of firms, the 'Structures' observed in the food processing industries may also be a consequence of competitive interactions with downstream activities (retailing) because the ability to exercise market power upstream has been constrained by agricultural price support schemes. Thus, the structural concentration of the food processing industry may be as much a product of competitive interactions as a determinant of performance. For example, the number and size of firms in a sector may reflect a need, or a desire, to counter the market power of the food distribution system if a firm is to maintain a visible (e.g. brand) presence in the market (see for example, Howe, 1983 or Shaw, Burt and Dawson, 1989).

Market Concentration

Clearly then, any consideration of structure in the food industry must take these broader factors into consideration, although this is not to under-estimate the importance of examining more traditional measures of industry structure such as concentration. Traditionally, the level of concentration has been one of the standard theoretical and empirical measures of market structure and there is (at least in relative terms) a considerable amount of information available in this area.

The published summary measures for the United Kingdom are concentration ratios (CR_k). Chapters Three to Nine utilise these ratios wherever possible, to illustrate the concentration in each of the sectors of the industry. These ratios indicate that the majority of the food industry groups often exceed a concentration ratio above which substantial price-cost margins may arise, i.e., CR_4 = 45-59%. Indeed, the UK food sector is thought to be one of the most concentrated in Europe (Shaw, Burt and Dawson, 1989). The high level of concentration in food processing in the UK is not unique; other European countries do have relatively high levels of concentration and similar patterns have been observed in the US food sector (Connor *et al*, 1985). But, for an open economy, the extent to which the observed levels of concentration reflect a correspondingly high level of market power has been questioned because of the (alleged) pro-competitive benefits of trade (Maunder, 1988), and the explicit recognition of the size of markets in the EU when deciding competition policy in Europe (DTI, undated). However, when compared to the information provided by Herfindahl indices (Slenwaeger and Delaudschutter, 1986), it has been argued that concentration ratios may be biased indicators of industry structure where industry concentration is high (CR4 > 50%). Hence Herfindahl indices have been estimated from Census of Production data for food industries on the bases of Net and Gross Outputs by establishments.[4] However, these estimates may be simultaneously underestimates of supply-side concentration and overestimates of demand-side concentration. Summary measures of the structure of the UK food processing industries (Tables 2.1 and 2.2), on the basis of the given product definitions, indicate that the degree of concentration is high and has increased over the period 1980-92; and further, that concentration is, with few exceptions, greater on a net output than on a gross output basis.

In some cases the use of principal products as the basis for the classification procedure may generate overestimates of demand side concentration as a consequence of both cross substitution between products and competition from imported processed food products. For example, concentration measures for the margarine market may indicate a relatively high degree of concentration in production, but from the perspective of the consumer there is actually a much greater choice of suppliers because of the opportunity to substitute butter for margarine. In addition, it is probable that these summary measures to some extent understate the degree of supply-side concentration because of the growth of conglomerates with subsidiaries operating across a range of different product categories, and because the Herfindahl Index (H-index) estimates are based on an average firm share derived as mid-points from summary data presented by employment size categories in the Censuses of Production.

A comparison of concentration on a Net Output (Table 2.1) and a Gross Output (Table 2.2) basis at both establishment and enterprise level shows that the degree of concentration is, for the vast majority of cases, greater on the Net Output basis (Table 2.1). This suggests that advantages of 'scale' (of production) exist for food processing, i.e., the size of the representative, or average, establishment/plant is greater on the Net Output basis. There is some suggestion of economies of 'size' from the

---

4   It was not considered appropriate to use data on the number of enterprises because of the element of double counting of enterprises in the Censuses of Production data. The Herfindahl Index for the jth industry is defined as

$$H_j = \sum_{i=1}^{n} s_{ij}^2$$

where s_{ij} = the share of the ith firm in the jth industry's output;

n = the number of the firms in the jth industry.

See Sawyer (1971) on the estimation of summary structure measures from Census of Production data.

Herfindahl indices based upon enterprise data, but double counting of enterprises in the Censuses of Production distorts the estimated Herfindahl indices and hence makes deductions from the estimates dubious. More generally, although there is some evidence of economies of scale and size, it is generally felt that these effects by themselves are insufficient to explain the observed level of concentration and that they do not constitute substantial barriers to entry (Connor et al, 1985; Maunder, 1988). The exclusion of non-industrial services may thus produce a biased picture; indeed if the consistent trend from 1973 to 1979, whereby non-industrial services were an increasing proportion of net output for food processors, held over the period 1958-72 then the net output proxy would tend to increasingly overstate the relative percentage value-added for food processors.

Table 2.1: Herfindahl Indices Food Processors, (Gross Output and Establishments)

Group		1980	1984	1988	1992
411	Organic oils and fats	0.0601	0.0948	0.0756	0.0638
		16.6	10.5	13.2	15.7
412	Slaughtering of animals and production of meat and by-products	0.0086	0.0039	0.0025	0.0055
		115.8	253.4	404.9	181.7
413	Preparation of milk and milk products	0.0205	0.0252	0.0304	0.0243
		48.8	39.7	32.9	41.2
414	Processing of fruit and vegetables	0.0311	0.0226	0.0280	0.0220
		32.1	44.3	35.7	45.4
415	Fish Processing	0.0450	0.0659	0.0678	0.0458
		22.2	15.2	14.8	21.8
416	Grain milling	0.0398	0.0453	0.0473	0.0474
		25.1	22.1	21.1	21.1
419	Bread, biscuits and flour confectionery	0.0126	0.0110	0.0081	0.0064
		79.1	91.2	123.5	156.9
420	Sugar and sugar by-products[5]	n/a	n/a	n/a	n/a
421	Ice cream, cocoa, chocolate and sugar confectionery	0.0536	0.0736	0.0670	0.0787
		18.6	13.6	14.9	12.7
422	Animal feeding stuffs	0.0120	0.0142	0.0245	0.0313
		83.5	70.2	40.8	32.0
423	Starch and miscellaneous foods	0.0245	0.0214	0.0222	0.0268
		40.8	46.7	45.1	37.3

Source: Census of Production(various years).

There is no unambiguous pattern with regard to the first-stage/second-stage distinction. However, on average, first-stage processors are more concentrated than second-stage processors, but little can be deduced from this evidence. Specifically, since first-stage processing industries

---

5   The Censuses of Production do not report data for 'Sugar and Sugar by-products' by employment-size categories because of the non-disclosure agreements upon which data are collected.

are, on average, appreciably smaller than second-stage food processing industries, both in terms of employment, and gross and net output, it is hardly surprising that they record higher Herfindahl indices. Having noted that, it is probable that if the characterisation of first-stage processing as being more orientated towards bulk processing was correct it would not be unreasonable to expect to find evidence that firms/plants were, on average, larger.

Table 2.2:   Herfindahl Indices Food Processors (Net Output and Establishments)

Group		1980	1984	1988	1992
411	Organic oils and fats	0.0708	0.1115	0.1183	0.0841
		14.1	9.0	8.5	11.9
412	Slaughtering of animals and production of meat and by-products	0.0139	0.0078	0.0024	0.0079
		72.1	128.3	411.3	126.8
413	Preparation of milk and milk products	0.0201	0.0255	0.0276	0.0222
		49.8	39.3	36.3	45.1
414	Processing of fruit and vegetables	0.0392	0.0213	0.0293	0.0390
		25.5	46.9	34.2	25.6
415	Fish Processing	0.0623	0.0860	0.0894	0.0582
		16.1	11.6	11.2	17.2
416	Grain milling	0.0426	0.0531	0.0521	0.0492
		23.5	18.8	19.2	20.3
419	Bread, biscuits and flour confectionery	0.0133	0.0136	0.0088	0.0071
		75.3	73.6	113.2	140.7
420	Sugar and sugar by-products	n/a	n/a	n/a	n/a
421	Ice cream, cocoa, chocolate and sugar confectionery	0.0574	0.0841	0.0780	0.0875
		17.4	11.9	12.8	11.4
422	Animal feeding stuffs	0.0264	0.0347	0.0522	0.0564
		37.9	28.8	19.2	17.7
423	Starch and miscellaneous foods	0.0318	0.0249	0.0285	0.0304
		31.4	40.1	35.1	32.9

Source: Census of Production(various years).

Other Dimensions of Structure

While concentration is often seen as one of the simplest dimensions of market structure, particularly for the purposes of statistical analysis, other dimensions of structure should not be ignored. Indeed in the context of the food industry, dimensions of particular relevance are product differentiation, branding and advertising, buyer and supplier power and barriers to entry.

Descriptive studies of the food industry indicate the potential importance of product differentiation, as does any visit to a supermarket. An understanding of the role of product differentiation in competition within the food industry is complicated by the existence of branded and own-label products which emerge from both food processors and food retailers. Hence, a truly general model of product differentiation within the food system requires the consideration of not only competitive interactions between food processors, but also between food retailers and between food processors and food retailers. The current discussion will be restricted to the first two types of interaction while the third form will be discussed under the heading of vertically related markets.

The two most common approaches to product differentiation are Lancaster's (1966) characteristic approach and the spatial analogy owing to Hotelling (1929). Both these frameworks provide explanations for product differentiation that are based upon differences between products and provide broadly similar insights into product differentiation. Lancaster's characteristics approach argues that consumers purchase commodities for the characteristics embodied within the commodities and hence, because consumers have a variety of tastes, each commodity will have a demand curve over a range of prices. A crucial presumption of the Lancaster model is that products are combinable, and although this may be a difficult concept for certain commodities, e.g. cars, it is not for food. Indeed, to the extent that all food products supply nutrients, i.e. protein, energy, vitamins, minerals etc., the Lancaster approach is especially useful for analysis of the demand for food. Clearly, many food products are substitutes for each other. Combined with a consideration of other characteristics of possible interest, e.g. texture, flavour, etc., this is a particularly useful conceptual model.

Hotelling was concerned with the location of consumers in space, but with care his analysis can be extended to encompass product differentiation. In particular the spatial analogy can be applied to particular characteristics of commodities, e.g. sweetness, such that consumers can be assumed to be located over a continuum according to their preferences for the particular characteristic. This type of model requires two key assumptions:

i)   the particular characteristic is supplied at a positive cost, and that the cost increases with the intensity of the characteristic;

ii)   the industry is characterised by scale economies, or otherwise the commodities produced would be consumer specific.

An important result derived from Hotelling models is that product differentiation provides the necessary conditions for the persistence of long-run equilibrium profits. Schmalensee (1978) demonstrates that entry will continue, i.e. new products will be produced, provided the product space available, i.e. the size of the market that can be captured, is sufficiently large as to generate profits. If the location of existing firms is fixed, i.e. the characteristics of their product are fixed, then the optimal location for a new product will be midway between two existing products which implies it will only be able to capture half the number of consumers that had previously purchased from its neighbours.[6] In a dynamic context an increase in the density of customers, and/or a decrease in the costs of production (technical progress), would encourage entry, but this would not alter the conclusion that profits can persist in the long-run.

Moreover, Hotelling models of product differentiation provide an explanation for product proliferation as a means of entry deterrence. If an existing market is characterised by a single producer but the market density is increasing, then ultimately space will exist in the market that encourages entry. Existing firms could pre-empt entry by locating products in these spaces before new firms enter the industry and hence preserve long term profits. Furthermore, if an existing firm enjoys either cost advantages when introducing a new product, or can locate the new product so as to realise larger future profits, it is likely to be willing to introduce a new product before a new entrant would wish to enter the market.[7] Schmalensee (1978) has argued that the ready-to-eat breakfast cereal industry in the USA used brand proliferation to "deter entry and protect profits" (p 305).

The issue of brands and advertising has many links to the discussion of product differentiation. Whereas the discussion of product differentiation implicitly presumed the existence of 'real' differences between products, this discussion of advertising will assume no 'real' differences but the existence of differences in perception relating to brands.

Standard textbook discussions of advertising draw upon the Dorfman-Steiner condition which defines the optimal ratio of advertising expenditure to revenue i.e.

$$\frac{A}{R} = \frac{|\eta_A|}{|\eta|} \tag{11}$$

where A = advertsing expenditure;

R = revenue;

$|\eta_A|$ = advertising elasticity of demand;

$|\eta|$ = price elasticity of demand.

---

6   Eaton and Lipsey (1978) provide a general model that supports this conclusion.
7   Under a standard Hotelling model a new entrant would have an incentive to locate towards the centre of the spectrum of possible products, whereas an existing firm would seek to locate so as to evenly distribute the market. Even relaxing the assumptions in the Hotelling model would still leave the entrant with an incentive to locate nearer the existing product than would the existing firm.

This condition indicates that the advertising/revenue ratio should increase with the absolute value of the advertising elasticity of demand and decline with the absolute value of the price elasticity of demand, which implies that *ceteris paribus* the advertising/revenue ratio would be relatively high for the food industry. As table 2.4 shows, this is not the case. This standard Dorfman-Steiner condition implicitly refers to circumstances of the firm as the industry whereas for an oligopolistic industry a number of firms would exist. It is therefore instructive to ask whether the advertising/revenue ratio would increase or decrease as the number of firms in the industry increases. A simple model developed by Waterson (1984, pp 131-133) suggests that the effect on the advertising/revenue ratio may be ambiguous[8]. Assuming, among other things that all firms have the same cost functions, and therefore are equal sized, and adopt a Cournot strategy, a variant of the Dorfman-Steiner condition that includes the number of firms in the industry is derived, i.e.

$$\frac{A}{R} = \frac{|\eta_A| + N - 1}{N^2 |\eta|} \qquad (12)$$

where $N =$ the number of firms in the industry;

As Table 2.3 shows, for low advertising elasticities of demand a monopoly would have a smaller advertising/revenue ratio than an oligopoly with a small number of firms, but that as the number of firms increases so the optimal advertising/revenue ratio would decline.

Table 2.3:   Advertising/Sales Ratios for Selected Food Products (1990)

Product	Advertising/Sales Ratio
Bread	0.41
Flour	0.41
Milk	0.49
Sugar	1.25
Biscuits	1.12
Cereals	10.34
Confectionery	2.98
Frozen Pasta	14.26
Margarine	8.86
Potato crisps/snacks	3.67
Frozen Veg	0.85
Frozen meat/meat products	0.89
Food	1.46

Source: Advertising Association (1992)

---

8   For a development of the Dorfman-Steiner model for 'optimal' generic advertising of food products see Strak (1983).

Models based on the expenditure/revenue ratio may present a biased image. The Dorfman-Steiner condition presumes that advertising expenditure is an appropriate measure of the quantity of 'messages' conveyed. An important potential role of advertising by food processors may be the creation and/or sustaining of barriers to entry, and by reinforcing brand loyalty to protect their market share.

The evidence for the existence of barriers to entry based on production economies of scale is limited, although there is rather more evidence of the existence of economies of scale and size in relation to marketing. In particular, there is evidence to suggest that sunk costs in the form of advertising expenditure may constitute a significant barrier in some, but not all sectors of food processing (Sutton, 1992). However, the extent of advertising, as indicated by the advertising/sales ratios, for different product categories varies substantially (Table 2.4).

Moreover, the existence of national and international brands may be of particular significance and while these do not prevent entry they tend to imply that where entry occurs it is more likely to be in the form of mergers with, or acquisition of, established players rather than through the entry of new players.

Table 2.4:   Advertising Expenditure and the Number of Firms

Price Elasticity of Demand = 0.5				
	Number of Firms			
Advertising elasticity of demand	1	3	5	10
0.1	0.20	0.47	0.33	0.18
0.5	1.00	0.56	0.36	0.19
1	2.00	0.67	0.40	0.20
1.5	3.00	0.78	0.44	0.21
Price Elasticity of Demand = 2.0				
	Number of Firms			
Advertising elasticity of demand	1	3	5	10
0.1	0.05	0.12	0.08	0.05
0.5	0.25	0.14	0.09	0.05
1	0.50	0.17	0.10	0.05
1.5	0.75	0.19	0.11	0.05

Source : Calculations from equation 12

Market Performance

The structure-performance paradigm argues that there should be a positive correlation between the measures of an industry's structure and its performance. To simply define the measure of performance as the absolute level of profits is obviously dubious. A more sophisticated approach would be to evaluate profit rates in food processing (and food retailing) against a suitable comparator. Usable data have been reported by the MMC (1981) and Slater (1987) with profit rates defined as a percentage of capital worth. Unfortunately the series are not continuous, and Slater's series is available with capital valued at historic cost only; even so the data can provide an indication as to the general movement in relative profit rates. One method of doing this is to re-express the profit rates of the two food industry sectors relative to those of a comparator sector, e.g. all UK manufacturing, and then regress the resultant series against time (a similar technique was used by Howe, 1983). The magnitude of the slope coefficient then indicates the rate of change in relative profit rates, and its sign the direction of change; the intercept term indicates the relative profit levels in a base period.

The results for the UK are presented in Table 2.5. They indicate that both food processing and retailing earned above average profits in the base periods (Equations 1, 2, 4 and 5) and that the relative profit rates for retailers increased over time. The evidence for food processing is conflicting: for the 1965-77 period there was no substantive and significant change in food processing's relative profit rate (Equation 1), but for 1970-85 there was a minor but significant upward trend in the relative profit rate (Equation 4). Within the food system there is evidence that not only did food retailing earn significantly greater absolute profits than food processing, but that the differences were increasing over time (Equations 3 and 6). The estimates are consistent with the presence of market power in the food processing sector that is greater than that typical for manufacturing, and that this remained broadly constant over the data periods. Similarly the evidence supports the conjecture that retailing possesses appreciable market power, and was able to increase its market power relative to both food processing and the rest of the economy. These results should be treated with caution. The matters of the correct valuation of capital and the appropriate definition of profits alone raise doubts about the data, and the estimates are not as robust as the test statistics may indicate.[9]

---

9   Note the omission of observations when using the Slater series - their inclusion generates a negative slope coefficient which plots of the observations suggest to be anomalous.

Table 2.5:   Profit Rates in the UK Food Industry
(Linear (OLS) Regressions of Relative Profit Rates Against Time)

	Dependent Variable	Constant	Slope	R2
PERIOD 1965-1977: Current Cost Basis:*				
1)	FM/AUM	1.23 (8.95)	0.018 (0.45)	0.02
2)	RD/AUM	2.33 (8.52)	0.15 (1.91)	0.27
3)	RD/FM	1.93 (14.3)	0.096 (2.49)	0.38
PERIOD 1970-1985: Historic Cost Basis:†				
4)	FM/AI	1.05 (56.8)	0.009 (2.15)	0.25
5)[10]	FR/AI	1.30 (39.1)	0.029 (3.28)	0.49
6)	FR/FM	1.22 (52.5)	0.018 (2.95)	0.44

Sources:
Data
Current Cost, MMC (1981)
Historic Cost - Slater (1987).

Results
McDonald, Rayner and Bates (1989).

t-statistics in parentheses.
Definitions: FM = Food Manufacturing;
                          AUM = All UK Manufacturing;
                          RD = Retail Distribution;
                          FR = Food Retailing;
                          AI = All Industry.
* t = 0 in 1971; † t = 0 in 1978.

Hence it is necessary to seek additional information. Two obvious candidates suggest themselves: first, the distribution of value-added between profits and employment income, and second, productivity growth in the food industry. The distribution of value-added between profits and employment income indicates that profits accounted for an appreciably greater proportion of value-added in 1990, and that profits shares were particularly buoyant for first-stage processors. This latter result is contrary to the expected result, given the first-stage/second-stage hypothesis, although of course it may be a reflection of greater capital intensity.

---

10   First three observations omitted: See McDonald, Rayner and Bates (1989, p 103).

Table 2.6:   Percentage of Value-added Attributed to Profits for Input-output Industries (1990)

	1990
Oils and fats	n/a
Slaughtering and meat processing	36.2
Milk and milk products	52.7
Fruit, vegetables and fish processing	37.2
Grain milling and starch	56.1
Bread, biscuits and flour confectionery	24.4
Sugar	67.8
Confectionery	37.8
Animal feeding stuffs	51.2
Miscellaneous foods	46.7
UK Average	34.8

Source: CSO (1994). Input-Output Tables for the United Kingdom

Evidence on the total factor productivity growth performance of the food industry is contradictory, and relative to agriculture, sparse. Estimates of total factor productivity for the food industry disagregated by SIC activities/minimum list headings have been reported by Mordue and Marshall (1979) and Balasubramanyam and Nguyen (1991) and for the food industry as a whole by McDonald, Rayner and Bates (1992). For the period 1968-76 Mordue and Marshall estimate that 'food and drink' displayed a lower rate of total factor productivity growth than 'all manufacturing', a result that is confirmed by the estimates produced by McDonald, Rayner and Bates for the food industry as a whole over the period 1968-74. On the other hand, Balasubramanyam and Nguyen report estimates indicating that over the period 1979-86 'total food' outperformed 'total manufacturers' whereas McDonald, Rayner and Bates report a negative rate for the food industry over the period 1979-84. Furthermore, there is no consistent pattern with regard to the relative performances of first and second stage food processors in the estimates reported by Mordue and Marshall and Balasubramanyam and Nguyen. However, a major problem with productivity growth estimation is how to allow for changes in product quality. If the food industry is characterised by appreciable changes in its products, then estimates of total factor productivity are more likely to be under than over estimates.

Further Issues in the Economic Analysis of the Food Industry

Previous sections have outlined, in general terms, some of the conceptual issues in the economic analysis of industries and markets and considered their applicability in the context of the food industry. Even in such a brief treatment, it is apparent that some of the richness and complexity of the competitive process in the food industry is lost as a consequence of many of the simplifying assumptions which have to be made. In particular, the analysis in the previous pages pays little attention to the complex interlinkages between input markets, production and output, largely ignores location issues, and cannot readily accommodate the issue of own-label products. This section highlights some of the more important issues in each of these areas.

Vertically Related Markets

A fundamental characteristic of food systems is that they constitute a series of vertically related markets that, at least in developed economies, are relatively isolated from the rest of the economy in the sense that transactions with industries outside the food system are only a relatively small proportion of the total value of transactions. This characteristic of food systems coupled with the evidence of substantial structural concentration in both food processing and food distribution, are strongly suggestive of a need to investigate the operation of the food system using models of imperfect competition. But outside of models which presume perfect competition throughout the food system it is obvious that this analysis enters areas of great difficulty for economists, especially when this results in outcomes that are indeterminate, e.g. the classic monopoly monopsony problem. These difficulties probably go a long way towards explaining why "industrial economists have not pursued the area theoretically with anything like the vigour they have expended on the oligopoly problem" (Waterson, 1984, p 82). Consequently the comments in this section are based on a far less formal analysis than the previous sections.

A different aspect of structure concerns the relative market power of buyers and suppliers and may be of particular relevance in the context of food. Traditional S-C-P frameworks tend to under-estimate the importance of input suppliers and implicitly assume that input markets are competitive. While in principle this would appear to be a reasonable assumption for the food industry given its dependence on agriculture, such a view ignores the impact of government policy and the marketing strategies developed by farmers.

A key distinguishing feature of input markets in the food and drink industry is that inputs are predominantly agricultural and thus input supply is characterised by seasonality in many instances and a degree of quantity, quality and cost variability. In some instances, these conditions induce processors to forward contract with suppliers to induce a degree of certainty with respect to price and availability. In other instances, some processors will undertake a degree of backwards integration to guarantee input availability. In principle, the input markets faced by food processors are generally competitive; agriculture in general is highly fragmented and the typical farm is small relative to the typical food processor. The development of various co-operative and marketing organisations has been seen as a strategy to counter-balance the market power of the food processors, but perhaps of much greater significance in this context is the role of government intervention. Government intervention, primarily through the CAP in the EU, has effectively raised prices above world levels and in so doing has raised input costs to processors. The existence of price support, in whatever form, effectively constrains the exercise of market power by processors, at least with respect to price because it effectively imposes a floor to the market. However, market intervention may not necessarily be harmful to food processors; in particular, first stage processors may benefit because market intervention effectively guarantees sales (Harris *et al*, 1983). More likely, market intervention may benefit some processors and harm others in the Single Market (for example through the agrimonetary system); similarly, the effects of reduced agricultural support may be ambiguous and depend not only on the first- stage/second-stage distinction but also on the existing patterns of behaviour in the market. Thus for example, McCorriston and Sheldon (1992) suggest that policy reform which results in excess capacity in the processing industry may have adverse consequences for consumers but may actually benefit processors.

While input markets appear, in principle, to be highly competitive, the reverse is true for output markets and it is clear that for the UK food processing sector, the bargaining power of buyers (food retailers) is significant. The degree of concentration in the retail sector and the growing importance of the supermarkets is well documented (Shaw, Burt and Dawson, 1989). It is difficult however to determine the extent to which concentration in the food retailing sector has adversely affected food processors. Research has indicated that food retailers may have substantial scope for the exercise of market power (Handy and Padberg, 1971, and McDonald, Rayner and Bates, 1989), but empirical evidence as to the extent to which food retailers have actually exercised market power in the UK has not been reported. Among the many difficulties facing empirical research are the multi-dimensional nature of society's goals[11] , an underdeveloped theory of pricing in joint supply retail outlets and chronic shortage of data on the retailing sector. Furthermore, although specialist food shops continue to be important, the growth and diversification of the major retailers has involved substantial

---

11   For example, how are changes in welfare (variety and quality of commodities), economy
       (prices) and efficiency (advertising, brand proliferation) to be reconciled.

segmentation of the food retail market, with the major supermarkets developing specialist product lines; a process reinforced by the growth in both the quantity and quality of own brands. More recently, it has been suggested that competition within food retailing may be increasing (Wrigley, 1994) with the growing market presence of discounters (e.g., Aldi, Netto). If this suggestion proves correct, it is likely that food retailers will face greater incentives to exercise downstream market power.

Location and Distribution

Analysis of the criteria used by firms to determine their 'optimal' location, and the market areas that firms control, has a long history. Early theories focused upon costs, in particular transport costs, whereas later research has emphasised locational interdependence, the determination of market-areas and the importance of demand factors. A major outcome of this work has been the identification of the importance of interactions between the choice of location and the pricing policies of competing firms. There appears to have been limited research into these issues within the agricultural economics literature, which is probably regrettable given the location specific nature of substantial proportions of agricultural activity. The comments here are therefore brief and more concerned with suggesting the desirability of further research.

Transport costs are clearly a subject of substantial concern, especially as many of the commodities used and produced by food processors have high moisture contents. Von Thünen's concern with the optimal allocation of agricultural land between competing production activities was based upon the costs of transporting different products to market. The simple conclusion that, *ceteris paribus*, the higher the per unit transport cost of a commodity the more densely will its production be concentrated in the vicinity of the market, clearly remains valid despite the reductions in transport costs witnessed since von Thünen's time.

More generally, Weber was concerned with the choice of industrial-location and the minimisation of costs involved in accessing intermediate inputs and marketing outputs. In its simplest form this extension simply amounts to a (transport) cost minimisation problem but has been extended to incorporate a consideration of the potential benefits to firms of locality concentration via agglomeration economies. These cost-based theories have an appealing simplicity. Transport costs provide a compelling explanation for the clustering of sugar beet production in the vicinity of the beet factories, and the concentration of flour mills in the UK at the ports through which grain entered the country from the end of the nineteenth century. Whatever the product being transported, grain, coffee, cocoa or bananas, merchants and shipping companies will testify to the importance of transport costs - and the importance of market power in the shipping arrangements. In a similar vein, it is intuitively appealing to believe that the location of food processing activities will change with developments in the distribution of agricultural production and changes in relative transport costs. These models are, however, limited by their implicit presumption that producers enjoy local monopolies, or that competitors' locations are fixed.

The incorporation of location-interdependence is generally attributed to Hotelling (1929). Hotelling suggested that with two sellers of a commodity both would gravitate towards the centre of the distribution of customers in their attempts to maximise their market shares, but the generality of this conclusion has been challenged with later research arguing that with more than two sellers the agglomeration tendency would be reversed (Eaton and Lipsey, 1975).

On the other hand, Löschian theories (Lösch, 1938) suggest the possibilities of intra-industry dispersion and inter-industry agglomeration. Again the analysis has intuitive appeal. It would be reasonable to expect, *ceteris paribus*, that industries may benefit from locating near to their major input suppliers, and hence it might be expected that there would be clustering of related first- stage and second-stage food processors. Similarly, 'inter-industry' agglomeration may go some way to explaining the appeal of shopping centres for retailers. These models have been criticised for their simplistic treatment of demand, and while they provide intuitively appealing explanations for certain phenomena it is all too easy to identify examples that contradict the expected outcomes. Hence, whereas traditional theories of imperfect competition have arguably under acknowledged the importance of location choice, so location theory has under-recognised the importance of demand factors. But, as Greenhut *et al*, (1987) observe, in a review of developments of traditional location theory, "One of the major problems in an analysis of imperfect competition is that a slight increase in model complexity can generate an intractable increase in mathematical complexity" (p 271), and hence conclusions drawn from models based on highly restrictive assumptions must be cautious ones.

Of the general conclusions that emerge from the literature, the most clear is that while cost considerations remain an important factor in location choice, the presence of imperfect competition, and hence the possibility of a range of pricing strategies, complicates the results. Indeed, for any given set of cost conditions it would appear that there are a range of location choices available according to the pricing strategies adopted. Thus it has been argued that "Standard location theory also requires full recognition of the demand (price) factor of location" (Greenhut *et al*, 1987, p 290).

Own-Label Products

A widely recognised facet of the modern food and drink industry is the importance of own-label products. Nickell and Metcalf (1978) employed a development of Cowling and Waterson's model to examine the hypothesis that the producers of proprietary branded products realised increased profit margins through advertising. They argued that own-label products "marketed under the name of the supermarket itself" (Nickell and Metcalf, 1978, p 254) were often essentially the same as proprietary branded products, but that advertising activities allowed the producers of proprietary branded products "to maintain a fixed differential between its own price and the prices offered by the other firms" (p 255). The recent controversy about 'look-a-likes' in the UK noted in the previous chapter has added interest to this whole question.

Nickell and Metcalf sought to relax the constraints imposed by the static nature of most performance-structure models by including terms to capture the barriers-to-entry from a limit pricing strategy and technology, and to accommodate the effects of the growth of demand and the minimum efficient scale of production, i.e.

$$\frac{C'}{p} = \frac{p_1}{p} = 1 - \frac{a}{p} + \alpha\beta\frac{H}{|\eta|} + \beta g + \gamma m \tag{13}$$

where C' = marginal cost;

p = proprietary branded product price;

p_1 = own - label product price;

a = average unit advertising expenditure;

β = a "measure of the level of ..... technological barriers to entry";

H = Herfindahl index of concentration;

$|\eta|$ = price elasticity of demand;

g = rate of growth of industry demand;

m = " ratio of the minimum efficient scale to own [label] sales";

This model was estimated using UK data, in particular price data gathered from products on the shelves of supermarkets, for a sample of UK industries that included food processing. The results indicate that there were significant and negative relationships between the concentration, industry structure, and advertising expenditure per unit of sales, i.e. that these variables were associated with proprietary branded products having higher prices relative to the matching own-label products. The only other variable that appeared to be relevant was the ratio of the minimum efficient scale to own-label sales whereas the other coefficients on the other variables were "generally speaking, not significantly different from zero" (Nickell and Metcalf, 1978, p 266). However, an interesting feature of the Nickell and Metcalf results is the inclusion of a dummy variable for food processing. This indicates that while producers of proprietary branded products realised monopoly profits they were lower for the food industry.

A very similar methodology was employed by Connor and Peterson (1992) to examine the price differences between proprietary branded and own-label products for regions of the USA.[12] The models for which estimates were derived were broadly similar to those derived by Nickell and Metcalf with some adaptations to suit US circumstances. The results indicated that concentration and advertising intensity were significant and positive determinants of price-cost margins, as was the price elasticity of demand (used to adjust the Herfindahl measure of concentration). Both these studies indicate the potential importance of advertising as a barrier-to-entry in the food processing industry. Moreover, they do so by drawing upon the easily observed fact that a substantial proportion of the items for sale in supermarkets carry the brand name of the supermarket, but they depend on the presumption that the own-label product provides an acceptable proxy for the minimum long run average cost of producing the products. This presumption is increasingly dubious in the UK since several of the supermarket chains may have been able to get their own-label products regarded by customers as being equivalent to the 'traditional' proprietary branded products[13].

Concluding Comments

The food and drink industry remains an important but relatively neglected component of the UK economy for economic researchers. In part this neglect probably reflects the lack of interest offered by a sector that is apparently declining in relevant importance. It also reflects difficulties with data and the theory. Yet, it is doubtful if a full understanding of the operation of food systems can be obtained without the development of economic analysis of the food and drink industry. Not only is the industry now more important to the UK economy than

---

12   The terminology used in the text differs from that used by Connor and Peterson, and
      other American authors. They call proprietary branded products 'national or regional
      brands' and own-label products 'private-label' products.

13   See McGoldrick (1984)

agriculture, in terms of contributions to GDP and employment, it also occupies a pivotal role in the processes by which food is delivered to consumers and is the source of many of the changes in food quality and presentation that reflect the growth and evolution of consumer demand.

While this chapter has adopted the well known S-C-P framework of analysis, it is important to maintain an awareness of the limitations of the framework. In particular, although the S-C-P framework recognises the importance of interdependency between firms within an industry, it is far less adept at providing a conceptual framework in which competitive interactions within an industry, and between industries that are vertically related, can be analysed. However, the S-C-P framework does provide a useful starting point. Without evidence that an industry is characterised by structures that may provide the necessary conditions for imperfect competition, it is unlikely that research on the consequences of such structures will be initiated. The evidence presented in this chapter is consistent with an industry where imperfect competition is likely. The food industry displays high degrees of concentration (which at the product level are more likely to be under- than over-estimates) and relatively high profit rates (given the arguably lower levels of risk).

Moreover, consideration of the food system as a whole suggests that the interactions between processors and retailers may be particularly important for food; structural characteristics (specifically administered prices on the major inputs to food processing and high concentration in retailing) suggest the appropriateness of bi-lateral oligopoly models that seek to accommodate oligopolistic behaviour within and between both sectors. Such models have not yet been developed, but the potential for reform of agricultural policies, notionally offered by GATT, coupled with an apparent increase in competitive pressures within the food retailing sector, indicate a growing need to understand the post-farmgate food system if the effects of agricultural policy reforms upon the food system, are to be predicted and explained.

References

Advertising Association (1992). *Advertising Statistics Yearbook*. NTC: Henley.

Bain, J (1958). *Industrial Organization*, John Wiley, New York.

BSO/CSO (various). *Census of Production*, HMSO, London

Balasubramanyam, V.N. and Nguyen, D.T., (1991). Structure and Performance of the UK Food and Drink Industries, *Journal of Agricultural Economics*, **42**, 56-65.

Connor, J.M. and Peterson, E.B., (1992). Market-structure Determinants of National Brand-Private Label Price Differences of Manufactured Food Products, *Journal of Industrial Economics*, **40**, 157-171.

Connor, J M, Rogers, R T, Marion, B W and Mueller, W F (1985). *The Food Manufacturing Industry*, Lexington Books, Lexington, Mass

Cowling, K.G. and Waterson, M., (1976). Price-cost Margins and Market Structure, *Economica*, **43**, 267-274.

CSO (1994). *Input Output Tables for the United Kingdom 1990*. HMSO

Cubbin, J., (1983). Apparent Collusion and Conjectural Variations in Differentiated Oligopoly, *International Journal of Industrial Organization*, **1**, 155-163.

DTI (Undated). *Merger Control in Europe*. HMSO, London.

Eaton, B.C. and Lipsey, R.G. (1975). The Principle of Minimum Differentiation Reconsidered: Some New Developments in the Theory of Spatial Competition, *Review of Economic Studies*, **42**, 27-49.

Greenhut, M.L., Norman, G. and Hung, C., (1987). *The Economics of Imperfect Competition: A Spatial Approach*. Cambridge: Cambridge University Press.

Handy, C.R. and Padberg, D.I., (1971). A Model of Competitive Behavior in Food Industries, *American Journal of Agricultural Economics*, **53**, 182-190.

Harris, S., Swinbank, A. and Wilkinson, G., (1983). *The Food and Farm Policies of the European Community*. Chichester: Wiley.

Hay, D.A. and Morris, D.J., (1991). *Industrial Economics and Organization: Theory and Evidence*. Oxford: Oxford University Press.

Hotelling, H., (1929). Stability in Competition, *Economic Journal*, **39**, 41-57.

Howe, W.S. (1983) Competition and Performance in Food Manufacturing, in *The Food Industry. Economics and Policy* ed. J.A. Burns, J.P. McInerney, and A. Swinbank. London: Heinemann.

Lancaster, K., (1966). A New Approach to Consumer Theory, *Journal of Political Economy*, **74**, 132-157.

Lösch, A., (1938). The Nature of Economic Regions, Southern Economic Journal, **5**, 71-78.

Maunder, P (1988). Food Processing, in Johnson, P *The Structure of British Industry*, Unwin Hyman, London

McCorriston, S., and Sheldon, I M (1992). Policy Induced Capacity Constraints and Strategic Interaction in Processed Food Markets, *Journal of Agricultural Economics*, **43**, 149-159.

McDonald, J.R.S., Rayner, A.J. and Bates, J.M., (1989). Market Power in the Food Industry, *Journal of Agricultural Economics*, **40**, 101-108.

McDonald, J.R.S., Rayner, A.J. and Bates, J.M., (1992). Productivity Growth and the UK Food System 1954-84, *Journal of Agricultural Economics*, **43**, 191-204.

McGoldrick, P.J., (1984) *Grocery Generics - An Extension of the Private Label Concept, European Journal of Marketing*, **18 (1)**, 5-24

MMC (1981) *Discounts to Retailers*, HC311. London: HMSO.

Mordue, R.E. and Marshall, J.D., (1979). Changes in Total Factor Productivity in UK Food and Drink Manufacturing, *Journal of Agricultural Economics*, **30**, 159-167.

Nickell, S. and Metcalf, D., (1978). Monopolistic Industries and Monopoly Profits or, are Kellogg's Cornflakes Overpriced?, *Economic Journal*, Vol 88, pp 254-268.

Pickering, J F (1974) *Industrial Structure and Market Conduct*, Martin Robertson, Oxford.

Porter, M E (1980) *Competitive Strategy*. Free Press, New York

Porter, M E (1985) *Competitive Advantage*. Free Press, New York

Sawyer, M.C., (1971). Concentration in British Manufacturing Industries. *Oxford Economic Papers*, **23(3)**, 352- 383.

Sawyer, M C (1981) *The Economics of Industries and Firms*, Croom Helm, London.

Schmalensee, R., (1978). Entry Deterrence in the Ready-to-Eat Breakfast Cereal Industry, Bell Journal of Economics, **9**, 305-327

Shaw, S A, Burt, S L and Dawson, J A (1989) Structural Change in the European Food Chain, in Traill, B (ed) *Prospects for the European Food System*, Elsevier, London.

Slater, J.M., (1987). The Food Sector in the UK, paper given at Conference on *Competition Policy in the Food Industries*, University of Reading, September 1987.

Sleuwaegen.L., and Dehandschutter. W., (1986). The critical choice between the concentration ratio and the H-index in assessing industry performance. *Journal of Industrial Economics*, **35(2)**, Dec 1986, 193-208.

Sosnick, S (1958) A Critique of the Concept of Workable Competition, *Quarterly Journal of Economics*, **72**

Strak, John (1983). *Optimal Advertising Decisions for Farmers and Food Processors*. Journal of Agricultural Economics, Volume 34(3).

Sutton, J (1992) *Sunk Costs and Market Structure* MIT Press, Cambridge, Mass.

Waterson, M., (1984). *Economic Theory of the Industry*. CUP, Cambridge.

Wrigley, N., (1994). After the Store Wars: Towards a New Era of Competition in UK Food Retailing?, *Journal of Retailing and Consumer Services*, **1**, 5-20.

Chapter 3: Cereals and Oilseeds Products

Robert Bojduniak and Ian Sturgess[1]

Introduction

The economic activities undertaken in the cereals and oilseeds sectors in the UK depend upon the production and harvesting of a small group of arable crops. In the UK these are principally; wheat, barley, oats, and rape. An amount of maize is grown but mainly for forage, and there has been an increasing area of linseed which recently has declined sharply (reflecting the rise and fall of EU subsidies).

The introduction of the EU cereals and oilseeds regimes has had a significant impact on the UK's production and processing sectors. Because many other farm products (intensive livestock) and food products (bread, confectionery, starch, distilling, etc.) depend upon cereals as a raw material the effects of farm policy on the value-added cereals processing sector are also important.   For example, the availability of different qualities of cereals and the competitiveness of cereals and processed cereals exports are two of the aspects of the market that the CAP regime has influenced: similarly for oilseeds production and vegetable oil processing.

The chapter begins with a brief overview of the end markets for cereals and oilseeds that sets the processed products considered here in context. However, the processing demand for cereals and oilseeds raw materials is examined here only at the first-stage of transformation i.e. not beyond their intermediate demand. But market by market, the changes and developments that have occurred are spelt out at this level. The policy background that has affected production and processing decisions is covered in a separate section in the chapter but linked, wherever possible, with actual or perceived changes in the marketplace. For both cereals and oilseeds, the main changes and players in the company sector are identified in a succeeding section.   Value-added (final demand) product areas for cereals such as; biscuits, pasta and breakfast cereals are dealt with in Chapter Nine.   Compound feed, however, is briefly discussed in this chapter.

1   Robert Bojduniak is editor of a UK farm business newsletter 'Farm Brief', Norfolk; Ian Sturgess is Director of the Agricultural Economics Unit, Department of Land Economy, University of Cambridge. The Editors are grateful for the comments of Freddie Rees on earlier drafts of the chapter and for the assistance of various trade associations in providing information including the HGCA and NABIM.   Any opinions, errors or omissions in this chapter remain the full responsibility of the Editors and the reader's attention is drawn to the caveat in the Appendix of Chapter One.

End Markets for Cereals and Oilseeds

Cereals and oilseeds are not generally thought of directly as "food products". Apart from breakfast cereals their common usage is as raw materials in primary and secondary transformation processes and this may disguise their important place in the daily diet. Consumer demands for cereals and oilseeds are expressed through products like bread, cakes, cooking oils and vegetable oil spreads, etc. but these value-added products mainly originate from the further processing of intermediate products. The intermediate demand and consumption of first-stage transformation products is a derived demand for these final consumer products. This aspect of consumer demand is not unique to the cereals and oilseeds sectors but it is especially relevant to them. Comprehensive consumption data tends to be for final products. This has encouraged the approach taken here of discussing their consumption and market structure in a later chapter (Chapter Nine) which deals with further processed and branded products. Hence, biscuits and breakfast cereals are considered there and not in this part of the book. This chapter, meanwhile, deals with the production of:

- flour

- starch and gluten

- malt

- vegetable oils and oilseed residues

- compound feed

A short note on the final use and transformation of each of the key cereals' and oilseeds' intermediate products is presented here: key markets are;

Bread, Baking, Confectionery

Wheat flour's milling and baking properties vary according to the moisture, protein and other technical characteristics of the wheat. To achieve a longer shelf life for bread for example, imported high protein North American hard wheats - primarily from Canada - are needed in the bread flour grist (or there is a need to reinforce soft wheats with gluten). Northern Europe predominantly produces soft wheats. However, the percentage of wheat used in all millers' grist rose from 54% in 1985/86 to an 88% peak during 1990/91 and has subsequently fallen to c. 72%.

There are three classifications for wheat bought for milling: Groups 1, 2 and 3. Group 1 are preferred bread-making varieties based on tests by millers themselves and at the industry funded Flour Milling and Baking Research Association. The four autumn and three spring varieties regarded as suitable for bread-making have also to meet the following criteria: a minimum protein content of 11% on a dry 14% matter basis, a specific weight of 76 kilos/hectolitre and a Hagberg falling time of at least 250 (this is the basis for which the main market premia over feed quality is paid). Group 2 varieties are those which produce flour that may be blended in bread grists, but are primarily used for cake and biscuit production and animal feed. Group 3 varieties, the vast majority of wheat produced in the UK, are mainly used for feed and biscuit flour production. One Group 3 variety, Riband, has taken up to 32% of autumn 1993 plantings, the period when the vast majority of the crop is sown.

Starch and Gluten

Maize gluten and maize starch are not used in bread production. Maize starch, however, is used in the cake and confectionery baking industries to assist the cooking process. Wheat gluten, which is part of the UK starch industry, is an important ingredient for the UK bread industry. It is primarily used to fortify the protein fraction in bread flour grists (and thus reduce dependence on North American wheat imports). It takes 7.5 tonnes of flour to produce one tonne of wheat gluten.

UK produced maize gluten is essentially a by-product of the starch process and is primarily used for animal feed. Maize gluten feed is imported into the UK from America where it is a by-product of the federal government's subsidised ethanol programme and the production of corn sweeteners. Maize and wheat starch and gluten production have various end uses. Maize is a much more versatile raw material for starch use in various end markets. For example, wheat brans could show up in high quality stationery. The UK industry also uses potato starch, but none of it is produced domestically due to its prohibitively high processing costs.

Alcohol from Malting Barley

Converting malting barley into malt uses relatively low technology, with the exception of computer controls in processing. The barley is brought into the maltings at around 16% moisture across the UK where it is steeped. Water is added at a high temperature to cause the barley to germinate and convert the starch present in the grain into sugar. It then goes through the kilning process which ultimately dries down what has become malt to 8%. Normally, this process takes five to seven days, depending on the end market for the malt; ales, lager beer, malt whisky, vinegar, or the food sector.

Compound Feed

The by-product from cereal milling, wheat feed, is sold into the animal feed market as loose bulk or pelleted, either into compound plants or directly on to farms. The extraction rate of flour from a tonne of wheat ranges from 72% to 78%. With a relatively high protein content, it normally secures c.80 - 85% of the prevailing cost of feed wheat.

The residue from oilseed 'crushing' (now usually by solvent extraction) is high in protein and fibre and is used in compound feed production. Compound feed demand for rapeseed has a potential for major growth. This is due to the development of 'double zero' varieties (with very low levels of glucosinolates) which avoid the toxicity (for monogastric animals - pigs and poultry) of single zero varieties which contain higher levels of glucosinolates. Double zero rape varieties can be safely used in monogastric diets at inclusion rates of between 10% and 20%, compared to maxima of 3% for single zeroes. Variety plantings show that UK growers since 1988/89 have made a wholesale switch from single zero to double zero rape. Trade estimates suggest that around 97% of UK rape production in 1995 will be of double zero type. This is a major competitor for US imported soyabean meal.

Margarine and Shortenings

Margarine and cooking fats, the traditional mainstay of the oils and fats business remain a major user of vegetable oils. In some cases vegetable oils are blended with maize oils or animal fats. Oils sold as such, for frying and salad use are an increasingly important use.

Retail Oils

Branded and private label cooking oils are produced either as straight soya, sunflower, corn or olive oil or as blends mainly composed of rape, soya or sunflower oil. The growth in EU rape and sunflower production means that many of the bottles on supermarket shelves labelled 'vegetable oils' are usually a compound of one or both of these oils. The bottles are in 0.5 litre, 1 litre and 4 litre sizes, while canned oils for the catering sector are supplied in 4.5 and 20 litre tin plate containers.

Soaps

These are mainly based on blends of palm kernel or coconut oils with tallow. The addition of colours, perfumes within a milling extrusion and stamping process provide the standard toilet soap.

Baking and Catering

These two sectors are the largest trade users of vegetable oils and fats. A range of shortenings is based on blends of solid fats and liquid oils. They are used in the production of cakes, confectionery, pastry, bread and snack foods. In this area such characteristics as plasticity tolerance and minimal palate cling are required. Oil is also used for frying in catering outlets.

Ice cream fats

To allow ice cream to melt in the mouth and yet retain its structure in warm weather requires a particular fat: hardened and hydrogenated palm kernel oil.

Emulsifiers

A combination of base fats and glycerine are spray dried to produce a free flowing powder. These products are used to improve the shelf life of bread, prevent ice cream from crystallising in the deep freeze, and even reduce the stickiness of toffee.

Industrial demand

Oilseed rape is high in erucic acid is used as a technical oil for non-food purposes. Vegetable oils can be used to replace mineral oils in certain applications. Over the past two years a relatively new market for rape oil has opened up in the UK - biofuel[2]. The European Commission has allowed production on set-aside land, provided there is a bona fide contract for non food use.

---

2   Significant quantities of biodiesel are reported to be produced in Europe. British Farmer (1993) estimates annual production of c. 600,000 tonnes by 1997 (about 1% of total EU diesel consumption).

The Policy Background for Cereals and Oilseeds

The CAP regime for cereals, since its first application in 1967, has made prices of cereals for both producers and users higher than they would have been in a free market. This has been achieved primarily by; controls at the border, import levies which have maintained the levy paid import prices at fixed, pre-determined levels and export subsidies which have bridged the gap between fixed, so-called intervention prices and world prices which have been normally lower[3]. The import levy system has normally kept internal prices high enough to avoid intervention buying. But public intervention activities and export sales of intervention stocks have sometimes occurred for reasons of internal finance or external politics. Consequent "grain mountains" in the EU attracted unfavourable media and political attention.

A more persistent pressure for modification of the regime since the late 1970's has come from its budgetary cost. High support prices by stimulating production and inhibiting consumption, especially in compound feeds. They have also converted the EU from a net importer to an increasingly large net exporter, despite a brief breathing space given by the accession of the UK as a major net importer in 1973. As exports increased on to a world market, which in the 1980's was generally weakening in real terms, so the cost of financing export subsidies became an increasing burden to the EU taxpayer. After the introduction of dairy quotas in 1984 political attention focused on cereal surpluses (along with deficiency payments on oilseeds) as the main cause of increasing, and increasingly unacceptable, public expenditure on the CAP. At times the cost of the CAP cereal regime rose significantly because of variations in the Dollar/ECU exchange rate.

The initial policy reaction was to manipulate the intervention system, for example, by reducing monthly increments and deferring payments. These reduced effective support prices but not enough, especially after 1988 when more stringent budgetary controls (the budget 'Guideline') were placed on the CAP. "Stabilisers" were then tried. These followed the principle that if production exceeded a pre-set level then all producers incurred a price penalty. The severity of the measures was further weakened by the agrimonetary system and contradictory actions by the Agriculture Council at its annual price fixings. A more direct control was essayed in 1988 through a system of voluntary set-aside of land partly financed by the EC. Outside Germany however this was taken up with little enthusiasm by national governments and even less so by farmers.

---

3   See Neville and Mordaunt (1993) or Leguen de Lacroix (1992) for further detail on the CAP regime for cereals.

The EU entered the 1990's with the budgetary problem unresolved, and with new pressures arising from enlargement of the Community (recent and potential) and environmental concerns about intensive farming. Crucially, there was also a desire to save the Uruguay Round GATT negotiations on liberalisation of international trade which had stalled largely on agricultural disputes between the EC and US. In 1991 Commissioner MacSharry responded to these pressures with a bold plan for reform. In part this plan, which was focused on cereals, oilseed and protein crops, followed the pattern long favoured by economist commentators on the CAP - a progressive cut in support prices combined with direct income payments. However the payments were decoupled from production decisions only in respect of yield, being paid per unit of area planted and were conditional on leaving idle an area of land in fixed ratio to that planted to CAP crops - the concept of compulsory set-aside. In June 1992 the version of this reform adopted by the Council of Ministers was more favourable to farmers and less so to the budget but was nevertheless a radical change.

To a degree that is hotly disputed, the CAP reform may enable the EU to meet the GATT settlement of the Uruguay round signed in April 1994[4] and to take effect from 1995. For cereals the critical commitments are reductions over six years from a 1986-90 base of spending on export subsidies by 36% and in the volume of subsidised exports by 21%. Partial tariffication of imports will attempt to link internal EU prices more closely to world prices and there is an unresolved issue of whether supplementary import levies, under a safeguard clause, will be assessed cargo by cargo or more generally[5].

Compulsory set-aside of arable land within the current CAP reform rules[6] and the Uruguay Round GATT agreement has had, and will continue to have, the greatest impact on UK cereal production. The UK larger farm structure makes it more liable to idling the 15% minimum than any other Member State. The exemption for those planting an area less than would produce 92 tonnes of cereals a year at average yields, is of little relevance in the UK. It implies an arable area farmed of around 16 hectares. MAFF analyses shows that less than 9% of the UK cereal area is covered by holdings of less than 20 hectares. By contrast almost 74% were 50 hectares or above. The UK cereal area fell by 469,000

4   The agriculture element of the GATT Uruguay Round was first agreed in late 1992 (the
     Blair House Accord) and after further clarification initialled in December 1993. See NFU
     (1994) and USDA (1994) for a fuller account of the agriculture elements of the Uruguay
     Round of the GATT, and De Maria (1994) for comment on prospects for cereals.
5   See, The Agreement Establishing the WTO Agreement on Agriculture, Misc No 17
     (1994), HMSO)
6   See MAFF (1993) for a precise description of the Arable Area Payments system as it
     operates in the UK.

hectares between June 1992 and the first year of compulsory set-aside in 1993 (-13%).

Over time, the cereals regime has often thrown up market anomalies i.e. discrepancies between the regime's valuation of specific qualities and the market's view of their worth. They include a temporary subsidy for Southern Italian imports of bread wheat that lasted for 14 years. Abolishing support buying for feed quality wheat also threw up a market anomaly that some officials failed to appreciate at the time. The trade's acceptable standard - common wheat - is equivalent to that used by UK flour millers for bread-making quality. In 1994/95 UK millers paid the maximum premia for specified varieties - four winter sown and most spring types with a specific weight of 76 kilos/hectolitre, 11% protein, 15% moisture and a minimum Hagberg falling time (a measure of the alpha amalayse activity in the resultant bread dough) of 250. This carries a premium over feed quality in the UK ranging from £5 to £35/tonnes - depending on average quality and quantity each year.

However, the EU cereal support price is the same for common wheat and feed barley. The latter - based on its nutritional value as an animal feed, particularly a lower protein content - has generally been valued at a £5 to £8/tonne discount to feed wheat. This institutional anomaly has not only distorted cereal markets, but has also ensured that some of the 500,000 tonnes of barley sitting in UK intervention is now 10 years old.

Around 80% of the 1995 wheat crop was made up of varieties that would fail the intervention standards. Moreover, the newer top yielding wheat varieties that are increasing market share - Brigadier and Hussar - are feed quality only. This feed standard is 72 kilo/hectolitre specific weight, 15% moisture and a protein content minimum of 10%. However, if farmers were to switch to quality varieties estimates suggest a maximum premia range of £5 to £10/tonne over base feed market quality would prevail. While the UK premia over feed quality for the 1994/95 season ranged from £10 to £19/tonne, the availability of French and German supplies effectively provided a price ceiling on UK domestic bread values. Unless there are radical changes in wheat varietal use in France, Spain, Denmark or Germany, this is likely to remain.

Unlike bread wheat the premia for malting barley over feed quality have become a fixed feature of the market. Moreover, to ensure supplies, maltsters and distillers are more inclined to offer farm contracts. As barley production has fallen - see Table 3.2 - these contracts have become more prevalent to secure supplies. About 55% of Scottish malting barley requirements are bought under contract and around 20% of English consumption. The malting industry typically pays about a 15% premium over the feed price shown in the HGCA weekly average. But the absence of specific institutional price support makes the sector totally dependent on supply and demand - both in the UK and across the EU.

In the short to medium term, one impact of the 1992 CAP reform's switch from price support to direct aid may have been to reduce the incentive to maximise output. A 1,000 acre farm in the UK with a familiar mix of wheat, barley, oilseed rape and linseed is eligible for a cheque of around £80,000 by Christmas each year as compensation for support price cuts and set-aside payments. Furthermore, these payments have increased in Sterling terms as Sterling has devalued within the agrimonetary system that translates EU market support and compensation payments into national currencies. Increasingly, farmers have adapted to the set-aside provisions and the implementation of the arable-aid compensation rules. Some commentators suggest that farmers are changing their behaviour in response to the variety of aid payments. There has been a major push to cut fixed costs - mainly labour - in order to cut production costs per tonne as part of a wholesale restructuring of the industry[7]. This mirrors the response to lower prices that cereal farmers have made in other major producing countries where subsidies have been much lower and are falling - such as Argentina, Canada and the US. As always however the effects of these resource withdrawals on cereal production may be outweighed by new technology.

In contrast, the linseed area, which had risen almost ninefold in five years to 150,000 hectares in 1993 more than halved to just under 60,000 the following year - entirely due to the lower aid paid relative to other arable crops. At the same time, edible oilseed rape planting which had also declined from a 1991 peak of 440,000 hectares to 376,000 hectares in 1992/3, recovered to over 400,000 in 1993/4. Lower aid rates for protein crops - peas and beans - relative to wheat are set to reduce pulse plantings across the EU. Yet it is EU policy to cut its protein trade deficit by substituting imported vegetable proteins (soyabeans and meals) with pulses.

Some UK farmers believe that EU arable aid payments will be sharply cut after 1996. But the European Commission points out that in the absence of any politically controversial change by the Farm Ministers' Council, the scheme continues at 1995/6 rates. It is part of the 1992 CAP reform that the European Commission regards as being largely successful: intervention grain stocks have fallen from 30 million tonnes to below 10 million, while EU 12 cereal production has fallen from 180 million tonnes before reform to 162 million tonnes in 1994. This has not been without cost. Combined CAP expenditure on the cereal, oilseed

---

7   For example farmers in the UK have restructured their operations and there has been a
     large growth in contract farming. Many farmers have left farming but retain ownership
     of their land. This is raising actual unit sizes well beyond those shown in official MAFF
     figures. While there are 68,000 arable farmers listed in the UK, it is estimated that c.
     35,000 make the daily production decisions.

and protein regimes which was just under £6 billion during 1989 increased to an estimated £10.7 billion for 1995 at prevailing green pound rates.

With regard to oilseeds, an important feature of the new post-Uruguay Round GATT oilseeds regime is that it effectively limits the total EU planted area for vegetable oil production as follows:

Rape   2.377 million hectares
Soya beans   0.509 million hectares
Sunflower   1.202 million hectares for the EU 10, (Spain is currently allowed to grow 1.411 million hectares and Portugal 122,000 hectares under transitional agreements).

These base areas are predicated on 1990/91 plantings and penalties are imposed in terms of cutting the direct farmer area aid subsidy by 1% for each 1% that the area is exceeded if the base area is larger than this. The total EU rape crop for 1994 was c. 6.5 million tonnes, compared with 7.3 million tonnes two years earlier. Production in 1994 included an estimated 1.1 million tonnes planted on set-aside land for industrial use.

The Supply of Cereals and Oilseeds

Wheat

Table 3.1:   UK Wheat Area and Production 1991 - 1995

	1991	1992	1993	1994	1995
Area (000 ha)	1,980	2,067	1,759	1,811	1,910
Output (million tonnes)	14.38	14.09	12.89	13.15	14.0-14.5

Source: MAFF census, Seed certification figures, Trade/Farm Brief
Notes: The figure for 1994 is based on 1991-93 three year average yield of 7.11
         tonnes/hectare. A ten year average is a lower , and probably
         more indicative, 6.83 tonnes/hectare.

The UK is the EU's third largest wheat producer and has been a net exporter since 1982. Some major world players in the grain trade - such as Bunge with Kenneth Wilson and Louis Dreyfus - have left the UK internal market in recent years. There has also been a major decline in the independent merchants operating in the grain markets (from c.1500 in 1984 to c.400 in 1994), and the rise of Allied Grain, Associated British Foods' subsidiary and Dalgety. Between them the two groups now account for a third of all ex-farm grain purchases.

Table 3.2:   UK Wheat Supply and Demand 1991-94 (million tonnes)

	1991/92	1992/93	1993/94*	1994/95+
Production	14.60	14.10	12.89	13.2
Intervention	0.01	0.01	0.29	0.18
Imports	0.75	1.35	1.6	0.75
Total Supply	15.36	15.46	14.78	14.3
Feed	4.50	5.06	5.4	5.2-5.4
Milling	5.00	5.10	5.10	5.1-5.2
Distilling/Starch	0.60	0.50	0.68	0.65
Seed/Sundries	0.60	0.50	0.51	0.51
Domestic Demand	10.70	11.16	11.69	11.46-11.76
End June EU exports	2.92	2.78	1.86	1.96
End June Non EU exports	1.72	1.69	1.02	0.44

* Estimate
+ Forecast
Source: MAFF, Farm Brief, Trade estimates
Note: UK export destinations have changed from being primarily third country to other EU
          Member States., which account for over 70% of trade. However, this includes an
          element of trans-shipment, especially with movement to Belgium and the Netherlands

As Table 3.2 shows, UK domestic demand has grown since 1992. Weak prices during the peak animal feed period - October to March - are likely to have raised usage on livestock farms and by compounders to new record levels. Imports rose sharply during 1993/94 due to the poor quality of the UK crop - average protein content across the country was 1% lower at 9.3%. However, the previous season's harvest produced the worst samples on record. Its disposal - mainly on the export markets - was primarily due to Sterling's decline against key currencies such as the French Franc and the US Dollar and thus produced higher market prices - factors that continued during 1994/5.

Barley

The advent of oilseed rape, and latterly set-aside during the 1990's, has accelerated the decline in the plantings and production of barley in the UK. Until comparatively recently, 1983, the UK's climate made barley the dominant cereal crop. But the consistently higher average yields (and higher prices) achieved by winter wheat, 1.16 tonnes/hectare more than winter barley and a 2.52 tonnes/hectare yield above spring sown barley, have encouraged farmers to switch. UK plantings are split between winter and spring barleys. In recent years this has been 60:40 in favour of winter. Climatic factors, however, ensure that 90% of the Scottish crop is planted in spring.

Table 3.3:   UK Barley Area and Production 1980/81 - 1993/94

	Total Area (thousand hectares)	Production (million tonnes)
1980/81	2.33	10.33
1981/82	2.33	10.23
1982/83	2.22	10.96
1983/84	2.14	9.98
1984/85	1.98	11.10
1985/86	1.97	9.74
1986/87	1.92	10.01
1987/88	1.83	9.23
1988/89	1.88	8.77
1989/90	1.65	8.07
1990/91	1.52	7.89
1991/92	1.39	7.60
1992/93	1.31	7.36
1993/94	1.16	6.04
1994/95	1.11	5.88

Source: MAFF, HGCA, Trade Sources

Production in other European countries is also predicated on spring sowing.   This is a key reason for the majority of UK malt export destinations being outside the EU. Combined with a higher proportion of spring sown barley of malting quality, stimulated by the availability of new higher yielding varieties, plantings may swing towards spring in future years.

Table 3.4:   Estimated UK Malting Barley Output and Usage (thousand tonnes)

	1991/92	1992/93	1993/94	1994/5[*]
Total Barley Production	7,600	7,360	6,010	5,885
Potential Malting Production	3,063	3,194	2,584	3,054
Actual Malting Barley Purchases	1,830	1,713	1,729	1,750
Winter	695	789	907	910
Spring	1,135	924	823	840
Malting Barley as a percentage of total Barley Production	24	23	29	30

Source : MAFF seed certification figures, Institute of Brewing, Farm Brief
* Forecast

Trade in Cereals

Wheat

As a proportion of total UK wheat exports, the rest of the EU's share has varied from 40% (1989) to 76% (1987, 1991). In 1993 the EU's share was less than 50%. This volatility is partly due to the quality and size of the UK crop, and partly to the UK price relative to the rest of EU. On a fob basis, the UK is usually the cheapest source of wheat in the European Union. This is often a function of internal market movement and freight levels since the fob gap between UK and French ports narrows as the season progresses, especially for deep-water 25,000 tonne vessels. With most export trade moving eastward and the cereal crop grown on the eastern side of the country, these UK areas have only four major deep-water ports for this business (terminals at Southampton, Tilbury, Teesside and Hull).

This poses a problem for mills sited near major ports since they are competing with shippers for available internal supplies. RHM's Southampton mill competes with two export terminals at the port, while Allied Mills' Rochford and Hull plants compete with Tilbury and Hull export facilities respectively. This means that when shippers need to fill boats quickly they may pay a premium and distort the local market for periods during the season up to April when UK fob markets traditionally lose their price advantage. It should be borne in mind that the Tilbury terminal is owned by Allied's sister company Thames Grain and accounts for all or virtually all of the port's wheat shipments.

The largest wheat export terminals by volume are as follows: Immingham, Ipswich, Southampton, Tilbury, Hull, Middlesborough, King's Lynn and Cardiff - all shipping 100,000 tonnes plus per annum.

Table 3.5:   UK Wheat Trade July-June (thousand tonnes)

	Third Country		EU		Total	
	Imports	Exports	Imports	Exports	Imports	Exports
1985/86	848	587	1,221	1,940	2,069	2,527
1986/87	714	2,465	537	2,936	1,251	5,401
1987/88	492	1,134	1,654	1,299	2,146	2,433
1988/89	561	1,458	626	758	1,187	2,216
1989/90	389	2,558	405	1,116	794	3,674
1990/91	321	900	421	3,162	742	4,062
1991/92	343	1,722	520	2,925	863	4,647
1992/93	212	1,694	1,093	2,782	1,305	4,476
1993/94	176	1,023	1,426	1,885	1,602	2,907
1994/95*	180	450	670	1,950	850	2,400

Source: HGCA, Farm Brief
* Forecast

Figure 3.1:   Wheat Trade Balance July-June ('000 tonnes)

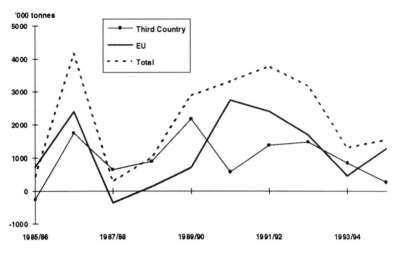

Source : HGCA, Farm Brief, Euro PA

Starch/Maize

Table 3.6:   UK Maize Imports and Usage (thousand tonnes)

	Imports	Feed Usage	Human/Industrial
1984/85	1,440	195	1,197
1985/86	1,450	330	1,125
1986/87	1,485	280	1,180
1987/88	1,385	240	1,150
1988/89	1,405	250	1,155
1989/90	1,700	240	1,330
1990/91	1,480	150	1,395
1991/92	1,545	220	1,300
1992/93	1,580	190	1,375
1993/94*	1,550	180	1,355

Source : MAFF, HGCA

Until the 1988/89 season, starch processors received an EU subsidy to encourage the use of wheat and maize in the Union. It was phased out on the grounds that starch products used in the food industry were already protected under the CAP. In addition, the subsidy did not fully compensate industrial users for the higher EU cereal price compared to world levels and thus failed to prevent undercutting by imports based on the cheaper raw material cost.

While cereals are the dominant raw materials used by starch processors, there is also limited usage of other raw materials. The biggest player

Cerestar, also processes rice for speciality markets, such as freeze/thaw stability of food for microwaves and paper coatings.

On average, UK starch processors account for 63% to 65% of all maize imports. Breakfast cereals producers, animal feed compounders and grain whisky distillers take the remainder. France overtook America as the biggest supplier in the middle of the 1980's and now accounts for around 80% of all UK imports, while US shipments have fallen below 5,000 tonnes (less than half of one percent of imports). Increased domestic production of starches has tended to reduce imports which are mainly based on maize and potatoes (see Table 3.7).

Table 3.7:   UK Starch Imports by Product (tonnes)

	1987/88	1988/89	1989/90	1990/91	1991/92	1992/93
Maize	44,969	40,620	39,713	37,760	31,350	33,330
Wheat	5,337	15,187	15,242	17,027	13,558	11,951
Potato	86,781	79,373	87,176	81,749	84,850	85,108
Rice	384	396	345	338	256	285
Other	2,420	1,852	2,644	1,290	1,924	846
Total	139,891	137,426	145,120	138,164	131,936	131,521

Source : Customs and Excise, Intrastat

Malt and Malting Barley

The weather plays a crucial role in trade flows in the unsupported European malting barley market. Drought in Denmark in 1992 reduced its overall barley production by 40% against the previous year. This helped raise the delivered UK price of spring malting barley, Alexis, from £141/tonne in August to £180/tonne for January, even before the collapse of Sterling in September.

Continental EU malt markets are more affected by the existence of co-operative maltsters such as in France. These maltsters are said to have lower expectations on capital requirements and profits. Also, credit provision from French Credit sources e.g. Credit Agricole[8] may have been easier. Surplus malting capacity on mainland EU may also be a

---

8   A key reason for the co-operatives' dominance in major agricultural and food processing sectors on the Continent, as opposed to their minor presence in the UK, is that they were the main conduit for agricultural and social investment. This ranged from the ability of French co-ops to borrow from Credit Agricole at 1% below base rate and, until recently, the general availability of EU grants for up to 25% of the capital cost of a project. Farmer-owned groups were more likely to get EU grant aid than a private limited company (plc).

factor and is estimated by the UK industry at upwards of 300,000 tonnes. This exacerbates the seasonal factors, such as the weather, that can make UK sales maltsters lose European export markets.

Malt imports were just under 60,000 tonnes in 1987 and then doubled to 122,000 tonnes during 1991, but fell back to 74,000 tonnes in 1993. Total UK malt exports to Europe have fallen from 155,000 tonnes in 1983 to between 110,000 and 116,000 tonnes during the 1990's. This has been largely compensated for by the growth of exports to Asia and the Far East, especially Japan, which have grown from 90,000 tonnes to 160,000 tonnes over the same period (see Table 3.8).

Table 3.8:   UK Malt Exports by Destination (tonnes)

	1991	1992	1993
Germany	54,608	69,583	77,909
Netherlands	24,099	20,298	26,943
Eire	3,623	2,153	1,516
Denmark	5,589	9,187	6,231
Portugal	12,989	4,382	-
Other EU	3,566	2,753	2,647
Total EU	**104,476**	**108,356**	**115,246**
Brazil	18,745	12,079	13,610
Cameroon	10,682	8,190	5,350
Ghana	6,772	4,605	9,197
Japan	116,395	118,331	116,679
Jamaica	13,272	2,315	3,217
Malaysia	5,066	6,377	5,781
Norway	12,548	10,404	11,759
Peru	13,272	4,000	6,000
Philippines	10,527	13,526	7,054
Singapore	2,591	5,889	4,642
South Africa	50,573	29,335	34,088
Thailand	5,580	3,420	7,598
Venezuela	19,379	30,176	24,570
Other	20,165	27,075	45,632
Non EU Total	305,567	275,722	295,177
Total	**410,043**	**384,078**	**410,423**

Source : Customs and Excise

The impact of the Uruguay Round GATT agreement on malt exports is not clear. If malt is not treated as a processed added value product but as a grain the impact could be negative. The UK industry will be the worst hit in the EU since over 70% of its malt exports are to third country destinations (28% to Japan alone), compared with 45% of French shipments.

Table 3.9:   UK Malting Barley Trade (tonnes)

	Exports			Imports		
	1991/2	1992/3	1993/4	1991/2	1992/3	1993/4*
France	-	17,263	1,005	6,810	11,119	14,548
Belgium/Lux	32,534	117,415	26,373	22	1,529	1
Netherlands	12,943	58,867	41,227	-	-	-
Germany	11,698	97,655	23,610	1,935	2,269	687
Denmark	-	58,656	7,214	63,891	2,721	29,371
Greece	-	-	5,636	-	-	-
Eire	-	-	-	50	4,213	8,252
USA	-	-	-	-	612	6,650
Other	3,019	358	3,085	1,142	128	28
Total EU	**60,194**	**350,014**	**108,150**	**73,850**	**22,591**	**59,517**

Source : Customs and Excise
* July to December only

Processed Cereals Products

Flour Milling

UK flour milling has restructured and rationalised to an extent that has yet to occur in most of Continental Europe. In 1994/95 there were around 35 companies producing flour in the UK, compared with, for example, over 900 in Italy. While there are major commercial players in France, such as Soufflet - with over two million tonnes of milling capacity in French and Belgian mills - there are still a large number of mills. However, in France around 70 mills account for about 70% of total flour ouput so the UK/Continental comparison is not a straightforward one.

There are two major reasons for any differences in structure: British taste (conditioned by traditional supplies of wheat) and ABF. The UK bread market was dominated by the cut slice loaf with a shelf life of four to five days, whereas daily purchasing of bread was the norm in the rest of Europe. The longer-life, easily wrapped "high rise loaf" produced in the UK lent itself to larger scale bakeries, flour milling and distribution operations.

The UK 's position in the Commonwealth and its longstanding trading connections with North America resulted in a constant supply of relatively cheap North Amemerican wheat. This supply of raw material enabled British millers and bakers to produce the "high risen loaf". In turn the British consumer acquired a taste for bread that also had a longer shelf life and a whiter colour and could be sliced and wrapped easily. North American hard wheats, therefore, were an important part of the UK's demand for bread wheat. The Community Preference adopted by the UK upon entry into the EEC increased the price of wheat imported from third countries. This price effect plus the advent of new baking processes and the addition of wheat gluten to soft wheats has allowed substitution of some (11% minimum protein) EU produced wheat for imported hard wheats (see Table 3.5).

UK millers traditionally use between 4.8 million and 5.1 million tonnes of wheat to produce flour for white and wholemeal bread, biscuit, cake, retail and household markets. With imported wheat more costly, including those from other EU countries, the pressure to utilise a greater proportion of domestic supply has been a technical priority, hence the use of gluten to improve the protein fraction when less of the crop is at the 11% protein minimum.

Table 3.10:   The UK Flour Market (thousand tonnes)

	1987/88	1990/91	1993/94
White Bread Flour	1,950	2,000	1,970
Brown and Wholemeal Bread Flour	398	329	414
Biscuit	475	512	528
Cake/Self-Raising	84	233	88
Household	205	184	178
Other (incl. starch)	533	403	522
Total	**3,650**	**3,661**	**3,700**

Source : MAFF, Farm Brief, Trade

Table 3.11:   Estimated UK Bread Wheat Harvest Output 1989-94 (million tonnes)

	Group 1 Varieties (% Of total)	Total UK Wheat Output	Potential Bread Wheat Output
1989/90	27.0	14.04	3.79
1990/91	21.0	14.04	2.95
1991/92	21.3	14.36	3.06
1992/93	24.7	14.10	3.48
1993/94	21.4	12.89	2.76
1994/95*	20.5	13.15	2.70

* Forecast
Source: National Institute of Agricultural Botany/Farm Brief

As noted at the beginning of this chapter there are three classifications for wheat bought for milling: Groups 1, 2 and 3. Group 1 contains the preferred bread-making varieties. Group 2 varieties are those which produce flour that may be blended in bread grists, but are mainly used for other flours and animal feed. Group 3 varieties, the most common in the UK, are usually used in feed and biscuit flour production.

Bread flour producers claim to be increasingly concerned over the drop in Group 1 plantings by UK farmers. Currently only 8% to 15% of bread wheat demand is contracted. Due to the yield penalty for growing bread wheats, farmers calculate a minimum 15% premium over feed is required as sufficient financial incentive to grow it. As Table 3.12 shows this level has rarely been reached consistently. This suggests that the reliance on imported wheat will not fall.

The earlier reference to ABF's influence on the milling industry needs further elaboration[9]. Unlike the two other major players, Ranks and Spillers - ABF integrated backwards from baking into flour milling with Allied Mills during the 1950's and 1960's. Occasional supermarkets' bread price wars and actions by some smaller "rogue" millers contributed to the squeeze on industry margins. Some commentators, therefore, argue that ABF's position has helped maintain a consistent pressure on its competitors in the bread and flour industry to raise productivity and achieve lower unit costs of production.

Table 3.12:   UK Bread Wheat Premium Over Feed 1980/81 - 1993/94

	Feed Wheat Price	Bread Wheat Price	Premium
	£/tonne	£/Tonne	%
1980/81	101.4	106.2	4.7
1981/82	108.8	118.8	9.2
1982/83	113.9	120.3	5.6
1983/84	121.1	135.9	12.2
1984/85	107.2	120.2	12.3
1985/86	106.5	130.4	22.4
1986/87	109.0	121.4	11.4
1987/88	105.1	136.6	30.0
1988/89	109.3	119.2	9.1
1989/90	112.0	115.0	2.6
1990/91	128.2	137.7	7.4
1991/92	120.9	135.1	11.7
1992/93	135.6	174.0	22.5
1993/94*	108.9	130.4	19.8

* Forecast
Source: HGCA, Farm Brief, Trade Sources

9   Now effectively dormant, the Millers Mutual Association also played an important role in industry rationalisation before and after the 1939-45 war. Millers paid a levy into a central fund which was available to those leaving the industry provided that their capacity was dismantled. Similar schemes have been used in other EU countries.

Cereal Starch

The high cost of entry and the technology required to produce starch and gluten from the two main cereal raw materials, wheat and maize, ensure the sector is dominated by pan-EU and multi-national groups. There is significant price volatility in the sector - vital wheat gluten prices ranged from £450/tonne to £1,600/tonne during 1991-94. The production of wheat starch/gluten started in the UK with relatively minor involvement of some independent firms. Even when the parent company was quite large e.g. RHM, the production of the starch/gluten enterprise was small. The high price of gluten in the early days and millers/bakers seeing the advantages nevertheless, caused the wheat starch producers to have a significant market impact on maize starch producers. This probably encouraged the larger company involvement and scaling up of existing operations seen today. Around 80% of wheat starch is now estimated to be produced by companies which are predominantly maize starch producers e.g Cargill, Roquette, Cerestar, Amylum.

The interchangeability of maize and wheat as a raw material is limited by availability and market pressures. In the UK, the main obvious constraint is that climatic conditions make the production of grain maize, as opposed to fodder maize and sweet corn, an impossibility. Table 3.13 illustrates the relative levels of production of grain maize in the EU.

Table 3.13:   EU Grain Maize Production (million tonnes)

	1988/89	1989/90	1990/91	1991/92	1992/93	1993/94
France	14.7	13.3	9.3	12.9	14.9	15.1
Germany	1.5	1.6	1.5	1.9	2.1	2.7
Greece	2.3	2.3	1.6	1.9	2.0	2.1
Italy	6.3	6.4	5.9	6.0	7.2	7.5
Spain	3.6	3.3	3.2	3.2	2.8	1.7
Others	0.7	0.7	0.7	0.7	0.7	0.8
Total	29.1	27.6	22.2	26.6	29.7	30.0

Source: International Wheat Council

UK maize starch processors formerly imported most of their raw material from North America, but the CAP-supported production growth in France was an obvious substitute and this now accounts for up to 80% of UK maize starch use. The third country import levy also caused a sharp reduction in imports. EU crop production was badly affected by drought during 1990/91 and caused processors to source US supplies. Overall UK maize imports during 1993/94 were 1.55 million tonnes, of which starch processors used 62%. The remainder went for distilling, breakfast cereals and animal feed.

Table 3.14: UK Maize and Wheat Usage for Starch (thousand tonnes)

Marketing Year (July-June)	Maize	% of Total	Wheat	% of Total	Total Cereals
1981/82	804	91.6	74	8.4	878
1982/83	812	83.8	157	16.2	969
1983/84	830	77.1	247	22.9	1,077
1984/85	857	73.6	307	26.4	1,164
1985/86	768	71.5	306	28.5	1,074
1986/87	856	70.1	367	29.9	1,223
1987/88	804	67.0	397	33.0	1,201
1988/89	815	66.5	412	33.5	1,228
1989/90	560	67.7	410	32.3	1,270
1990/91	925	70.3	390	29.7	1,315
1991/92	915	70.1	390	29.9	1,305
1992/93	975	72.5	370	27.5	1,345
1993/94*	1,005	73.9	356	26.1	1,361

* Forecast
Source : MAFF, Government Statistical Office, Trade

Malting Barley

In the UK the malting barley industry is concentrated to an extent that does not occur in the rest of Europe. Again, this reflects the dominance of the co-operative system in Continental Europe. Malting barley is broadly defined by those varieties appearing on the Institute of Brewing's (IoB) preferred list, usually with a nitrogen content of below 1.8%. Export and European markets use a similar criteria, except that it is traded on an equivalent protein content of 11.5%.

UK malt consumption by brewers, sales maltsters and distillers has remained fairly static at between 1.75 million and 1.95 million tonnes over the past five years. Formerly, this represented less than a quarter of the barley crop, but the continued fall in plantings has pushed the proportion closer to 30%. With malting varieties representing a much higher proportion of sowings (40%) theoretical availability ranges upwards of 2.5 million tonnes.   But climatic variables and varietal characteristics actually produce a 40% to 70% usage range for the nine varieties listed by the IoB as suitable for malting, in any season. Other non-listed IoB varieties are used for malting, but the proportion actually processed falls to around 25% in most seasons.

Malting barley is predominantly grown in southern England, East Anglia, the Yorkshire Wolds, the Borders and north-east Scotland and mainly bought by merchants going onto farms. In England, merchants traditionally bid the farmer for the crop, subject to analysis. Hitherto, less than 10% of the English malting barley crop has been bought under farmer contract at harvest by end users via merchants. The decline in barley plantings has prompted a greater interest in contracts and the proportion under contract is estimated to have grown to c. 25%+ for 1994/95 as end users seek to guarantee supplies. Maltsters have also sought to ensure supplies by acquiring merchants with a strong farmer connection with which they have enjoyed a lengthy trading relationship. Examples are Munton and Fison, the malting subsidiary of Charles Wells at Stowmarket in Suffolk, buying C K Squirrell near Ipswich in 1992, and Essex maltster Hugh Baird taking over Mark Lawrence (Grain) in the same county. In Scotland, around 55% of the malting crop, ranging from 650,000 tonnes to 750,000 tonnes out of a total barley harvest of 1.6 million to 1.8 million tonnes depending on the season, is bought under contract by merchants who in turn have a contract with a brewer, distiller or maltster.

Unlike milling wheat, malting barley premiums over feed quality are consistently above £25/tonne and have ranged up to £60/tonne in times of shortage. This provides a considerable element of risk in which end users prefer not to get directly involved. It is not uncommon, for example, for delivered prices off East Anglian and southern farms for the best parcels of a malting variety to collapse by £15 to £20 in less than a month. Prices tend to be lower in Scotland due to higher moisture contents (see Table 3.15).

Table 3.15:   Moisture Content and Drying Charges

Moisture Content	Drying Charges
<16.1%	Nil
16.1%-17%	Nil
17.1%-18%	Nil
18.1%-19%	£1.50-£2.50/tonne
19.1%-20%	£3-£4/tonne
20.1%-21%	£3.50-£4.50/tonne
21%+	As agreed

Source : Farm Brief

The trading period is compressed into the shortest period of all the main arable crops, partly because of the need for merchants to clear their stores for the wheat crop and partly due to the desire of end users to get it into their own stores where it will be kept in best condition. By the end of September up to 80% of the malting crop will usually have been bought by brewers, distillers and maltsters. Some will have been bought at corn exchanges around the country where merchants bring in samples and purchase initially by eye and subject to analysis.

Currently the industry operates on the basis of 1.33 tonnes of malting barley to produce one tonne of malt. This varies depending on variety and moisture at intake. While simple, the lengthy process is expensive.

23 FEB 1999

Norfolk's College of the Countryside

Current industry estimates are that construction of a maltings is £350 to £450 per tonne of malt capacity on a green field site. This compares to around £70/tonne of capacity for a compound feed mill.

Industry Structure and Performance

The UK Flour Market

Flour demand is widely regarded in the industry as static and forecast to remain so. Allied dominates the UK flour market as price leader, even though it holds just under a third of the total market. The flour sector is highly concentrated with RHM, Allied Mills and Dalgety dominating the market. These three have over 75% of the sales of flour, although part of their sales are to sister companies (e.g. Allied Mills to Allied Bakeries).

Table 3.16: UK Flour Market Shares

	Bread	Other	Total
Allied	24	8	32
RHM	22	6	28
Dalgety Spillers	6	9	15
Heygates	5	1	6
Carr's	3	2	5
Whitworths	2	8	4

Source : Industry

Notes: The war of attrition waged by the supermarkets over bread and subsequently the millers over flour prices since 1989 has also resulted in the majors gaining market share at the expense of the independents.

The major players' tied tonnage is conducted on a list price basis, which is up to £100/tonne more than free market bakers' flour levels. It effectively forms the transfer price within the biggest two players, Allied and RHM. Before financial results became consolidated, the majors' milling operation made a return on investment of 15% to 20%, while bakeries managed only 3% or a minus figure.

The big three millers; Allied, RHM and Dalgety Spillers, have tied tonnages for a high proportion of their throughput. For Allied and RHM a large proportion goes to sister companies, while Dalgety Spillers has a contract with Federated Bakeries and some other independents. There is also an element of supplied flour that is in a tied arrangement whereby some form of funding for a new bakery or refurbishment costs is provided by the miller. The remaining 10% of their business is traded on a free market basis. Allied, for example, is totally devolved with each mill a profit centre, sometimes competing with another mill in the same group for this non-tied market. Combined with the growing pressures of capital expenditure for food health and safety legislation, this 10% of free trade was also used to put pressure on independent millers and is a key factor in their demise. Since 1990, six independent companies have sold out or mothballed plants, Botley, Clark and Butcher, W L Duffield, Hills and Partridge, and Priday Metford. Table 3.17 illustrates the average performance of the major players over the three year periods shown

Table 3.17:   Summary of Average UK Flour Company Results (three year average)

	Turnover £m	Profit £m	Profit/ Sales(%)	ROCE (%)	Current Ratio (%)	Debt Ratio	Years
Flour							
Ranks Hovis McDougall Ltd	1620.67	125.33	7.73	10.97	1.27	0.37	89/90-91/92
Cereal Industries Ltd (Allied Mills)	659.32	67.38	10.22	58.60	1.06	0.67	90/91-92/93
Dalgety Spillers Foods Ltd	347.87	33.13	9.52	44.25	0.85	0.83	90/91-92/93
Carr's Flour Mills	16.80	0.67	3.99	8.76	0.97	0.52	90/91-92/93
Whitworths	49.83	2.51	5.04	16.14	3.65	0.45	90/91-92/93
Heygates Ltd	48.68	0.31	0.64	2.92	1.37	0.59	90/91-92/93
Average Weighted by Turnover		**94.50**	**8.37**	**26.58**	**1.21**	**0.51**	
Straight Average		**38.22**	**6.19**	**23.61**	**1.53**	**0.57**	
Total Turnover	**2,668**						

Source :   Kompass, McMillans, Euro PA

Note :   The figures shown above should be read in conjunction with the notes contained in the Appendix to Chapter One

The ROCE figures are very high although the aggregate figure is pushed up by Dalgety and Allied Mills' figures. The current ratio is, on average, also very high, although Allied Mills does have a below unity figure. The debt ratios on aggregate are very low compared to other food sectors. Whitworths and RHM have performed well. The figures for RHM go up to the end of the year in which they were purchased by Tomkins for almost £1 billion.

Starch

The three major UK players are

- Cerestar
- Tunnel Refineries/Amylum
- Cargill

Between them, UK starch processors use over 1.3 million tonnes of maize and wheat within a European industry total of around 8.5 million tonnes. To arrive at a starch production figure, each tonne of maize normally yields 0.8 tonnes of starch, while the same conversion is used for wheat into flour, 7.5 tonnes of which is needed to produce one tonne of starch/gluten. Companies in the industry estimate that a further 630,000 tonnes of wheat and 150,000 tonnes of maize are used by smaller European processing organisations. Thus the European industry as a whole produces about 4.25 million tonnes of starch from maize and 230,000 tonnes from wheat. The industry estimates another 1.3 million tonnes is produced from potatoes , a third of this in Holland.

In the UK, trade estimates are that National Starch at Tilbury, a part of the Unilever empire, and ABR at Corby (majority controlled by Associated British Foods via its British Sugar subsidiary) use another 150,000 tonnes of wheat between them.

ABR uses an estimated 80,000 tonnes of flour (100,000 tonnes of wheat equivalent), mainly from its sister company Allied Mills' mill a few hundred yards away. A large share of its starch production is used in cake and confectionery companies, mainly Allied Bakeries, within the ABF group. The starch plant was completed 13 years ago and among the incentives for building it were regional development grants, 10-year rates relief and employment subsidies to take on redundant British Steel workers following the closure of the nearby BSC factory. Close to a motorway, the plant and nearby flour mill are sited near to a major wheat growing area. There is a general consensus that the Corby plant investment would be unlikely to be made today without a similar level of UK or European Commission grant aid.

Cerestar, the subsidiary of the troubled Italian agribusiness, Feruzzi, is by far the largest operator in the UK and throughout Europe. With total maize and wheat processing capacity of just over 2.8 million tonnes, it accounts for almost a third of the EU market. Its EU plant processes an estimated 425,000 tonnes of maize annually. Cerestar also has plants in Germany, where it is building another 400,000 tonne capacity maize processing plant, and Holland, where both maize and wheat is processed. In addition there are maize-only factories in France, Italy and Spain.

Tate and Lyle subsidiary Tunnel/Amylum is the UK's second largest processor using an estimated 250,000 tonnes of maize and 150,000 tonnes of wheat for its Greenwich plant. With operations in Belgium, Holland and Spain, it is also Europe's third largest player. It also recently bought a small ageing potato starch plant in eastern Germany.

Cargill, the biggest cereal trader in the world, processes an estimated 300,000 tonnes of maize at its UK plant and a similar total of both maize and wheat in Holland. The French based group Roquette is Europe's second largest cereal starch producer, but does not operate in the UK.

While UK wheat starch producers' gross margins have grown rapidly to around 12% by 1993, there is a threat to profitability: the EU support system. If UK farmers finally switch to bread quality wheats to obtain institutional price support, the protein cost may fall. This would produce downward price pressure on vital wheat gluten (VWG), a key by-product of the starch production process. With Britain's bakers the biggest current market for VWG, processors would have to rely on much smaller volume demand sectors, such as petfood, to maintain demand. It should be noted, though, that there are other technical possibilities e.g. competition with casein which, if feasible, would raise VWG demand and prices.

Figure 3.2 illustrates that gross output concentration ratio in the starch and miscellaneous food industry is around 30%. The graph below shows that this concentration has been growing steadily since the early 1980's. The fact that the gross value-added ratio is always above the gross output ratio indicates that the five largest firms have, on average, better margins than smaller starch processors. This underlines the key point that economies of scale are very important in this sector. If figures were available for just starch then the concentration ratios would probably be significantly higher.

Figure 3.2:   5 Firm Concentration Ratios - Starch and Miscellaneous Food

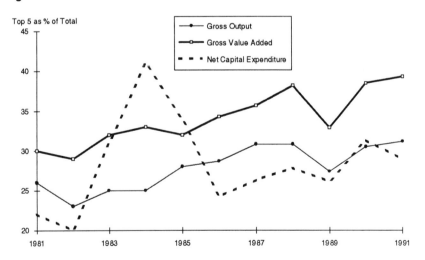

Source : Business Monitor PA1002 selected years, Euro PA

Note :   The fact Miscellaneous Food is included in the graph obscures the concentration of
            just the starch sector which is significantly above that shown in Figure 3.2.

The major UK players' plant locations are Cerestar in Manchester, Tunnel/Amylum in Greenwich and Cargill in Tilbury.

Table 3.18:   Summary of Average UK Starch Company Results (three year average)

	Turnover £m	Profit £m	Profit/ Sales(%)	ROCE (%)	Current Ratio (%)	Debt Ratio	Years
Cerestar UK Ltd	173.84	5.36	3.08	7.14	1.31	0.81	91-93
Tunnel/Amylum	102.61	6.23	6.07	10.49	1.41	0.55	90/91-92/93
Cargill[a]	figures given under Oilseeds section						
Average weighted by turnover		**5.68**	**4.19**	**8.38**	**1.35**	**0.71**	
Straight Average		**5.80**	**4.58**	**8.82**	**1.36**	**0.68**	
Total Turnover	**276**						

Source :   Kompass, McMillans, Euro PA
(a) starch is only a small proportion of Cargill's turnover
Note :   The figures shown above should be read in conjunction with the notes contained in
the Appendix to Chapter One

The Malting Industry

Pauls Malt became the UK's and Europe's largest sales maltster when it bought industry number one Associated British Maltsters from Dalgety in a £32 million deal in June 1987. It brought in seven maltings, five of which were operational; Bury St Edmunds, Louth, Knapton in North Yorkshire and Carnoustle and Airdrie in Scotland, while two other Scottish plants were effectively mothballed.

At the time Pauls had plants at Ipswich, Ware, Mendlesham, Grimsby, Gainsborough, Grantham and Buckie in Scotland and industry estimates were of a 450,000 tonne surplus malting capacity. Malt capacity at the time of the enlarged Pauls was around 600,000 tonnes, while throughput at the combined operation was estimated at below 500,000 tonnes. Mendlesham near Ipswich with 80,000 tonnes of capacity was the first to be shut down within months of the deal.

In general, maltings operate to full capacity or production lines are closed down. Since there is not a vast amount of machinery within the plant, a maltings can also act as a grain store, an option used by Pauls with Mendlesham.

Table 3.19:   UK Sales Maltsters Estimated Output and Capacity (thousand tonnes)

	Throughput			Capacity	
	1990	1991	1993	1991	1993
Pauls	402	370	365	465	410
Simpson	162	155	153	180	180
Hugh Baird	105	125	122	165	165
Moray Firth	150	145	142	165	165
Munton and Fison	100	100	98	125	125
Anglia/Crisp	96	96	95	115	115
Masham	36	36	35	40	40
Peach	14	12	12	17	17
Additional Capacity	-	-	-	88	73
Totals	**1.060**	**1,039**	**1,022**	**1,350**	**1,290**

Source : Farm Brief, Trade Sources

There has also been pan-European and global concentration involving UK companies. Tate and Lyle exited the industry when it sold its Hugh Baird malting subsidiary to Canada maltsters; the world's largest with throughput estimated at over 850,000 tonnes annually (1992). Cargill, the US-based biggest global agribusiness, vies with Canada as the number one maltster and is in the process of expanding capacity in mainland Europe.

Sales maltsters operate by producing malt for domestic and export markets. Their domestic (UK) market has been put under pressure by brewers increasing their own malting capacity and the threat from players across the Channel. Whitbread began importing malt in the mid 1980's. This caused some consternation in the trade but the company has steadily increased its import levels to a current 30,000 tonnes plus. Industry reactions since include Paul's shut-down of its Carnoustie maltings and removal of 30,000 tonnes of capacity. Bass and latterly, Guinness, have also closed capacity.

Table 3.20:Summary of Average UK Sales Maltsters Company Results(3 yr av.)

	Turnover £m	Profit £m	Profit/ Sales(%)	ROCE (%)	Current Ratio (%)	Debt Ratio	Years
Pauls plc	320.74	25.31	7.89	56.63	0.61	0.88	91-93
Simpsons Malt Ltd	61.56	1.57	2.55	6.89	1.52	0.59	90/91-92/93
Hugh Baird	37.15	1.29	3.46	2.93	1.83	0.59	91-92
Average weighted by turnover		**19.70**	**6.71**	**44.57**	**0.85**	**0.81**	
Straight Average		**9.39**	**4.63**	**22.15**	**1.32**	**0.69**	
Total Turnover	**419**						

Source :   Kompass, Euro PA
Note :   The figures shown above should be read in conjunction with the notes contained in the Appendix to Chapter One

Table 3.20 above illustrates the average performance of the largest three sales maltsters over a three year period. These three companies account for over 60% of the volumes by sales maltsters.

Pauls seems to have performed most impressively with its profit margin and ROCE figures well above the other companies.

Distinctions between sales and brewer maltsters are increasingly blurred. For example, Moray Firth is owned by Scottish and Newcastle, while Munton and Fison is controlled by the Charles Wells brewing family.

Table 3.21:   UK Brewers Malt Output and Capacity (thousand tonnes)

	Output	Capacity
Bass	150	170
Allied	60	105
Courage	16	25
Guinness*	20	20
Wolverhampton and Dudley	5	6
Green King	5	6
Home Breweries	3	3
Total	**259**	**335**

Source: Farm Brief, Trade Sources
* Guinness closed its three small floor maltings within its E S Beavan subsidiary in East Anglia during 1994

Currently, the UK malt industry is under a double squeeze depressing both domestic demand and third country exports. The UK Treasury's refusal to reduce excise duty in line with other EU countries may have encouraged both legitimate and illegitimate cross-Channel trade by consumers. The UK drink's industry estimated losses of £1 billion in sales during 1993. Cross-channel beer purchases doubled to 1.25 million barrels, equivalent to 3.5% of the UK market. This is against the background of already declining domestic beer consumption; beer consumption fell from 37.7 million barrels in 1982 to 36.25 million barrels in 1992. While some major brewers have shipped bonded beer to France for sale to UK consumers, it is not likely to stem the decline in domestic consumption.

Table 3.22:   UK Distillers Malt Output and Capacity 1990/91 (thousand tonnes)

	Output	Capacity
UDC	200	215
Allied Distillers	32	40
Highland Distillers	21	28
Morrison	5	6
Grant	5	6
Chivas	1	1
Total	**264**	**296**

Source : LIS, Trade Sources

The UK Oilseeds Industry

Supply of Oilseeds

Production

UK oilseed production, and that of the rest of the EU, are almost totally a function of CAP subsidies. Linseed, oilseed rape, soya and sunflower simply would not be grown by arable producers to anything like the same extent without the level of support given. At its peak every extra hectare planted in the EU cost the CAP £1,200. This was mainly outside the UK where the climate militates against any commercial scale production of soya or sunflower.

But during the 1992/93 season, UK linseed plantings of just under 150,000 hectares accounted for two-thirds of the EU total. Production subsidies, rather than the crop itself were the main factor in the area's ninefold rise in just four years. As a spring sown crop, it is more susceptible to poor weather and in many cases, farmers have found it more economic to plough in their linseed rather than harvest it. Its massive dependence on CAP aid was underlined in spring 1994 when a reduction in subsidy more than halved the crop area to 58,000 hectares.

By contrast, the oilseed rape area has more than surpassed its 1990/91 peak of 493,000. Total 1993/94 plantings were at 520,000 hectares, this includes about 110,000 hectares for industrial use, mainly on set-aside land. Thus, edible rapeseed production is expected to return to previous levels of around 1.2 million tonnes with another 300,000 tonnes for industrial use. The latter is grown under a policed system whereby industrial production is only permitted with a contract specifying non food end use.

Table 3.23:   UK Oilseed Rape Area and Production

	1987/88	88/89	89/90	90/91	91/92	92/93	93/94	94/95
Area ('000 ha)	388.0	347.0	320.7	489.9	439.9	421.1	376.7	520
Output ('000 tonnes)	1353	1040	976	1231	1250	1150	1430	1550

* Includes industrial crops
Source : MAFF, Farm Brief, Industry

However, price relativities are almost certain to distort these figures. Edible rapeseed prices have ranged from £170 to £180 a tonne on the farm for the 1994 harvest, and weakened on the prospect of a larger than expected Canadian crop and higher American soyabean plantings. This compares with contract values of £100 a tonne for industrial use. Both varieties can meet both market requirements

The Processing of Oilseeds

UK oilseed crushing capacity is estimated at 1.4 million to 1.6 million tonnes 1994/95. The main outputs from this are edible oils (used mainly in food manufacturing and for cooking), and the protein and fibre oilseed residue (used in compound feed formulations). In addition to domestic oilseed crops, the major crushers also process a wide range of imported oil-bearing products for edible markets including palm kernel, soya and maize. The UK crushing and refining industry processes the entire British crop extracting an average of 40% oil, leaving a residual of 60% meal for the animal feed market from each tonne. This represents 35% of the UK edible oil market.

The mid 1994 price for crude rape oil was the equivalent of c. £355/tonne, while palm oil values were at around £305/tonne. Demonstrating market distortions, soya oil was trading at a discount to rape oil. Traditionally, soya oil trades at a premium to rape oil and downward pressures inevitably bear on the latter as global values weaken. However, these values reflect the rises in edible oil prices over the previous two years, even if they do not accurately mirror relative prices. In 1992, crude oil was £220/tonne and £260/tonne for refined oil. Palm oil was at the same level, while soya oil traded at £30/tonne premium and sunflower oil at £260. The latter's higher crude oil price is due to its greater demand for margarine production.

Mid 1994 ex factory prices for rapemeal for use in animal feed were just under £110/tonne compared with £80/tonne two years earlier. This compares with delivered prices of £130/tonne for feed wheat in 1992 and £125/tonne two years later. Their price relativity is important since it forms the basis of the EU oilseed regime, a radical reform agreed for the 1992/93 crop year, that switched support from a crushing subsidy to processors and crop intervention support to an on farm payment system allowing rapeseed to meet its own true market level. The change was in response to the rising cost of the original oilseed regime and pressure from America in the GATT Uruguay Round[10].

Crushing and refining margins are around zero in the summer months as there is no raw material, but usually range between £17/tonne and

---

10   The EU's oilseed's regimes have been the subject of two GATT panels and in the summer of 1992, a USTR 301 action. The latter threat of trade sanctions effectively brought about the agreement on a new oilseeds regime finally put together as part of the Blair House Accord in late 1992.

£28/tonne to produce a return on capital of below 9%. The exception is Unilever with a higher ROCE of about 12% presumably due to its brand led activities in the yellow fats market, margarines and spreads.

Industry Structure and Financial Performance

Archer Daniels Midland (ADM) is the UK's and Europe's largest oilseed crusher. The US-based agribusiness achieved that position by taking over Unilever's Unimills business at Erith, near London and its 600,000 tonne capacity plant at Mannheim in Germany. Unilever's exit from the primary crushing market was completed with the sale of its BOCM Silcock subsidiary to Pauls' parent company Harrisons and Crosfield in April 1992.

BEOCO is the subsidiary of South America's Bunge and Born family interests whose activities range from global agricultural commodity trading to denim manufacture. Its Liverpool plant was bought from the J Bibby group in 1983. The plant has a maximum crushing capacity of 1,400 tonnes per day with actual throughput during peak production of 1,000 tonnes. It is the only major operating in the UK producing a branded rapeseed oil, Golden Fields. With an integrated plastic bottling unit at the plant, the company apparently seeks a 5p to 6p a litre premium above standard vegetable oil for its brand. The company also crushes maize for Mazola corn oil.

Table 3.24: UK Crushers and Refiners

	Activity	Plants	Throughput* ('000 tonnes)	Product Throughput ('000 tonnes)
ADM	Crushing	Frith	700	Rape 750, Sunflower 200
BEOCO	Crushing /Refining	Liverpool	280	Rape 250, Maize 30
BOCM Pauls	Crushing	Selby, Yorks	100	Rape 60, Linseed 20 Speciality 30
Cargill	Crushing /Refining	Liverpool	300	Soya 400, Rape 120
		Hull	180	Rape 180, Linseed 30
Anglia	Refining	Manchester	200	
Central Edible Oils	Refining			
Karlsrahms	Refining		50	
Unilever	Refining		400	Linseed 30

Source :Farm Brief, Industry
* This is oil produced. Crushers and refiners work at full capacity during the period based on the availability of raw material and crude oil, thus plants are traditionally closed for varying periods during the summer months for maintenance.

Cargill, the world's largest grain trader and primary processor also has a plant in Liverpool which it bought from a fellow family owned giant, Continental, and was originally designed to crush soya imported from its American operations. It subsequently added a rapeseed processing line. Cargill's operations include another crushing plant at Hull.

These changes of ownership underline the major structural changes in the oilseed crushing sector. One other global commodity trader, Louis Dreyfus, bought Scotland's only crushing plant in Glasgow from the receiver and has subsequently closed it down. A key factor for the plant was its distance from any rape production area. Thus for crops grown in the north east of Scotland the nearest crushing plant is in Norway, but the nearest practical point of delivery is, of course, Liverpool. Only Erith, Hull and Selby have oilseed rape production areas in close proximity.

As Table 3.25 shows the industry appears to have surplus crushing capacity which is made up in Erith's case by importing sunflower from France. However, this problem is even worse in Continental Europe where industry estimates put total crushing capacity at upwards of 20 million tonnes (per annum) compared with rape, sunflower and soya production which has not been higher than 14 million tonnes.

The five firm output concentration ratio in the oilseeds sector was around 80% in 1991. Throughout the 1980's this ratio was around 70% and was falling in the second half of the decade, though it rose in 1990. The gross value-added ratio is significantly less than this at 70%.

Figure 3.3: 5 Firm Concentration Ratios - Oilseed Sector

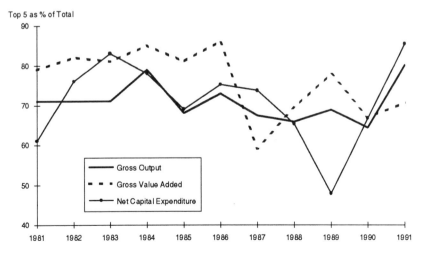

Source : Business Monitor PA 1002 selected years, Euro PA

Table 3.25 displays average company results for the main oilseed companies

- The companies in this sector show much the same performance as those in the starch sector.

- Profit margins (profit/sales) are very low at around 1% on average.

- The weighted average sector ROCE figure is over 7.5% but is mostly due to Cargill plc. With Cargill and BOCM Pauls excluded from the calculation the weighted average would be 4.7%.

- BOCM Pauls made an average loss in the period but this was entirely due to a large loss in 1992/93. Without this, profit would have averaged (straight) just over £5m. Even so, this represents a 1% profit margin.

- No company has performed outstandingly in what seems to be a difficult sector in which to operate.

Table 3.25: Summary of Average UK Oilseed Company Results (three year average)

	Turnover £m	Profit £m	Profit/ Sales(%)	ROCE (%)	Current Ratio (%)	Debt Ratio	Years
Cargill plc	1292.00	12.27	0.95	11.61	1.05	0.82	90/91-92/93
BOCM Pauls	387.12	-3.69	-0.95	-3.14	1.91	0.30	90/91-92/93
Archer Daniels Midland International	291.78	6.88	2.36	4.50	1.63	0.36	90/91-92/93
BEOCO	85.33	1.48	1.74	5.32	0.74	1.14	90-92
Average weighted by turnover		**8.05**	**0.83**	**7.56**	**1.28**	**0.67**	
Straight Average		**4.24**	**1.03**	**4.57**	**1.33**	**0.66**	
Total Turnover	**2,056**						

Source :   Kompass, McMillans, Euro PA
Note :   The figures shown above should be read in conjunction with the notes contained in the Appendix to Chapter One

The Compound Feed Industry

Output

Compound feeds are finished diets for livestock and thus an animal needs no other food source. They contain a range of raw materials, wider for ruminant than for monogastric stock. Their inclusion rates are determined by their nutritional value for each species and market price, by least cost formulation computer programmes. Demand is highly seasonal since ruminant stock (cattle and sheep) have a major alternative food source, grass, usually from April through to October. Thus peak demand generally operates from October through to March.

Table 3.26:   GB Feed Output Jan-Dec (thousand tonnes)

	1991	1992	1993	1994	1993/94 % change
Cattle and Calf	3,571.3	3,592.6	3,853.1	3,989.5	3.5
Pigs	2,110.7	2,193.8	2,276.2	2,267.0	-0.40
Poultry	3,468.9	3,410.7	3,439.0	3,475.0	1.00
Sheep	525.3	512.4	494.0	484.6	-1.90
Others	274.6	301.0	341.1	364.4	6.80
Total	**9,950.8**	**10,010.5**	**10,403.4**	**10,580.5**	**1.70**

Source : MAFF

Livestock farmers, especially pig producers on the eastern side of Britain, grow cereals to feed directly to their animals. In addition, large integrated poultry production companies have their own feed mills manufacturing compounds for stock kept at nearby sites. Having lost a large proportion of the generally low margin poultry feed business to these integrated operations, UK compounders have effectively integrated back into pig production and marketing. This provides a tied tonnage for the year long demand.

23 FEB 1999

Norfolk's College of the Countryside

Raw Material Use

Table 3.27: GB Compound feed raw materials usage (thousand tonnes)

	1991	1992	1993	1994	1993/4 % change
Wheat	2,518.9	2,429.6	2,523.5	2,865.3	13.5
Barley	851.8	661.1	599.0	562.7	-6.1
Maize	106.5	100.8	93.7	91.8	-2.0
Cereal - by-products	821.6	829.3	961.6	958.0	-0.4
Maize gluten feed	322.3	468.3	537.6	517.0	-3.8
Vegetable oil - cake & meal	2,210.6	1,977.7	1,953.9	2,085.3	6.7
Peas & Beans	305.7	290.9	285.9	387.4	35.5
Animal & Fish meals	381.9	356.4	392.1	393.0	0.2
Other	2,707.2	3,055.0	3,261.2	2,986.6	-8.4
Total ingredients	**10,026.5**	**10,232.1**	**10,608.5**	**10,847.1**	**2.2**

Source : MAFF

The 260,000 tonne rise in wheat usage and the 45,000 tonne fall for barley is primarily due to their price relativity during the peak October to March feeding period. Wheat is nutritionally superior to barley and is valued at £5 to £8/tonne more in compound feed diets, while the use of enzyme additives reduces that differential by £1-£2/tonne. The total rise in raw material use was due to the UK pig herd expansion and dairy producers' greater milk production in response to improved market prices.

The vast majority of raw materials used in compound feed are domestically produced. Protein in the form of soyameal and fishmeal are the major exceptions. Cereal usage is relatively stable, but will vary due to the relative prices of the other ingredients. Among them is imported maize gluten (MGF), a by-product of the US maize ethanol programme and production of corn sweeteners, along with rice bran. MGF is among the raw materials described as cereal replacers. Another major substitute is wheat feed, the by-product of the flour milling industry. This product provided an opportunity to those companies with both flour and feed mills on the same site. Among those who may be using this potential cost advantage are Dalgety at Avonmouth and Heygates at Bugbroke.

Industry Structure and Financial Performance

The compound feed market is dominated by three national companies:

- Bibby, a subsidiary of Associated British Foods via British Sugar,
- BOCM Pauls, owned by Harrisons and Crosfield,
- Dalgety.

Between them, they account for over 50% of the compound UK market. This rises to over 75% in south west England; Gloucestershire, Wiltshire and west to Cornwall. Independent companies, including integrated operations, account for c. 42% of production and co-operatives less than 8%.

Table 3.28: Summary of UK Compound Feed Company Results (3 year average)

	Turnover £m	Profit £m	Profit/ Sales(%)	ROCE (%)	Current Ratio (%)	Debt Ratio	Years
J. Bibby and Sons	654.33	24.86	3.80	14.10	1.48	0.59	90/91-92/93
BOCM Pauls	387.12	-3.69	-0.95	-3.14	1.91	0.30	90/91-92/93
Dalgety Spillers Foods Ltd	347.87	33.13	9.52	44.25	0.85	0.83	90/91-92/93
Average weighted by turnover		**18.98**	**3.91**	**16.85**	**1.44**	**0.57**	
Straight average		**18.10**	**4.12**	**18.40**	**1.41**	**0.57**	
Total Turnover	**1,389**						

Source : Kompass, McMillans, Euro PA
Note : The figures shown above should be read in conjunction with the notes contained in the Appendix to Chapter One.

- The three companies displayed in Table Table 3.28 account for over 50% of the compound feed market.

- Two of the companies in this sector have already been mentioned in other sectors of the cereals and oilseeds industry.

- J Bibby and Sons is the only company not yet displayed and is the largest of the companies in the sector. The figures shown above are for the entire group, not just the compound feed division. This compound feeds division was sold to ABF in April 1994 for £35m.

- Bibby's has had solid growth throughout the period culminating in its purchase by ABF in early 1994 for £35m. This company has now been incorporated into British Sugar plc and complements British Sugar's sugar processing by-product - beet pulp products - through its Trident Feeds subsidiary.

Summary

The consumption of the end products of the cereals and oilseeds industries - bread and confectionery products, animal feed, cooking fats and oils, manufactured foods and beer and alcoholic beverages is relatively static and in some sectors declining. However, there have been profound structural changes within each sector - both in response to changes to the CAP and to increasingly intense competition. The most fundamental change in administered prices was the 1992 arable reform, shifting CAP spending from crop price support to direct producer payments. Assisted by the weather, another measure - set-aside - has cut EU cereal production from 181 million tonnes in 1991 to 162 million tonnes in 1994.

A common feature of these industries is that a major source of uncertainty is changes to the CAP and, internationally, the GATT - not only in terms of material supplies, but also markets. For example, the compound feed industry is vulnerable to changes in milk quota or beef support prices, which provide the highest margins of mainstream volume production, the malting and brewing industry to excise duties, and the oilseed crushers to changes in dairy support and subsidies for biofuel.

The system of arable aid payments favours wheat, instead of pulses for example, and has already caused a recovery in UK wheat plantings - a process reflected elsewhere in the EU with a 4% rise. As the highest-yielding cereal, there are growing dangers future EU wheat production could undermine the EU's obligations under the Uruguay Round GATT agreement. Apart from changes in supply, UK processors and merchants have to adjust to farmers' improved cash flow because of direct income payments which strengthen their market position.

These changes have accentuated the differences between the UK industries and their EU counterparts operating in more fragmented producer markets. Concentration of ownership has accelerated in the UK processing sectors, while the co-operative-dominated Continental EU industries remain plagued by greater surplus capacity. The pace in the UK has been forced by major players restructuring their agribusinesses.

ABF has moved from its milling and baking base to becoming the monopoly buyer of sugar beet, the second largest UK arable merchant and third largest compounder with the takeover of Bibby in 1994. The latter complemented its large beet pulp feed business (in British Sugar). Harrisons and Crosfield subsidiary Pauls became Europe's biggest sales maltster when it took over Dalgety's interests, and the largest feed compounder when it bought BOCM Silcock from Unilever in 1992. While Bunge and Dreyfus have withdrawn from internal UK markets, ADM bought Unilever's oilseed processing plants and ConAgra and Soufflet have moved into on-farm trading. Meanwhile, Dalgety has consolidated its position as the largest on-farm supplier of arable inputs and buyer of outputs and has gained compound feed market leadership. Partly to reduce dependence on a few majors, malsters have taken over long-standing small merchant suppliers.

Contractual arrangements predominate in baking flour, compound feed supplies for pig and poultry production and are becoming more common in the sale of barley for malting. It remains much less a feature of wheat for milling where quality premia are lower and much less consistent that for malting barley - a key reason for feed varieties accounting for 80% of UK plantings.

Generally, returns from oilseed crushing have been modest, rather better for feed compounding, relatively high for starch processing and sales malting and good for flour milling which has generated a ROCE of over 25%. Ease of entry varies considerably between the industries. Technological considerations and economies of scale deter new players in oilseed and starch processing, which is dominated by pan-EU and multinational companies. At the other extreme, independent feed compounders flourish in some areas, but the three nationals - Bibby, BOCM Pauls and Dalgety - have increased their collective market share to over 55% and in the pig sector account for more than 64%.

References

British Farmer (Oct 1993). *Making Industrial Oilseed Production Pay*. NFU Publications Department, 22 Long Acre, London.

DeMaria (1994). *CAP, GATT and World Cereal Prospects,* speech given to BCE conference, International Wheat Council, London.

DTI (1994) The Uruguay Round of Multilateral Trade Negotiations 1986-94, Cm 2579 HMSO, London

Euro Analysis (1992) unpublished report R42. *A Study of the Export Refunds in the Processed Cereals and Rice Sector.* Volume 1. Euro PA & Associates, 11 Church St, Northborough, Cambs. PE6 9BN

Farm Brief (Various). Lakebourne Publishing Limited, 6 Cley Road, Holt, Norfolk, NR25 6JD.

GATT, (1994). *Agreement Establishing the World Trade Organisation Agreement on Agriculture*, Cm 2559, Misc No 17, HMSO, London

HoL(1991).   Select Committee on the European Communities. *Development and Future of the Common Agricultural Policy*. HMSO, London.

Leguen de Lacroix, E. (1992). *Basic Principles and Mechanics of the New CAP in the Main Agricultural Sectors: Cereals, Beef and Milk* in Proceedings of CEPS Business Policy Seminar No. 46, CEPS, Rue Ducale 33 B-1000 Brussels

Lorenz, K. and Kulp, K (eds) (1991). *Handbook of Cereal Science and Technology*, Marcel Dekker inc.

MAFF (1993) Arable Area Aid Payments 1993/94, Explanatory Guide Vols I & II, HMSO, London.

Neville, W. and Mordaunt, F (1993) A guide to the reformed Common Agricultural Policy. *Estates Gazette.*

NFU Briefing Paper (1994). *GATT Settlement in Agriculture*, Economics Department, NFU, 22 Long Acre, London, WC2E 9LY.

Roberts, I and Andrews, N. (1992).   Market Effects of the 1992 EC Reforms for Cereals and Beef, *ABARE Agriculture and Resources Quarterly*, Vol 4, No 4, Canberra.

Sturgess, I. M. (1991) The Future of the Common Agricultural Policy. *Review of Marketing and Agricultural Economics*, 59(2).

Tyers, R. and Anderson, K. (1992) *Disarray in World Food Markets: A Quantitative Assessment*, Cambridge University Press, Cambridge.

USDA (1994) *Agricultural Provisions of the Uruguay Round*, Foreign Agricultural Service, USDA, Washington.

Chapter 4: Sugar and Sweeteners

David Hallam and Peter Midmore[1]

Introduction

The production and processing of sugar beet in the United Kingdom provides an interesting case study of interaction between the market and policy arrangements that are made for the commodity. In this instance, the specialised agricultural activity - which is highly profitable for farmers - is governed by considerable vertical integration, itself made possible and desirable as a result of quotas governing the overall level of production. The position of Britain is somewhat different from that of the rest of the European Union, since it is the entry point for most of the preferential imports of raw cane sugar for refining from developing countries (particularly member-states of the British Commonwealth, for whom concessionary arrangements were negotiated upon entry to the then EEC). Within the context of rapidly changing consumer attitudes to diet and health, a detailed understanding is required of the way the industry structure has evolved and will continue to change and adapt to new circumstances.

In this chapter, we begin by describing the changing conditions of consumption. Though retail demand has reduced considerably, it has effectively been replaced by new uses in food manufacturing. Supply conditions are then examined in detail, with special consideration given to the way in which production controls have contributed to the current market environment. The role of competitive pressures, giving rise to fewer, more efficient processing factories, are also examined. The chapter concludes with a comparison between the relative financial performances of the two major sugar producers in the United Kingdom.

---

1   Dr David Hallam is Senior Lecturer at the Department of Agricultural Economics and Management, University of Reading; Dr Peter Midmore is a Lecturer at the Welsh Institute of Rural Studies, University of Wales, Aberystwyth. The Editors are grateful for the comments of Simon Harris of British Sugar plc on earlier drafts of this chapter and also for the help of British Sugar plc and Tate and Lyle plc with various data and information sources. The Editors are responsible for the opinions expressed herein and any errors or omissions remaining. The reader should also note the caveat in the Appendix to Chapter One.

The Consumption of Sugar

The UK sugar market has annual sales of around 2.25/2.35 million tonnes with a wholesale value of around £1.3 billion. Nearly three quarters of these sales are to industrial customers, notably in the food and drink industries, where sugar is valued not only as a sweetener, but also for its bulking, textural and preservative properties. Retail sales for direct consumption account for the remainder.

Recent years have seen little growth, and most recently some slight decline, in the size of the UK sugar market. The stability in overall consumption masks an increasing divergence between the retail and industrial markets. Over the last two decades there has been a steady decline in retail sales for direct consumption, but this has been offset by a corresponding increase in industrial consumption. The UK sugar market is now split approximately 70% industrial and 30% retail demand. Prior to the UK's entry into the EU in 1973, the proportions were reversed. The same development has also been seen in the sugar markets of other industrialised countries.

Retail sales have declined steadily, as a result of changes in consumer lifestyles - e.g. the decline in home-baking. The trend towards 'healthy' eating may have been a factor, as this is often taken as requiring a reduction in sugar intake. Recommendations for a healthier diet in the UK usually involve reductions in sugar intake (interestingly this is not the case in the USA or Canada[2]), and this has long been popularly regarded as an important element in dieting for weight loss as part of a calorie controlled diet. National Food Survey analysis reveals that these kind of trend effects have dominated price and income as determinants of sugar consumption. The price elasticity of demand for sugar does not appear to be significantly different from zero. The income elasticity is significantly different from zero and negative with a value of around -0.2 indicating that sugar is an 'inferior good'. There does not appear to be any significant seasonal variation in retail demand.

Industrial demand for sugar reached a peak in 1989/90 but has fallen back slightly since then due to the recession in the first part of the 1990's. Around 80% of industrial sugar sales are to the food and drinks industry, and virtually all food and drink manufacturers are customers of the sugar producers. Sugar is obviously valued as a sweetener, but also has several other desirable and equally significant properties for food manufacturers as a preservative, a flavour and texture enhancer, and especially as a relatively cheap bulking agent. Sugar's texture and

---

2   See for example Canadian Ministry of Health and Welfare (1990) and USDA (1990)

flavour characteristics mean that it is favoured by confectionery manufacturers. However, for some uses - soft drinks manufacture, for example - isoglucose is a direct substitute and has a price advantage over sugar. In the US beverage industry there has been massive substitution of isoglucose for sugar. However, in the UK the availability of isoglucose is limited by quota to a very small percentage of the total sweetener market. There is some limited substitutability between sugar and other cereal-based sweeteners (such as glucose and fructose). Saccharin and aspartame are widely used in 'diet products', although these artificial sweeteners do not have any price advantage over sugar and raise issues about the use of artificial products in the diet.

Not surprisingly, industrial sugar sales very much reflect the output of the food and drinks sector: econometric analysis suggests that around 85% of the variation in industrial demand for sugar can be attributed to variations in the level of output of the food and drinks industry. In spite of the availability of alternative sweeteners, no significant price effects could be ascertained in modelling industrial demand for sugar. This may be due to the less than perfect substitution possibilities facing most industrial sugar uses, and also to the quota limitations on the availability of alternatives as noted above. Figure 4.1 shows how the output of major food and drink industry sugar users has evolved since the mid-1960's.

Figure 4.1: The Output of Key Sugar Users in the Food and Drink Industry 1966-1990

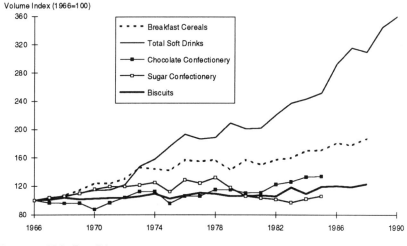

Source: CSO, Euro PA

The main users of sugar in the UK food manufacturing sector are those producing biscuits, chocolate and sugar confectionery and breakfast cereals. Chocolate and sugar confectionery output has been relatively static since 1966, growing at less than 1% per year. Biscuit manufacture grew just over 20% over roughly the same period. The growth in output of breakfast cereals has been more pronounced at over 80%. However, the fastest growing sector has been soft drinks, whose output rose 360%, and which has become the largest user of sugar. Figure 4.2 shows a breakdown of this part of the drinks industry. It can be seen that the growth area is in unconcentrated soft drinks, which account for almost all the growth in output. Growth in concentrated soft drinks has been virtually zero.

Figure 4.2:   The Soft Drinks Industry

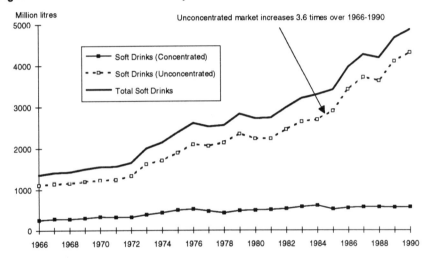

Source : CSO, Euro PA

Sugar Supplies and the EU Sugar Regime

Supplies

Most sugar consumed in the UK is produced in the UK, with imports of sugar for direct consumption (as opposed to refining) accounting for only a small proportion. The make-up of UK sugar supplies is shown in Table 4.1.

In statistical terms , the UK is close to balance from domestic sources, with the total of UK beet sugar production and raw cane sugar refining (some 2.26 million tonnes) being close to demand - at 2.25/2.35 million tonnes annually. The UK has an export of sugar, however, representing the re-export of quantities equivalent to; imports from the rest of the EU (around 135/150 thousand tonnes annually), imports of direct consumption raws (cane sugar specialities, such as muscavado and demerara, which are not further refined before consumption) and imports of other caloric sweeteners (glucose and fructose) from the rest of the EU.

Table 4.1:   UK Sugar Supply 1989/90 - 1991/92 average (million tonnes WSE*)

UK quota beet sugar production	1.144
UK cane refining	1.115
Imported raw sugar for direct consumption	0.037
Imported white sugar from the rest of the EU	0.135
(Exported white sugar	0.197)
Total Supply	**2.232**

Source : MAFF worksheets
*WSE - White Sugar Equivalent
Notes :   Excludes stock change, and the sugar content of manufactured foodstuffs exported from, or imported into, the UK

The principal element of imports - white sugar imports from the rest of the EU - is that they represent a 'Third Source of Supply' for industrial users of sugar. The possibility of importing from elsewhere in the EU strengthens the hand of sugar users in their price negotiations with domestic suppliers (Monopolies and Mergers Commission, 1987 and 1991). The result is that the level of UK market prices is effectively determined by the offer price of imports from the rest of the EU.

Figure 4.3:   The Formation of Sugar Selling Prices

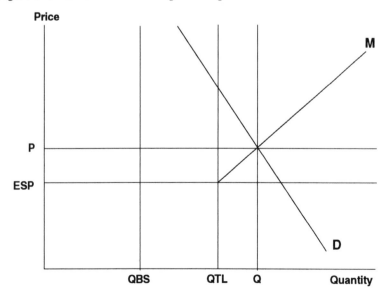

In recent years, British Sugar has probably acted as the price leader in determining the selling price of domestically produced sugar, setting prices at a level which does not encourage imports of sugar from elsewhere in the EU. A simplified illustration of the formation of sugar selling prices is shown in Figure 4.3.

QBS is the supply of sugar to the UK market by British Sugar, and is equal to the UK maximum quota. QTL-QBS represents the supply of sugar to the UK market from Tate and Lyle: in practice, there is a level of exports by Tate and Lyle which effectively represents production displaced by imports from the rest of the EU. The horizontal difference between the sloping line M and QTL measures the quantities of sugar which would be imported into the UK at different UK price levels. D represents the demand curve for sugar. ESP is the 'effective support price' for sugar in the EU, equal to the intervention price plus the storage cost levy.

At the EU effective support price, exporters would find it profitable to sell into intervention rather than to export to the UK, and imports would be zero. As UK prices rise above ESP, exporting to the UK becomes more attractive. UK selling prices represent a margin over the EU effective support price at P. The size of this margin depends on transport costs from the Continent, and the alternative trading opportunities open to EU exporters. At price P, total supply to the market will be given by Q, made up of the policy-determined supplies from British Sugar and Tate and Lyle, and the small quantity of imports attracted.

It is apparent from this analysis that the EU effective support price is a major influence on sugar selling prices in the UK. Econometric analysis of sugar selling prices indicates that around 90% of the variation in UK selling prices can be 'explained' by reference to the effective support price. The estimated coefficient linking the two prices has a value not significantly different from one, which implies close to perfect price transmission between the institutional and the market price.

British Sugar and Tate and Lyle compete through discounts on list prices and on service, and buyers do switch between the two suppliers. However, price competition in the sugar market is closely circumscribed by the constraints on potential market shares set by the quota system. The Monopolies and Mergers Commission Report on the proposed merger between Tate and Lyle and British Sugar in 1991 commented:

"There was a distinction between aggressive price competition found in a number of industries and the somewhat lesser degree of price competition which existed in the sugar market because of the nature and structure of the industry" (Monopolies and Mergers Commission, 1991, p 36).

The EU Sugar Regime

The major influence on the availability and price of sugar in the European Single Market is EU policy which provides for beet sugar and isoglucose production quotas, cane sugar import quotas, and price guarantees for both beet and cane sugar. Like other CAP commodity support regimes, the sugar market used to make provision for the charging of variable import levies on imports from Third Countries, and the payment of export refunds on exports to Third Countries. The EU regime was renewed in 1995, for a six year period to match the GATT Uruguay Round implementation period. This takes the regime upto 2000/2001. Essentially, the new regime represents a prolongation of previous regimes. The European Commission appears to have taken the view that there was sufficient flexibility within the regime to allow the EU to fulfil its GATT obligations without having to rewrite the regime.

The only major changes are the conversion of variable import levies to fixed tariffs (tariffication) and the introduction of a mechanism to ensure the EU does not export too much sugar with export subsidy. On the cane side, import quotas were introduced to ensure security of supply for cane refiners. (The quota of Tate and Lyle in the UK is set at 1,130,000 tonnes, white sugar equivalent, annually - meaning an increase of 15,000 tonnes a year over recent refining levels.

Beet sugar production in each member state is subject to quotas set under the EU sugar regime. The maximum quota for sugar has two parts: 'A' and 'B'. These differ in the rate of 'production levy', used to finance market support, which they attract; 2% of the intervention price for A, with up to an additional 37.5% of the intervention price for B alone. A 'storage cost levy' to reimburse producers for storage costs is also charged on all sales, except those into intervention. The intervention price plus the storage cost levy represents the 'effective support price' which market prices must exceed if selling into intervention is not to be the most profitable outlet. This effective support price sets a floor to market prices for sugar throughout the EU.

Actual market prices in the EU fluctuate in a band between this minimum level and the price at which Third Country imports (import duty paid) can enter the EU. In practice, market prices are somewhat higher in the deficit areas of the EU than in the surplus areas, due to transport costs. The surplus of EU quota sugar production is not allowed to depress market prices as the Commission manages the market to avoid sales into intervention. This ensures there are no sales to intervention, and thus avoids the cost to the EU Budget these would entail.

Only A and B sugar qualify for price support in the form of intervention arrangements. The support commitment, therefore, is not open-ended. Sugar production in excess of the A and B quota is classed as 'C-sugar' which is not eligible for intervention buying, but must be exported to the world market without the benefit of export refunds. However, provided the returns to A and B quotas cover fixed costs, C sugar can be produced profitably. Price support is aimed at the processed product, sugar, in order to ensure support for the farm product, sugar beet. Minimum beet prices are set, based on the intervention prices for sugar, and processors are obliged to pay sugar beet growers at least this much. In practice, intervention support buying is seldom used in the sugar regime, because of the effectiveness of the export arrangements as discussed above and the EU's dominant role in the supply of white sugar to the world market which ensures there is a ready market for its exports.

Beet sugar quota allocations and overall production levels in each member state are shown in Figure 4.4. For the UK the 'A' quota is 1.04 million tonnes and the 'B' quota is 140,000 tonnes. This gives a maximum quota of 1.144 million tonnes. Quotas were last altered in 1981/82, when the UK was one of only two countries to have its quota cut (by 13.7%), while most other countries had their quotas increased.

Figure 4.4:   EU Sugar Quotas and Production Levels 1991/1992

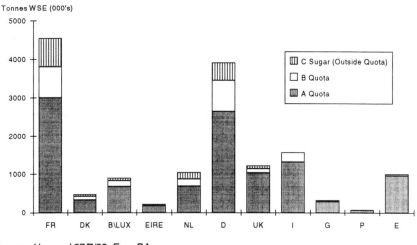

Source : Hansard 27/7/93, Euro PA

As Figures 4.4 and 4.5 show, in most EU states the maximum quota exceeds consumption. France and Germany have by far the highest quota and production, significantly in excess of consumption levels, while the UK quota covers only about half of consumption requirements. The UK can therefore claim not to contribute towards the overall EU sugar surplus.

Figure 4.5:   EU Sugar Production[1] and Consumption Levels 1991/92

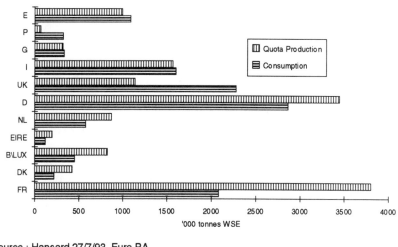

'000 tonnes WSE

Source : Hansard 27/7/93, Euro PA
[1] Sugar produced from sugar beet

The bulk of UK requirements which are not covered by domestic beet production are met by imports of 'preferential' cane sugar from the ACP States. Under the Lomé Convention Sugar Protocol, imports of raw cane sugar from the ACP states into the EU, as a whole, are permitted to enter tariff-free and at guaranteed prices for 'an indefinite period', up to a quota of just over 1.3 million tonnes (WSE).

Table 4.2:   Preferential Cane Sugar Import Quotas (tonnes WSE) under the Lomé Convention

Mauritius	491,030
Fiji	165,348
Guyana	159,410
Jamaica	118,696
Swaziland	117,844
Barbados	50,312
Belize	40,348
Trinidad	43,751
Zimbabwe	30,224
Malawi	20,824
St.Kitts	15,590
Madagascar	10,760
Congo	10,186
Ivory Coast	10,186
Tanzania	10,186
India	10,000
Zambia	0
Total	**1,304,700**

Source : Tate and Lyle

Prices are 'negotiated' annually, but have been at the same level as those guaranteed to EU producers because this is the Lomé Convention commitment. Should prices fall below the guaranteed level, the ACP states can sell sugar into intervention. Quotas are allocated to specific ACP sugar exporting States (Table 4.2).

Failure to fulfil the preferential import quotas allocated can result in the quota for the exporter concerned being reduced by the shortfall. Normally any shortfall is re-allocated to other ACP sugar exporting States. Occasionally, where the inability to fulfil the import quota is not just a matter of the occasional 'short crop', the quota is reduced permanently. Only Surinam, Kenya and Uganda have lost their quotas completely. However, the overall preferential quota has remained at 1.305 million tonnes.

Imports into the UK account for the majority of these EU quota imports, since only the UK has sufficient cane refining capacity. Consequently, although the Lomé commitment is on the part of the EU as a whole, it is fulfilled largely in the UK market.

With the current regime (1995/96 to 2000/01) a new category of cane raw sugar imports was introduced called Special Preference sugar. These import volumes will vary in quantity between years as they will used to balance-up the supplies to EU refiners. The majority of these imports come from the ACP States at a reduced rate of import duty.

Isoglucose is a direct substitute for sugar in some uses, and hence is also covered by the sugar regime with similar quota provisions to those for sugar. The UK's A quota for isoglucose stands at 21.7 thousand tonnes, and the B quota at 5.8 thousand tonnes. This quota is held by Tunnel Refineries - a subsidiary of Tate and Lyle. With availability restricted to these levels, isoglucose accounts for only a small share of the UK sweetener market.

The Structure of the Industry

The UK market is dominated by the activities of just two firms - British Sugar plc with a market share of around 50%, and Tate and Lyle with a market share of around 40%. British Sugar is the sole producer of sugar from home-produced sugar beet, while Tate and Lyle is the sole refiner of raw cane sugar imported from the African, Caribbean and Pacific States (the ACP) associated with the EU under the Lomé Convention.

British Sugar also produces animal feedstuffs as a major by-product[3]. The sugar output of both companies is constrained by EU policy which sets quotas for the production of beet sugar, the import of cane sugar, and the production of isoglucose (a competing caloric sweetener derived from cereals)[4]. The implementation of the GATT Uruguay Round outcome and the process of CAP reform will affect the economic and political environment of the sugar industry, but the immediate effects of this seem likely to be limited.

Processing of the sugar beet crop is carried out by British Sugar and the economic impact of the beet sugar industry in the UK is described in detail in Hallam *et al* (1994). Beet is purchased under contract from around 10,000 farmers, mainly in the Eastern counties, although it is also grown in the West Midlands and Yorkshire. Around 170,000 hectares of sugar beet are grown nationally. Sugar beet is an important part of arable farming in the areas it is grown, particularly in East Anglia. In Norfolk, for example, it accounts for a fifth of the total arable area.

The processing of beet sugar is carried out in British Sugar's factories, of which there were ten in the 1993/94 'campaign' employing over 3,300 people. The King's Lynn factory was closed at the end of the 1993/94 campaign and its capacity taken over by the nearby Wissington factory. The processing 'campaign' runs from September to February, the longest period of beet processing in the EU. British Sugar also operates three packaging centres. As with beet production, much of the sugar production and packaging is located in the Eastern counties. Sugar beet growers received £310 million from British Sugar in 1993, and sugar beet production contributed about 6.5% of total farm income. Only potatoes offer a higher net margin per hectare.

Over the three years (1991/92 to 1993/94), British Sugar's average annual revenue has been £684 million from average annual sugar sales of 1.312 million tonnes white sugar. Some 1.144 million tonnes of this - the quantity allowed under the beet sugar quota - is sold on the domestic market, with the excess (C sugar) being sold on world markets. The 1.144 million tonnes of sales to the domestic market would have an import cost at current CAP prices of around £600 million annually.

---

3   Tate and Lyle also produce molasses under its United Molasses subsidiary. Only a small proportion is used as an ingredient in animal feed.

4   Market shares do not reflect the size of the production and import quotas either in the UK or on the Continent. In the UK the Tate and Lyle cane quota is virtually the same as British Sugar's beet quota, so, statistically, each company has half of the market. But, in practice, British Sugar has 50% of the market, Tate and Lyle 40% and imports the rest. As a result, i.e. Tate and Lyle exports around a fifth of its production.

Animal feed is produced as a by-product from beet processing, utilising sugar beet pulp and molasses to produce molassed sugar beet feed. This is particularly suited to the needs of the dairy sector. Production averaged 715,000 tonnes in the three years 1991/92 to 1993/94, and sales via Trident Feeds, a subsidiary of British Sugar, provided £69 million (around 9%) of revenue.

Sugar cane is, of course, a tropical crop and raw cane sugar is imported according to the quotas listed in Table 4.2. Refining of raw cane sugar is located close to deep water port facilities, and is undertaken by Tate and Lyle in its Thames and Greenock refineries. Just as British Sugar's production and market share are limited by the level of the beet sugar quota, Tate and Lyle's production is limited by the quantity of ACP supplies of raw cane sugar it is able to purchase.

The actual refining process is similar whether for beet or cane sugar, once a sugar solution is obtained. (The principal difference between beet sugar processing and cane raw sugar refining lies in the raw material intake and initial processing). Crystallisation from the sugar solution produces the sugar for refining, leaving behind a syrup - known as molasses. Molasses are diverted primarily into the production of animal feeds, although they are also used in industrial fermentation processes. In the case of Tate and Lyle, it is only the final refining which is carried out in the UK. Production of raw cane sugar is carried out in the exporting countries.

Company Activity and Financial Performance in the UK Sugar Market

As noted earlier, the UK sugar market is dominated by the activities of just two companies, British Sugar and Tate and Lyle, which together account for nearly 90% of domestic sugar sales. The British beet sugar industry was established with governmental support in the 1920's. In 1936 the then 15 independent beet sugar processing companies were compulsorily amalgamated by the British Government to form the British Sugar Corporation Ltd (renamed British Sugar plc in 1982). The largest individual shareholder was the Government with, for much of the time, 36% of the shares and powers over British Sugar's actions. In 1981 the government sold its shares and, in 1982, the company was acquired by Berisford International. In 1991 British Sugar was acquired by Associated British Foods (ABF).

Tate and Lyle is the world's largest sugar and cereals sweetener group, with a turnover of £3.7 billion in 1993 from its international operations in cane and beet sugar, cereal sweeteners and starches and a worldwide production of around eight million tonnes annually of sweeteners. The company's UK activities focus on the refining of cane sugar and the production of glucose and isoglucose. Both British Sugar and Tate and Lyle are vertically integrated, undertaking processing, packaging and distribution. Both produce a comprehensive range of sugar products, which includes white and brown granulated sugars, liquid sugars, syrups and treacles, to meet the needs of both retail and industrial customers.

In common with the rest of Europe, the number of sugar processing factories and refineries in the UK has decreased significantly over the last twenty years in a process of rationalisation (see Figure 4.6). Sugar production is a capital intensive industry. The current construction cost of a 'standard' sized beet sugar factory producing 100,000 tonnes of sugar annually would be around £120 million. The capital intensity of the industry coupled with static nominal support prices in ECU terms have prompted a drive to secure economies of scale and size.

Figure 4.6:   UK and European Sugar Beet Factories

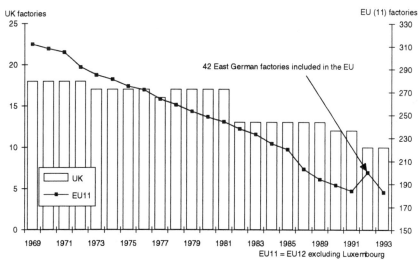

Source: CEFS (1994), Sugar Statistics 1993, Euro PA
Note: The UK, Denmark and Ireland joined the EU in 1973; Greece in 1981, Spain and Portugal in 1986. The figures for the EU include these countries for the years before accession. For example, production figures for 1970 incorporate figures for all the countries that are now part of the EU 12.

EU entry led to the lifting of the national controls imposed on the industry by the British Government, including, most importantly, the statutory market sharing agreement between British Sugar and the cane refiners. The effects of accession meant the cane refining industry had to rationalise and reduce capacity. This was brought about by Tate and Lyle which was allowed to acquire the only other remaining refiner (Manbre and Garton) in 1976 to become the sole UK refiner. Tate and Lyle then reduced the number of UK refineries from six to the current two and capacity from some 2.7 million tonnes to the present 1.13 million tonnes[5].

British Sugar, on the other hand, was allowed to expand its refining of white sugar (reclaiming its raw sugar which used to be refined by Tate and Lyle) and to invest in the modernisation and rationalisation of its factories. As a result, British Sugar has reduced the number of factories it operates from seventeen to nine since EU entry, and has invested half a billion pounds since 1981 in restructuring and modernising its factories. These factories are capable of processing about 70,000 tonnes of beet per day. Their annual capacity depends upon the length of the 'campaign'. In 1993 a record production of 1.475 million tonnes of sugar was achieved.

Figure 4.7:   UK Retail Sugar Market (1991/92)[6]

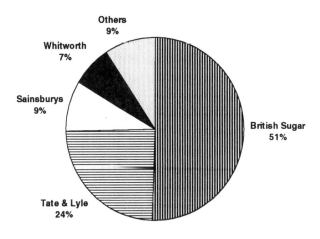

Total Retail Market for White Sugar = 550,000 tonnes

Source : Euro PA

Market shares differ slightly between the retail and the industrial markets, although British Sugar is dominant in both with 51% of the retail and 50% of the industrial market. Tate & Lyle is more prominent

---

5   Tate and Lyle operate two refineries, Thames and Greenock, which have annual
     production capacities of 985 and 145 thousand tonnes white sugar respectively
6   The Whitworths share of the retail market is supplied by British Sugar.

in the industrial rather than the retail market, with 43% in the former and 24% in the latter. Figures 4.7 and 4.8 illustrate the breakdown of the industrial and retail markets.

Competition between British Sugar and Tate and Lyle for market share is modified by the policy environment in which they operate. British Sugar's output is limited by the size of the UK beet sugar quota, while Tate and Lyle's output is limited by the quantity of ACP raw cane sugar it is permitted to import and its refining capacity (although Tate and Lyle rationalised its capacity to fit guaranteed imports). Tate and Lyle's ability to compete in the EU market is limited by its smaller per unit margin, as compared with the beet processors' margin which is set by the EU's institutional support arrangements. Given British Sugar's announced intention of selling its entire quota production domestically and the users' policy of having a sufficient level of imports to constitute a viable third source of supply, Tate and Lyle exports the margin of surplus arising on the UK market caused by imports.

Figure 4.8: UK Industrial Market for Sugar (1991/92)

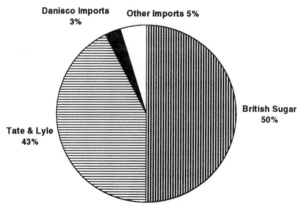

Total Industrial Market for Sugar = 1.6 million tonnes

Source : Euro PA

Obviously changes in the policy environment may lead to changes in the nature of competition. Competition from imported sugar is limited by the pricing of domestically produced sugar, and by the generally more profitable alternative for EU exporters of exporting to Third Countries with the benefit of export refunds.

Industry Performance

The five firm concentration ratio for the sugar industry is obviously 100% given that there are only two companies in the sector. The average financial performance of the two companies is shown in Table 4.3, as measured by Kompass and McMillans.

The sugar sector is the most concentrated of all the sectors in the food industry. This is due to the historical development of the sector which has resulted in only two sugar producing companies remaining (British Sugar and Tate and Lyle), plus several merchanting companies handling domestically produced and imported sugars.

Tate and Lyle refines sugar from the African, Caribbean and Pacific (ACP) countries, imported under the Lomé Convention. The figures in Table 4.3 refer to only Tate and Lyle's UK refining operations.

Both UK companies are part of large groups, Tate and Lyle plc and Associated British Foods (ABF).

Table 4.3:   Summary of Average UK Sugar Company Results (three year average)

Company	Turnover £m	Profit £m	Profit/ Sales (%)	ROCE (%)	Current Ratio (%)	Debt Ratio	Years
Tate and Lyle Industries Ltd	1,101.00	49.60	4.51	32.00	0.67	0.75	90/91-92/93
British Sugar plc (ABF Foods)	742.50	91.63	12.34	19.12	1.23	0.51	90/91-92/93
Average weighted by turnover		**66.53**	**7.66**	**26.81**	**0.90**	**0.65**	
Straight average		**70.62**	**8.43**	**25.56**	**0.95**	**0.63**	
Total Turnover	**1,843**						

Source : Kompass, McMillans, Euro PA
Note :   The figures shown above should be read in conjunction with the notes contained in
           the Appendix to Chapter One
           Tate & Lyle Industries Ltd covers all Tate & Lyle operations in the UK. These
           operations   include more than just sugar processing.

When comparing the financial performance of the two companies, as shown in Table 4.3, several points have to be taken into account:

- Both British Sugar and Tate and Lyle have rigid raw material restrictions - in terms of quotas and institutionally determined minimum prices that have to be paid for their agricultural raw materials.

- Cane sugar refining has smaller operating margins than that of beet sugar processing due to the EU institutional support arrangements.

- Processing of sugar beet is much more capital intensive than cane sugar refining as it is a complete process from the farm-gate product to the refined sugar. Whereas raw cane sugar refining is the final stage in the process of producing white sugar, with the agricultural processing aspects having occurred in the country of origin.

- Tate and Lyle operates its refineries all year round since it has a continuous supply of cane sugar. British Sugar factories, on the other hand, slice sugar beet for around a 140 days in the 'campaign' period. Following the campaign period sugar syrup that had been stored undergoes final stage processing (crystallisation). Only the final stage refining section of the factory is operational in this 2/3 month period.

- Tate & Lyle Industries Ltd includes all Tate & Lyle UK operations, not only sugar.

These factors indicate that the cost structure of each company is different and thus performance comparisons between them are problematic.

Summary and Conclusions

Sugar production is the most concentrated of all the sectors in the food industry, with just two companies supplying 90% of domestic market requirements. The resource base of these companies is very different, with British Sugar producing from domestically grown sugar beet, and Tate and Lyle producing from imported raw cane sugar. However, the output and market shares of the two companies, and the competition between them are constrained by the EU quotas for production of beet sugar and the imports of raw cane sugar. Competition from imports is limited by the pricing of domestic production. A roughly equivalent quantity of sugar is exported.

Both companies have rationalised their productive capacity leaving British Sugar with nine factories and Tate and Lyle with just two refineries. Their output is sold to both industrial and retail customers. Industrial demand for sugar, depending primarily on the level of food industry output, has grown to account for 70% of sales. Retail demand, on the other hand, has declined and there is little prospect that this trend will reverse. Thus far, competition to sugar from other sweeteners has not progressed as far as in the United States, but has been limited either by the extent to which these other sweeteners meet the physical requirements of food industry users, or by policy influences on their relative price or the quantities available.

The foregoing analysis of the sugar and sweetener market in Britain, and the production and processing industries which serve it, demonstrates the considerable flexibility that has been shown to adapt to changed circumstances. EU policy arrangements for sugar do not appear to have limited the productivity of these companies. Probably because of currently favourable returns for farmers producing sugar beet, and the comparatively sound financial structure of the domestic sugar production industry, institutional uncertainty may be tolerated more easily than in other commodity sectors. Only a major disturbance would upset its current profitability and stability.

References

Canadian Ministry of National Health and Welfare (1990). Report on the Scientific Review Committee, *Action Towards Healthy Eating*, Canada.

Coma (1992). *The Health of the Nation*, Cm 1986, HMSO, London

Comité Européen des Fabricants de Sucre (CEFS) (1993). *Sugar Statistics 1993*, Brussels, Belgium.

Central Statistical Office, (selected years). *Annual Abstract of Statistics*, HMSO, London.

CIUS (1992). *Reform of the Common Organisation of the Market for Sugar and Isoglucose*, A proposal from the Committee of Industrial Users of Sugar, 1 Rue Defaqz, 1050 Brussels, Belgium.

Euro Analysis (1992) unpublished report R55, *British Sugar: Input:Output Review*,. Euro PA & Associates, 11 Church Street, Northborough, Cambs, PE6 9BN, UK.

Hallam, D., Midmore, P. and The Lord Peston (1994). *The Economic Impact of the British Beet Sugar Industry*. Department of Agricultural Economics and Management, University of Reading, Reading.

Monopolies and Mergers Commission, (1987). Tate & Lyle PLC and Feruzzi Finanziaria SpA and S&W Bersiford PLC - A report on the existing and proposed mergers, Cm 89, HMSO, London.

Monopolies and Mergers Commission, (1991). Tate & Lyle PLC and British Sugar plc - A report on the proposed merger, Cm 1435, HMSO, London.

Murphy, M. (1993). *Report on Farming in the Eastern Counties of England 1992/93*, University of Cambridge, Cambridge.

US Department of Agriculture, (1990). Advisory Committee on the Dietary Guidelines for Americans, *Report of the Dietary Guidelines*, Washington, USA.

Chapter 5: Potatoes, Potato Products and Savoury Snacks

Laura Black, Phil Dawson, John Taylor and Ben White[1]

Introduction

Fresh and processed potato products are of great significance to the farm sector and to UK consumers. Potato production in Great Britain accounts for about 13% of the total output by value of the arable sector (1992-94) and represents 84% of output by value of the non-cereal arable sector. Consumers in Great Britain eat about 102 kg/head of potatoes each year, or around 2 kg of potatoes per week. In 1993, potatoes accounted for about 13% of the average household's expenditure on vegetables, and potatoes are the largest single item of vegetable consumption in the diet of the British consumer. Furthermore, a key trend in consumer purchasing habits for potatoes has been the move towards consumption in processed form.

Several key trends in the food consumption patterns are reflected in the development of the potato industry and the products it offers. First, the increasing demand for convenience foods. Second, the growth in demand for high quality premium. Third, the segmentation within food markets between the mainstream (price sensitive) sector, the premium sector and the children's sector.

Regular (par-fried) frozen chips[2] satisfy the economy/convenience segment. Oven, microwave-able and chilled chips satisfy the premium sector. They are convenient, healthy and have novelty value. Chilled chips have made little impact on the retail market as yet, but improved

---

1   Laura Black is a researcher at Euro PA & Associates, Cambs., John Taylor is Development Manager at the Potato Marketing Board, Oxford. Dr. Phil Dawson is a Senior Lecturer and Dr. Ben White is a Lecturer, in the Department of Agricultural Economics and Food Marketing, University of Newcastle upon Tyne. The Editors would like to express their thanks to the Potato Marketing Board and to KP Foods and Birds Eye Walls for the provision of data and statistics. This chapter quotes extensively from a PMB commissioned report on potato processing (Euro PA, 1994). Any opinions, errors or omissions in the chapter, however remain the responsibility of the Editors, subject to the caveat given in the Appendix of Chapter One.
2   The term 'chips' is used to denote parfried potatoes and French fries i.e. the British use of the term. The US version is 'French fries'. Similarly the British term 'crisps' describes what a US consumer would know as 'chips'.

technology and marketing may change this. Third, potato products, chips and other formats are well-suited to the fast food and takeaway segments of the catering market. Fourth, potato products are a basic ingredient in many frozen ready meals for which demand is growing rapidly. Lastly, potatoes are a fundamental part of most snack products, especially crisps. Premium crisps are a growth market in the UK and also offer export opportunities.

With this background, potato-based products can be expected to increase their share and their *per capita* level of consumption. Innovation in technology and marketing has played an important part in the development of the market in the UK, and the market's various segments should develop further in the future. In this chapter, the consumption of raw and processed potatoes in the UK is dealt with first, then the policy background (which is in a state of transition) and output, area and yields, and prices. The final section considers processed potato products including savoury snacks and provides coverage of the companies involved in these processing sectors.

Consumption of Potatoes and Potato Products

Figure 5.1 shows the consumption of potatoes in Great Britain 1956-94.

Figure 5.1: Potato Consumption in GB, 1956-94

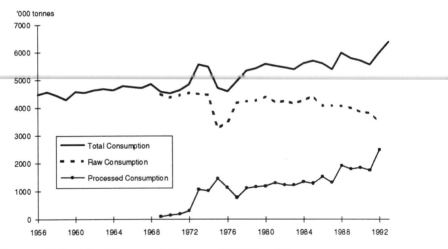

Source: National Food Survey - selected years, MAFF, Euro PA
Note :   Up to 1969, raw consumption is total consumption; thereafter, raw consumption is defined as total consumption less processed consumption.
         Figure for 1956 relates to the 1956/57 crop season (June to May), the 1957 figure to 1957/58 and so on.

Total consumption of potatoes has trended gently upwards since the mid-1950's. After the late-1960's, processed potatoes have become a significant substitute for raw potatoes. The demand for processed potatoes is dominated by chilled/frozen potatoes and crisped potatoes: both have risen over the last five years at the expense of canned and dehydrated potatoes whose consumption has declined.

Figures 5.2 and 5.3 illustrate potato consumption from all sources from 1980. Domestic (home) usage, that is all potatoes bought for the home, is shown in Figure 5.2. The consumption of raw potatoes sold in loose form fell by 20% from 1980 to 1990. Raw potatoes sold in prepack form, on the other hand, increased almost 25% in the same period. Unfortunately, from 1991 onwards statistics for raw loose and raw prepack are combined. Consumption of dehydrated/canned potatoes has been relatively constant from 1980/81 to 1993/94. The 250% increase in consumption of frozen and chilled potatoes (including chips), from 223,000 tonnes in 1980 to 564,000 tonnes in 1993/94 illustrates the move towards convenience foods. This trend is also seen in the consumption of crisped potatoes with a rise of over 100%. Great Britain is second only to the United States in terms of *per capita* crisp consumption.

Figure 5.2:   Domestic Potato Consumption in GB, 1980-94

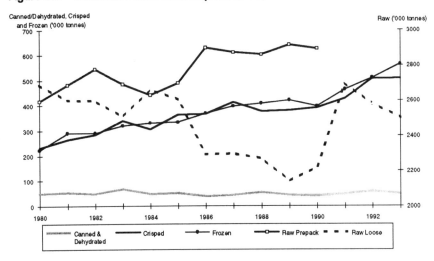

Source: National Food Survey - selected years, MAFF, Euro PA
Note :   Frozen = Frozen chips and Frozen Products
          Figure for 1980 relates to the 1980/81 crop season (June to May), the 1981 figure to 1981/82 and so on. In 1991 and 1992 'raw loose' includes all raw potatoes i.e. loose and prepack

Figure 5.3:   Non-Domestic Potato Consumption in GB, 1980-94

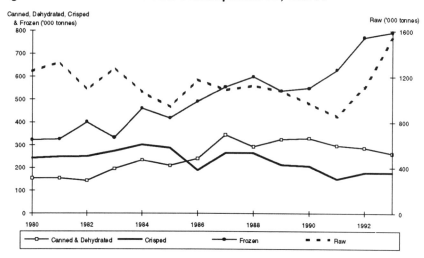

Source: HM Customs & Excise and MAFF, Euro PA

HM Customs and excise does not separate chilled chips from frozen, therefore the frozen category includes all frozen and chilled chips and other frozen and chilled products

Note :   Figure for 1980 relates to the 1980/81 crop season (June to May), the 1981 figure to 1981/82 and so on.

Figure 5.3 shows potatoes used for non-domestic consumption, that is outside the home. Non-domestic consumption of raw potatoes fell 12% between 1980/81 and 1992/93, from 1.245 million tonnes to 1.1 million tonnes. However in 1993/94 consumption jumped to 1.5 million tonnes the highest level of the last twenty years.

There was a decline in the amount of crisped potatoes consumed outside the home, from 243,000 tonnes in 1980 to 177,000 tonnes in 1993/94. A peak was reached in 1984 of over 300,000 tonnes since when consumption has fallen by over 4% per annum on average.

The use of dehydrated/canned potatoes increased over the period from 154,000 tonnes in 1980 to 263,000 tonnes in 1993/94. However a peak was reached in 1987 of 345,000 tonnes and since then consumption has fallen, as food processors have reduced demand due to consumers' tastes changing, moving to frozen/chilled potatoes. The demand for frozen potatoes is increasing, again illustrating both the move to convenience foods and catering establishments preferring to buy pre-prepared, competitively-priced frozen products that are more compact and easy to store (rather than using raw potatoes which involve much preparation time). In 1980 non-domestic consumption of frozen potatoes was 323,000 tonnes. By 1993/94 consumption had risen 145% to 793,000 tonnes.

Consumption of Frozen Potato Products

Frozen chips and potato products now account for over 40% of the total frozen vegetable market. The original frozen chip was for home frying but, in 1979, McCain launched the oven chip which is a more versatile product designed to be reheated in a conventional oven, grilled or fried if preferred. Oven chips are a value-added product within the frozen chip market and, because of the convenience and health aspects of a lower fat product, it commands a premium price.

The frozen ready-meal sector has grown by over 36% (1988-92), and including meal cores like cauliflower cheese and filled potatoes, was worth £304 million in 1992. Frozen ready-meals are important both to young consumers who have a high convenience priority and to older people, particularly single people, with over 30% of 65 year olds buying them at least once a week[3]. Table 5.1 shows the growth in retail sales of frozen chips and other potato products, 1987-91.

Table 5.1: **Retail Sales of Frozen Chips and Frozen Potato Products in the UK (£m at Retail Selling Price), 1987-91[4]**

	1987	1988	1989	1990	1991
Frozen Chips	109	123	132	158	166
Other	37	47	52	60	70
Total	146	170	184	218	236

Source: Trade sources, Euro PA Trade Sources

The precise size of the chilled chips and potato products market is difficult to quantify[5]. However, it is estimated (by trade sources) that chilled chips account for 20% of the prepared chips market (90,000 tonnes in 1992). Of this, 50,000 tonnes are imported from the Netherlands in the form of 'chilled parfries'[6], and 'gas flushed' products.[7,8] In contrast, chilled chips face difficulty competing in the domestic retail sector because they are not price competitive[9], and chilled cabinets in supermarkets may run at too high a temperature to maximise shelf life. Because of the extra cost, chilled chips compete at the premium end of

---

3   There is strong growth potential in the vegetable meals sector (Mintel: Market Research).
4   All figures in nominal terms for every table, unless otherwise specified.
5   Data tend to be included in a miscellaneous 'other' category in the Customs and Excise data.
6   Partly fried chilled chips with a five-day shelf life.
7   Gas flushing replaces the oxygen in the packaging with carbon dioxide and nitrogen, thereby allowing the product to be kept for 21 days.
8   Reasons for using chilled, rather than frozen, chips, in catering include improved taste, quicker cooking time, easier storage, convenient packaging, lower fat content and suitability for distribution through the fresh produce network.
9   The price premium is about 10% but some recent competitive price erosion has occurred.

the market, thereby gaining benefit from the 'freshness' image attached to all products in the rapidly growing chilled food sector. Moreover, they have attracted important sales outlets like Marks & Spencers.

Consumption of Potato Crisps and Potato Based Snacks

Crisps are potato-based products whilst savoury snacks are mainly extruded products which may use a variety of ingredients, including potato granules, wheat and maize.   The extrusion technique has facilitated the innovation of a wide variety of shapes and textures and have formed the cornerstone of the children's snack market.

The general snack market (including biscuits, crisps, potato products, extruded cereal products and fruit and nuts) is expanding rapidly with many examples of product and packaging innovation.   The UK is Europe's leading market for savoury snacks.   Annual *per capita* consumption was 4.08 kgs in 1991, compared with 1.67 kgs in continental Europe.   Changing demographic trends have had a major influence on this market: the shift towards an older population led manufacturers to innovate through adult snacks. In Table 5.2, children's products account for 35% of the savoury snack market. Family brands such as KP (parent company: UB Foods) Hula Hoops and Smith's (part of Walkers) Quavers represent around 60% of the market.   Derwent Valley foods is particularly strong in the market for premium adult products with the Phileas Fogg range.   The scope for development of adult-oriented savoury snacks has attracted new entrants to the market.   Proctor and Gamble introduced Pringles to the UK market in June 1991, backed by £2.6m of main media advertising.

Table 5.2:   Segmentation of the UK's Savoury Snacks Market, 1991

	£m	Per Cent
Family	252	49.9
Children's	176	34.8
Economy	52	10.3
Adult speciality	20	4.0
Adult mainstream	5	1.0
Total	505	100

Source: KP Snack Food Review 1991/Key Note

There are two main segments in the crisp sector, standard varieties and premium products (Table 5.3).   Standard crisps dominate the market with the four core varieties (Ready Salted, Salt and Vinegar, Cheese and Onion and Smoky Bacon), accounting for approximately 75% of sales. Premium products such as low-fat, vitamin enhanced and hard-bite crisps have provided the stimulus for market growth in recent years. These products are being targeted at the adult consumer and now account for 18% of the market with an estimated potential increasing to 30% by 1999.

Table 5.3:   Segmentation of the UK Crisp Market, 1991

	Per Cent by Value
Standard crisps	84.0
Thick cut/hard bite	9.0
Low fat	5.5
Other healthy	1.5
Total	100.0

Source: Euro PA, Trade sources.

In summary, since 1980 the total consumption of potatoes in Great Britain has increased steadily.   This overall trend masks falling consumption of raw potatoes which is offset by a larger increase in processed potatoes.

Frozen chips and other frozen products has been a particularly high growth area with the retail sales value increasing 60% in five years between 1987-1991. Sales of frozen ready meals has increased over 36% in this time. This illustrates the general move to convenience foods.

Crisp consumption *per capita* is almost two and a half times higher in the UK than in Continental Europe.   Demographic changes have led manufacturers to developing adult crisps snacks, though family and children's snacks still dominate the market.

Policy Background: The PMB and the PMS

Production policy for potatoes in Britain is in a state of flux in 1995. Potato production in Great Britain is currently directed through the Potato Marketing Board (PMB). This was established in 1933 with the objectives of stabilising prices and improving farmers' incomes. It is funded by a grower levy, and all growers of more than 1 ha[10] must register. The Joint Consultative Council (JCC) was set up in 1989 and comprises the PMB, potato processors, multiple retailers, merchants, seed merchants, the farming unions, and consumers. The JCC has an important role in determining the target area for potato quota. Notwithstanding this history, the 1993 Agriculture Bill in the UK Parliament laid down a timetable for the removal of the Potato Marketing Scheme (PMS) and the creation of a successor body for the PMB in 1997.

---

10   In late 1993 the PMB increased the cut-off point for registration from 0.4 to 1.0 hectare.

The PMB used the PMS to manage the potato market through area controls and intervention buying. A producer's basic area (in hectares) is determined by a three year average of plantings excluding any plantings in excess of quota (although basic area may be traded between producers). The JCC independently calculates a GB target area through estimated production requirements from all sources including net imports and estimated yields. Any potential discrepancy between base area and target area is adjusted for by the imposition of a quota area, i.e. the percentage amount of his base area that each grower can plant. Until November 1993 the PMS also operated the secondary mechanism of intervention in the market when high yields or other external factors led to surpluses which depressed prices below certain triggers. The PMB's other functions include promotion, research, and the supply of market and technical information.

There have been many amendments to the PMS which have resulted in the PMB's activities and functions changing over time. The most recent of these were at the end of 1993, and included the removal of intervention buying, increasing flexibility in area quota, reduction of grower levies and the end of compulsory registration and licences for potato merchants. The Minister of Agriculture at the same time announced the termination of the PMS (the area quota) by the end of 1997, and consultations are currently taking place to define a successor body to the PMB. The JCC sent its views on the functions and financing of a successor body to the PMB to the Minister in April 1995. The suggested functions include research and development, promotion, and market information; all to be funded by an area-based producer levy.

The European Commission brought forward a proposal for the creation of a potato regime in 1975 and 1992[11] but it has been unsuccessful in incorporating potatoes into the Common Agricultural Policy A decision on whether to present another proposal on this issue is due by July 1995, and a seminar on a CAP regime for potatoes is due to take place in June 1995. A common European potato regime is likely to be 'lightweight' in operation and be without intervention or area control powers. Its functions are likely to be restricted to ensuring unimpeded free trade, e.g. safeguards on third country import levels, removal of state aids, and common quality standards. However, some Member States wish to see a more interventionist regime.

---

11   See EC (1992), Ennew and Peston (1993), Hol (1993), Ecosoc (1993) amd European
     Parliament (1993).

The Supply of Potatoes

The Structure of Production

The structure of the potato sector at the farm level is competitive with about 14,250 registered producers growing one hectare or more in Great Britain at the end of January 1995. Figure 5.4 shows a typical planting and lifting/clearing[12] year, also shown is the potatoes' price for England and Wales. Plantings are concentrated between late March and early May.

Figure 5.4:   Average Plantings/Clearings and Prices

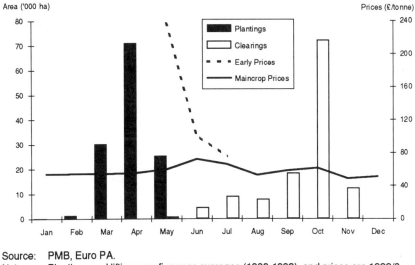

Source: PMB, Euro PA.
Note: Plantings and liftings are five year averages (1988-1992); and prices are 1992/3
          averages.

Early potatoes are defined as those lifted before 31st July. In most seasons, the first of the earlies are lifted in Cornwall and South Wales and command higher prices than earlies from later regions. Other early growing areas such as Suffolk, Essex, Shropshire and Lincolnshire produce similar volumes later in the season. Early crop prices start high as the very first crops are taken at low yields and then drop as supplies increase, but may fluctuate considerably depending on clearance rates, timing of clearing and imports.

---

12   By lifting the crop the land is cleared for planting next year. Figure 5.4 displays the year
     in terms of area cleared rather than tonnes lifted.

Main crop potatoes are defined as those lifted from 1st August, and harvesting is concentrated in late September and October. By mid-November the whole crop should have been lifted, but in some years a small percentage is left in the ground. Maincrop prices closely reflect production levels with shortfalls leading to sharp price increases. Indeed, their relationship can be used to estimate average maincrop prices with some accuracy. Within the season, maincrop prices fluctuate from relatively high prices in early summer when immature tubers are lifted at relatively low yields, falling to a low in autumn when yields are at their maximum and crops are sold at minimum unit cost since no storage costs are incurred, and gradually recovering in winter and early spring as storage levels fall. Table 5.4 shows the popular early and maincrop varieties grown in Great Britain.

Table 5.4: Areas Planted (Hectares) of Early and Maincrop Varieties in GB 1989-94

Earlies	1989	1990	1991	1992	1993	1994
Maris Bard	4,870	5,036	5,910	5,808	5,554	5,698
Pentland Javelin	3,432	4,032	3,347	2,786	2,205	1,810
Estima	13,814	14,515	14,149	14,414	16,285	15,958
Marfona	3,005	3,155	3,473	4,672	4,631	1,944
Wilja	12,153	10,678	7,926	7,677	6,716	5,814
Maincrop	1989	1990	1991	1992	1993	1994
Cara	10,657	10,853	13,097	13,159	9,482	8,346
Maris Piper	19,321	19,489	20,559	20,571	22,497	22,142
Pentland Dell	10,235	8,702	8,633	8,413	9,173	7,917
Pentland Squire	11,435	10,986	9,562	8,815	5,374	3,534
Record	17,742	17,187	16,488	15,372	14,284	11,670

Source : PMB

Figure 5.5 shows the total output of potatoes in Great Britain for 1980/81 to 1994/95. Variability in total output is an inherent characteristic of the potato market; despite technological and genetic improvements, the weather is an important factor determining yield and hence output. The matching of future supply to estimated future demand can therefore only partly be achieved by planning area to be planted against the future trend yield. Yield variation and its effect on total supply and hence price must be picked up subsequently either in the market or by intervention to remove surplus. Figure 5.5 also shows the historical trend of basic area. This highlights the falling area, from 192,000 hectares in 1980/81 to 152,000 hectares in 1994/95. In most seasons basic area falls as registered growers go out of production and grower numbers decline. Since 1989 the decline has halted and basic area has levelled out at around 152,000 hectares.

Figure 5.5:   GB Potato Output, 1980-95

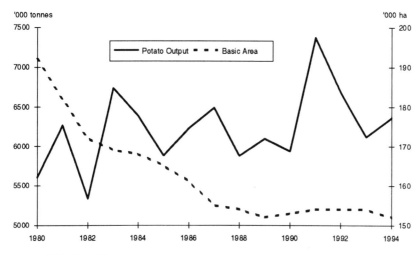

Source: PMB, Euro PA
Note :   Figure for 1980 relates to the 1980/81 crop season (June to May), the 1981 figure to
           1981/82 and so on.

Figure 5.6:   GB Potato Yields 1980-1995

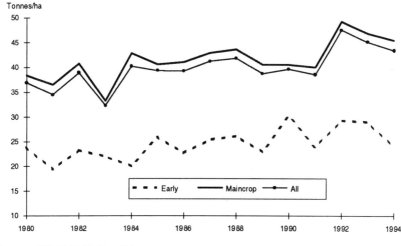

Source: MAFF, PMB, Euro PA

Counterbalancing the significant decrease in area is increasing yield - see
Figure 5.6.[13] In the period 1980/81-1994/95, the yield of early and main
crop potatoes has generally increased, though the 1994/95 level of 23.9

---

13   Although changes have occurred in the way yields are measured, Figure 5.6 indicates
      the trend in yields for all types of potato.

tonnes/hectare for earlies and 45.5 tonnes/hectare for maincrop was down on 1993/94. Overall, the changes in yields and efficiency are explained by two factors. First, increased technical efficiency of farming (from genetic and technical advances) has occurred in general and, improvements in fertilisers and agro-chemicals have led to increases in the efficiency of potato production by increasing yields and creating healthier plants. Second, there have been improvements in marketing skills and better storage facilities (in-storage treatment and a general increase in awareness of the importance of potato handling).

Quota was set on the basic area in order to set a target area for potato plantings. The primary criterion for judging the effectiveness of quota is the measure of how close aggregate planted area comes to target area after the application of basic area recalculation, quota percentage and quota allocation. The real test is the long term stability given to the market, in terms of sustained consumption, quality and reinvestment as well as price stability. On the first three of these measures, GB performance can be said to have been successful. On the last, price stability, the elements have prevailed in different seasons and yield variation coupled with inelastic demand caused price variation but significantly less so than on the Continent. UK growers were strongly supportive of self-funded floor price intervention up until 1992 when an exceptionally high yield resulted in a surplus of 1.25 million tonnes which totally removed the intervention fund. Processors, however, have seen this as an interference with their ability to buy potatoes at competitive price levels with their rivals in Europe.

The quota has varied from a low of 86% (of basic area) in 1973 to 100% in 1975-77. This highest level occurred when output was lowest due to drought. In recognition of this, the PMB attempted in the following years to maximise output levels from the given area, knowing that seed as well as ware was short, in order to minimise price increases. Despite this, prices in these years rose to relatively high levels (see Figure 5.7), with a resulting increase in maincrop imports.

Potato Prices

Figure 5.7 shows average nominal and real[14] prices in Great Britain for 1955-93. Underlying the real price is the balance of supply and demand and the influence of the PMS through target area control. It is gently trending downwards. But, potato production is particularly susceptible to weather and in drought years supply is greatly reduced. This,

---

14   Deflated by the Retail Price Index using 1985 as the base.

coupled with an inelastic price elasticity of demand of about -0.16 causes dramatic fluctuations in price: in 1974, the average price was £25.40/tonne but rose to £103.90/tonne in the drought year of 1975; in 1977, when crop output returned to more 'normal' levels, the price fell to £42.81/tonne.

It is worth noting that up until 1984 there was a system of guaranteed prices for potatoes moving into human consumption (see Figure 5.7). If the average price fell below intervention level the MAFF paid farmers the difference between the market price and the guaranteed price for each tonne sold for human consumption. In 1978, MAFF decided not to increase the nominal guaranteed price, thus in real terms the price fell. This represented a change in Government policy from supporting agricultural incomes to ensuring continuity of supplies. By 1984 the guaranteed price was so low that it was deemed irrelevant and scrapped.

Figure 5.7:   GB Potato Prices, 1955-94

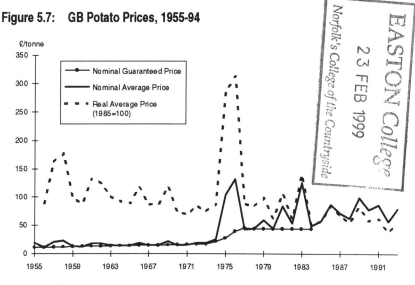

Source: PMB 'Historical data summary from 1960', Euro PA
Notes :   Real average price = nominal average price deflated by the RPI index 1985=100
             Figure for 1980 relates to the 1980/81 crop season (June to May), the 1981 figure to
             1981/82 and so on.

Figure 5.8 provides a comparison between potato prices in Great Britain and the Netherlands. Generally, the range of British potato prices is much narrower than for continental potatoes, but on average they tend to be above prices in Belgium, Netherlands and Germany.

Figure 5.8:   Potato Prices in Major European Countries 1987-1992

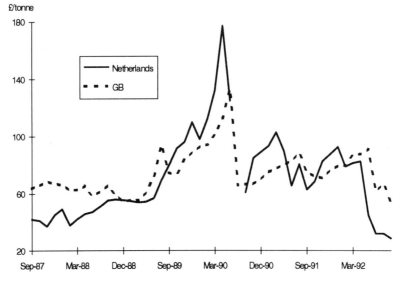

Source : PMB

Trade in Potatoes and Potato Products

Imports

Imports of fresh potatoes are determined by a number of factors
including the transport cost of bringing in supplies from abroad.
Seasonality and (especially for processors) the availability of appropriate
qualities and varieties play an important part.   Imports tend to be
competitive with domestic production when the price difference between
UK and foreign supplies is around £25-£30/tonne, reflecting the implicit
transport and transaction costs of exporting potatoes to the UK. Imports
typically arrive in the UK during spring when the home demand for
stored British maincrop holds prices in the UK at relatively higher levels
than those on the near Continent and, more particularly, because some
consumers want new potatoes which are out of season in the UK - see
Figure 5.9.

Figure 5.9:   GB Monthly Imports, 1992/3

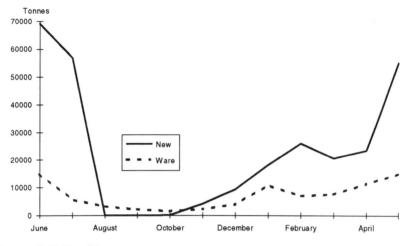

Source: PMB, Euro PA

Imports of new potatoes have varied little since 1955; they peaked at 441,000 tonnes in 1977 and reached a low of 215,000 tonnes in 1975. Figure 5.10 shows total imports to GB for 1980-93; most are from countries such as Cyprus, the Channel Islands, Egypt and the Canary Islands. New crop supplies affect ware prices if they arrive unusually early or late but in general they complement domestic production and represent another type of demand.

Figure 5.10: Total Imports to GB, 1980-94

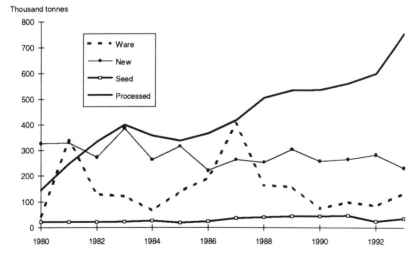

Source: PMB 'Historical data summary from 1960', Euro PA
Note :   Figure for 1980 relates to the 1980/81 crop season (June to May), the 1981 figure to
           1981/82 and so on.

There is a gradual increase in the long-term trend in seed imports which ranged from 12,000 tonnes in 1975 to 76,000 tonnes in 1984. Some controlled varieties of seed potatoes are brought in to Scotland under licence for further multiplication before being re-exported, because it provides a suitable climate. Seed imports are approximately 10% of total usage and either counterbalance seasonality or are for specialist markets.

Exports

Exports of raw potatoes have shown a steady increase in recent years. There is now a positive trade balance for Great Britain of raw ware potatoes. Most exports are destined for Eire, the Canaries or for southern European countries, where the climate means that consumer demand cannot be satisfied all year round with home produced potatoes or, where the growth of multiple retailers has encouraged a move to higher quality pre-packed potatoes. The export market in northern Europe is small, with Germany and Sweden as the main recipients although, again, there has been a growth in quality exports for pre-packing, and in 'baker' potatoes which are not easily sourced in Scandanavia for example. Figure 5.11 shows typical export destinations while Figure 5.12 shows total exports for 1980-93. Seed exports are mostly destined for southern European and north African countries.

Figure 5.11: GB Exports of Potatoes by destination (average 1988-94)

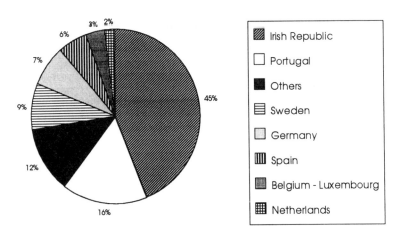

Source: HM Customs and Excise and Intrastat, Euro PA

Figure 5.12: GB Total Exports of Potatoes and Potato Products 1980-94

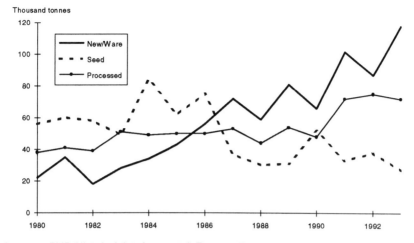

Source: PMB 'Historical data from 1960', Eurostat, Euro PA
Note :   Figure for 1980 relates to the 1980/81 crop season (June to May), the 1981 figure to
          1981/82 and so on.

Table 5.5: Potato Industry Balance Sheet for GB June/May Crop Yrs('000s tonnes)

	1989/90	1990/91	1991/92	1992/93	1993/94
SUPPLIES					
Home Crop					
From previous season	314	288	293	409	421
From current crop	5973	6198	6032	7481	6808
From next crop	8	5	17	20	12
Subtotal	6296	6491	6342	7909	7241
Imports					
New	303	257	264	283	230
Ware from outside GB	138	55	88	71	131
Ware from N Ireland	19	20	11	14	2
Processed (Raw Equiv)	517	524	545	599	753
Seed for next crop	44	44	46	24	35
Subtotal	1021	900	954	991	1151
Total	7316	7390	7297	8899	8393
DISPOSALS					
Home Disposals					
Human Consumption	5768	5716	5540	5991	6384
Seed for next crop	493	495	503	473	443
Intervention	0	32	0	869	44
Closing stocks	288	293	409	421	359
Home crop marketed pre June	11	8	5	17	20
Wastage	591	680	632	928	926
Subtotal	1383	1508	1543	2708	1792
Exports					
Ware/New	81	66	102	87	118
Processed (Raw Equiv)	54	48	72	75	72
Seed	31	52	33	38	27
Subtotal	166	156	213	200	217
Total	7317	7390	7297	8899	8393

Source: HM Customs & Excise, MAFF and PMB
Note: Intervention excludes potatoes sold back for human consumption.

Table 5.5 presents potato production and trade in GB for 1989 to 1994.

The Trade in Processed Potato Products

The UK imports a significant amount of processed potato products. Frozen and chilled chips form the bulk of imports, and there is also a smaller amount of crisps, snacks[15] and canned potatoes[16]. As a result the UK has a deteriorating balance of trade in potato products as shown in summary form in Table 5.6. This rise in imports of processed potatoes, plus the 10.8% increase in utilisation of raw potatoes by UK based processors, underlines the increasing UK demand for potato products. Imports of potato products bridge a supply gap currently not being met by domestic processors.

Table 5.6: Summary UK Balance of Trade in Potato Products (£m) 1988-1993 (calendar year)

	1988	1989	1990	1991	1992	1993
Exports (fob)	11.30	12.33	17.31	18.27	21.86	21.40
Imports	92.02	109.35	117.22	127.29	136.16	155.61
Trade Balance	-80.72	-97.02	-99.91	-109.01	-114.30	-134.21

Source: HM Customs & Excise

Tables 5.7 and 5.8 show that there has been a 43% increase in the volume of potato product imports in the period 1988 to 1993 with a corresponding value increase of almost 70%. The most significant increase in terms of both volume and value has been in the 'other' classification, which includes chilled products, snacks and crisps. Tonnage for this grouping increased by 71%, with a corresponding value increase of 72%. Although it is impossible to disaggregate the Customs data, most of this increase is thought to be accounted for by the growth in chilled products, particularly chilled chips.

The tonnage of frozen products (mostly chips) fell from 1989 to 1992 but has since recovered to almost 216 thousand tonnes in 1993, an increase of 38% overall since 1988 and a value increase of 61%.

---

15 From the Customs data it is impossible to distinguish between chilled products, crisps and snacks.

16 Customs headings were changed in 1986/7 and some semi-processed potato material may be under the heading which includes crisps, snacks canned products and chilled chips.

Table 5.7:   UK Imports of Processed Potato Products ('000 tonnes of product) 1988-1993 (calendar year)

	1988	1989	1990	1991	1992	1993
Frozen	155.89	170.19	156.79	159.38	160.66	215.78
Dehydrated	23.94	25.58	25.81	28.16	29.39	30.50
Other*	38.04	54.91	56.63	64.96	82.37	65.16
Total	217.87	250.69	239.24	252.49	272.42	311.44

Source: HM Customs & Excise
* Includes snacks, crisps, canned and chilled products.

Table 5.8:   Value of UK Imports of Processed Potato Products (£m) 1988-1993 (calendar year)

	1988	1989	1990	1991	1992	1993
Frozen	57.73	66.18	69.82	70.12	66.38	93.18
Dehydrated	13.18	14.44	16.07	17.95	20.56	26.22
Other*	21.11	28.73	31.33	39.22	49.22	36.21
Total	92.02	109.35	117.22	127.29	136.16	155.61

Source: HM Customs & Excise
Note :   * Includes snacks, canned and chilled products

Figure 5.13 shows that around 60% of all processed potato products imported into the UK (in raw equivalent[17]) in 1993/94 are sourced in the Netherlands, with frozen or chilled chips comprising over 85% of this total. Frozen products are also imported from Belgium, Luxembourg and France. For dehydrated products the main suppliers are the USA, Ireland, Sweden, Germany and the Netherlands.   Chilled potato products, snacks and crisps are sourced in the Netherlands, Belgium, and Luxembourg, Italy, USA and Germany, with the Netherlands (62%), Belgium (18%), and Italy (7%) accounting for 87% of the total.

Total imports from the Netherlands have been growing steadily, increasing over 20% between 1988/89 and 1993/94. Imports from other countries have increased more dramatically, rising 130% in the same period.

---

[17]   Figures in 5.13 are in thousand tonnes of raw equivalent. As such, they do not tally with the figures in Table 5.7 which are for thousand tonnes of product.

Figure 5.13: UK Imports of Processed Potato Products by Source 1988-94

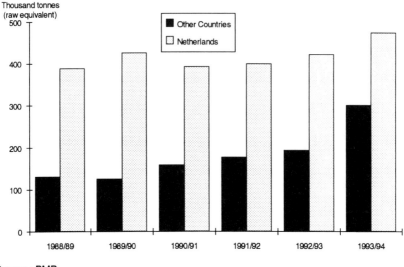

Source : PMB

Tables 5.9 and 5.10 show that in the period 1988-1993 the volume of UK exports of potato products increasing by 61%, and by 90% in value terms. This is largely due to a 200% increase in exports of dehydrated products. Exports in the chilled/snacks/crisps sector has also grown considerably (91% volume increase) adding greatly to the increase in value - an overall 140% increase, implying a shift to higher priced premium products. The frozen sector has been growing more slowly - by 32% in volume, and 56% in value.

Table 5.9: UK Exports of Processed Potato Products ('000 tonnes of product) 1988-1993 (calendar years)

	1988	1989	1990	1991	1992	1993
Frozen	11.95	16.14	19.90	17.14	16.38	15.77
Dehydrated	1.98	2.05	2.91	3.62	6.44	5.96
Other*	2.15	2.07	2.26	3.24	3.61	4.11
Total processed	16.07	20.26	25.07	24.00	26.43	25.84

Source: HM Customs & Excise
Note :   * Includes snacks, crisps, canned and chilled products

Table 5.10: Value of UK Exports of Potato Products (£m) 1988-1993 (calendar years)

	1988	1989	1990	1991	1992	1993
Frozen	6.63	7.97	11.50	10.02	11.12	10.33
Dehydrated	1.63	1.78	2.38	2.37	4.08	3.67
Other*	3.04	2.58	3.43	5.89	6.66	7.39
Total processed	11.30	12.33	17.31	18.27	21.86	21.39

Source: HM Customs & Excise
* Includes snacks, crisps, canned and chilled products.

Eire remains the largest single market for exports, but sales have declined over the last five years. Frozen products tend to be destined primarily for the Irish Republic, in addition to the Netherlands, Spain, Gibraltar and Belgium and Luxembourg.

The UK has shown a deteriorating balance of trade in potato products over the past five years with a deficit increasing from £80.72 million to £134.22 million. Breakdown of these figures suggests that the UK has apparently drawn in significant imports of chilled potato products, mainly chips from the Netherlands, and it is this sector in which the UK's trade balance has worsened most markedly, as Table 5.10 illustrates.

Table 5.11 also shows that the adverse balance of trade in frozen potato products deteriorated by about £31 million, or 61%, over the four year period. In contrast the trade gap in chilled potato products, crisps and snacks deteriorated by nearly £11 million or 60%.

Table 5.11: UK Balance of Trade in Potato Products (£m) 1988 and 1993

	Frozen		Dehydrated		Chilled, Crisps and Snacks	
	1988	1993	1988	1993	1988	1993
Exports	6.63	10.33	1.63	3.67	3.04	7.39
Imports	57.73	93.18	13.18	26.22	21.11	36.21
Balance of Trade	-51.10	-82.85	-11.55	-22.55	-18.07	-28.82

Source: HM Customs & Excise

This apparent deficit in processing ability implied by the growth in imports of chilled chips may be a function of the market structure of the industry in Britain. The frozen chips sector is dominated by a Canadian multinational (McCain) which has 60% of domestic capacity. Five firms control nearly 90% of the capacity. Economic theory suggests that this concentration would allow returns to processing to be higher than if a more competitive structure existed.

The Processing Sector: Frozen, Chilled and Ambient

Overview of the Total Frozen Food Sector in the UK

In the early 1960's frozen food manufacture was heavily concentrated in the hands of just one main producer, namely Birds Eye Wall's Ltd, owned by the multinational company Unilever PLC. However, over the years many other food manufacturers have entered the frozen food market, many of them specialising in particular product sectors, and the supply side of the frozen foods sector has become much more fragmented. Birds Eye's share of the total market has been steadily eroded from around 80% in the early 1960's to around 20% in 1991. Table 5.12 illustrates part of this trend. McCain is the only specialist potato products manufacturer large enough to feature in this table.

Table 5.12:   Estimated Shares of the Total UK Frozen Food Market (% by value) 1980, 1991 and 1994

Manufacturer/Brand	Ultimate Holding Company	1980	1991	1994
Birds Eye	Unilever PLC	31	20	20
Ross Youngs McVities	United Biscuits (Holdings) PLC	6	11	10
Findus	Nestle SA (Switzerland)	10	4	3
McCain	McCain Inc. (Canada)	-	4	3
Campbell	Campbell Soup Co. (US)	-	2	*
Other manufacturers' brands		31	18	21
Retail own-label		22	43	43
Total		100	100	

Source: Estimates based on trade sources
* Figure included in other manufacturers' brands

Most frozen food manufacturers specialise in particular products or manufacture for the retail own-label market. This has helped Birds Eye retain its brand leadership of the total market although it has lost market share to own-label frozen foods. Ross Youngs McVities has, in the last few years, taken the place of Findus as the closest competitor to Birds Eye in the total market. This followed United Biscuits' acquisition of Ross Youngs in 1988 from Hanson Trust PLC. This enabled United Biscuits to expand its existing presence in frozen foods through its McVities range of frozen cakes and desserts. Ross Youngs' operations were rationalised during 1991 and 1992, and Ross Youngs is now prominent in several major product sectors with sub-brands such as Tendergrill meat grills, Stir Fry vegetables, Ross meat pies, Ocean Classics fish products, Youngs' speciality seafood, McVities San Marco pizzas, McVities St Clements cheesecake and the Linda McCartney vegetarian products. Ross Youngs is also a major supplier of products to the retail own-label market.

Findus, owned by Nestle, used to compete with Birds Eye across a range of product sectors, but, after rationalisation measures in recent years, Findus has retrenched heavily and withdrawn from such sectors as frozen fish, frozen vegetables and frozen beef burgers. Findus then concentrated production on four main value-added lines of frozen foods, these being ready meals (including the Lean Cuisine range), French Bread pizza, filled pancakes, and other frozen snacks.

McCain's 4% share of the total frozen food market stems from its market leadership in sales of frozen chips and other frozen potato products and its leading position in the frozen pizza market, which is shared with Ross Youngs/McVities. More detail on McCain is provided in the following section on the frozen chips sector.

Campbells (best known for its canned soup) entered the UK frozen food market in 1988 when it acquired Freshbake, a fast growing brand. Campbells intention was to develop further Freshbake's range of pies, quiches, sausage rolls, cakes and desserts and to develop frozen products under the Campbells' label such as Kids ready meals and Burger-in-a-Bun. Campbells also manufactures for the retail own-label market.

Processed Potato Products

The processed potato products sector is a very dynamic one with new and innovative products produced almost daily. Processed potato products are defined here to include frozen potato products, potato based snacks, dehydrated potato and canned potatoes. It is convenient to view these as separate sectors in terms of their requirements for raw materials and their demand characteristics.

Crisps and other potato based snacks, account for 40% of the total quantity of potatoes processed (see Table 5.13), but in the case of crisps require a specialist variety, usually Record, which is grown on contract for crisping and has no other market in Great Britain. Other potato snacks use dehydrated potatoes as raw materials. Raw materials are estimated to represent approximately 25% of the total costs of production of Crisp.

Dehydrators utilise a wide range of potato varieties and accept potatoes which are of a relatively low quality. Canned and dehydrated potatoes account for 9.6% of raw potatoes used in processing in 1991/92. It is unlikely that a producer will grow specifically for a dehydrator, instead, potatoes are used which are not suitable for other uses. However, there are exceptions to this, dehydrated potatoes with a low level of reducing sugar are required for the snack industry. In the future there may be a development of specific starch potato varieties to produce starch for industrial use.

Producers of frozen potato products consider a small number of varieties as suitable, these include Pentland Dell, Russell Burbank and Maris Piper.   Contract specifications vary from company to company depending upon the product. For instance McCain, the largest company in the sector, have a payment system based upon tuber dry matter, tuber size, damage and reducing sugar levels which determines the colour of fried products. Bonus schemes reflect the higher conversion rates and lower processing costs associated with better quality product.   Raw materials represent approximately 40% of total costs of frozen potato products and this sector accounted for c. 55% of raw potatoes processed in 1991/92.

These products can also be viewed as distinct in terms of their consumption and use. It is reasonable to assume that frozen potato products, such as frozen chips represent a substitute for raw potatoes and other starchy foods such as pasta and rice. In contrast, crisps and other potato snacks are, not a direct substitute for raw potatoes and have quite different patterns of use to raw potatoes and frozen potatoes. Dehydrated potato products are best viewed as a raw material input into the production of other food products. Thus the three sectors identified have distinct patterns of demand for raw materials and different patterns of use by consumers and processors.

Over the period 1989-94, UK based processors increased their use of potatoes by 21.4% from 1.494 million tonnes to 1.814 million tonnes. Over the same period the proportion of potatoes supplied from the UK increased from 83.6% to 95.9%. Potatoes imported for processing are used predominantly for freezing and chilling, they accounted for 12.4% of the total frozen and chilled supplies in 1989/90 and 5.5% in 1991/92. This reduction in the level of imported potatoes for frozen and chilled production corresponded with an increase in the quantity of potato processed by this sector. This implies that the availability of potato supplies suitable for freezing and chilling has expanded in parallel with the expansion in processing capacity.   Some evidence for this is presented in Table 5.13 below.

Table 5.13:   Estimated Tonnage of Raw Potatoes used for Processing in the UK (thousand tonnes) 1989-1994

July/June	1989/90	1990/91	1991/92	1992/93	1993/94
Canned/Dehydrated/Other					
Home Grown	184	152	163	140	149
Imported*	0	0	0	0	4
Total	184	152	163	146	153
Crisped					
Home Grown	595	595	584	695	693
Imported*	6	11	10	2	4
Total	601	606	594	697	697
Frozen or Chilled					
Home Grown	621	668	742	838	911
Imported*	88	38	74	62	53
Total	709	706	816	900	964
Total UK Grown Usage	1400	1415	1489	1673	1753
Total UK Production	6325	6555	6267	7802	7065
Percentage Processed	22.1%	21.6%	23.8%	21.4%	24.8%
Total Processed in the UK	1494	1464	1573	1743	1814
% Share of UK Potatoes used in processing	93.7	96.7	94.7	96.0	96.7

Source: HM Customs and Excise, and MAFF
* Imports of raw potatoes used for processing in the UK
Note: The following ratios are used to convert raw potato to processed product:
               Dehydrated 6.2:1, Crisped 4:1, Frozen 1.9:1, Canned 1:1
               (In 1987/88 the ratio used for Crisped was 4.3:1 and for Dehydrated 6:1.)

Chips and Potato Products

Trade sources report that there are about 30 major processors of processed chips in the Benelux countries.   In the UK, which grows approximately the same quantity of potatoes, there are only eleven processors, excluding subsidiaries.   The major producer in the UK is McCain. The top five UK manufacturers of chips in terms of capacity are listed below in Table 5.14. In the chips sector, McCains have around 60% of current estimated capacity.   Everest, in second place with around 12% of estimated capacity.   Everest has bought up equipment from Merlin and Cwmbran Foods[18] in 1993 and trade sources indicate that there may be increases in capacity in 1995/96.

Imports are currently in excess of 20% of the processed chips market. The Dutch have a high quality processed chips image which some UK producers may not be able to match due to their production facilities - or UK processors' pricing behaviour may have encouraged imports.[19]

---

18   Companies going into receivership.
19   Recent research indicates that the increasing market share of British processors has led to a substantial increase in Dutch imports and considerable welfare loss.   See Dennis A.L. (1995)

**Table 5.14:   Estimated Capacity of Top Five UK Manufacturers of
                 Chips and Potato Products - 1991**

	Estimated Chip Capacity (kg/hour)
McCain Group	62,000
Everest	12,000
UB (Ross Youngs)	10,000
WCF	5,000
Garden Isle	5,000
Fisher Frozen	5,000
Total	99,000

Source: Trade Sources/Euro PA
Note :   McCains also have a substantial share of the own-label market via PAS Grantham

The Dutch processors' apparent disadvantages are the high cost of
transport to the UK and environmental constraints in the Netherlands.
Leading Dutch suppliers to the UK market are Boots Frites, Aviko (who
own Idwal Fisher), De Fritesspecialist, Farm Frites, Meijer Frozen Foods
and Vriezo. McCains also own a major plant at Lelystad in Flevoland.

The Frozen Sector

As Table 5.15 shows, McCains have a dominant position in the frozen
chip market, with Ross Youngs a distant second. Own-label is believed
to account for around 50% of sales.

Table 5.15:   Retail Brand Share of Frozen Chips in the UK, 1994

	% Value
McCain	33
Ross Youngs	5
Other brands	12
Own-label	50
Total	100

Source: Trade sources
Note :   McCains also have a substantial share of the own-label market via PAS Grantham

Table 5.15 covers all chips, including the premium varieties like ovenable
chips. If these premium types are excluded then the growing impact of
own-label on the 'commodity' frozen chip market is evident, as Table 5.16
shows.

Table 5.16:   UK Retail Brand Shares of Frozen Chips excluding Premium Chips (% value) - 1988 and 1991

	1988	1991
Own-label	50	78
Ross	14	7
Birds Eye	13	-
McCain	12	12
Other brands	11	3
Total	100	100

Source: Mintel analysis and Nielsen

The frozen potato products market has shown particularly strong growth since 1984 and has doubled in size. There is a wide variety of products and participating companies in this sector with a number of new product launches in recent years. All major manufacturers have been developing a range of potato specialities, and now offer many variations, for example:

Birds Eye: within the Country Club range are Potato Waffles, Alphabites, Crispy Potato Fritters, Potato Croquettes, Potato Cheesies, Crunchies, Crunchy Potato Grill, Crispers and jacket potatoes with a range of filling including cheese and onion, bacon and cheese and pizza.

McCain: in the children's range are Moon Waffles and Mega Monsters, in the family range are Croquettes, Hash Browns, Baby Bakers, Crispy Slims, Potato Fritters and Southern Fries.

Ross: within the Potato Greats range are Jacket Potato Wedges, Jacket Scallops, Oven Crunchies, Button Crunchies, Bubble and Squeak, Potato Pancakes, Hash Browns and Potato Waffles.

Findus: Sauté Potatoes and Jacket Sauté Potatoes.

Jus-Rol: Potato Bites and Rollers.

Fri d'Or: (from Olaf foods, Part of Hazlewood) Potato Shells with six different fillings including Cheddar Cheese, Cheese and Onion, Ham and Cheese, Butter, Corn and Pepper and Cheese and Broccoli.

Of these products the best selling line for a number of years has been Birds Eye's Waffles. Own-label Potato Croquettes, own-label Potato Waffles, Birds Eye's Potato Fritters and Alphabites are all key products in this market segment. The majority of these products are targeted at the children's market.

In the speciality potato products sector branded products have traditionally dominated and Birds Eye accounted for around 45% of this sector in 1994. Own-label speciality potato products have gained an increasing share in this market as indicated in Table 5.17 which illustrates brand shares in frozen potato products.

Table 5.17: UK Retail Brand Shares of Frozen Potato Products (% value) 1988, 1991 and 1994

	1988	1991	1994
Birds Eye	40	41	45
Ross	21	13	15
Own-label	19	37	40
Jus-Rol	6	5	*
McCain	6	2	*
Other brands	8	2	10
Total	100	100	100

Source: Mintel analysis and Nielsen
* Figure counted in all other brands

The Chilled Sector

The inability to disaggregate Customs and Excise data on chilled products, from frozen chips and the 'other' category, is a major problem in determining market shares in the chilled sector. However the Dutch are the main supplier to the UK chilled sector, with companies like De Fritesspecialist, following an aggressive marketing campaign in the UK. The UK-based leaders in chilled chips are Everest Frozen Foods and Idwal Fisher, although McCain have launched a premium chip range aimed at the chilled/frozen sector. Presumably the logic of this move is that many domestic purchasers of chilled products (possibly up to 60%) actually freeze their purchases on returning home. Other leading UK manufacturers of chilled chips are Warrell Morton and Axgro. Roy's Quality Foods produce a range of chilled potato products.

Warrell Morton estimate that the chilled chips segment is 25% of the prepared chip market, although the PMB catering survey put the figure at 32% of chipped products[20]. Both Warrell Morton and Axgro report their main markets as local authority school meals. Warrell Morton do supply some catering outlets via wholesalers and Axgro reported a move into this area via a new vacuum packaging system which will give ambient storage for up to six weeks. Their target market will be chip shops, kebab shops etc.

Export trade sources reported three grades of chips ranging in price from £4.00 to £5.50 per 10 kg box. They also reported increased competition and market pressure from the Dutch. Main Dutch competition comes from De Fritesspecialist, Bravi (bought by Farm Frites recently), Kuibo, Aviko and Boots Frites. De Fritesspecialist are estimated to be the single

---

20   The GB Catering Market for Potatoes March 1993, PMB. This study excluded the major
     fast food catering chains.

largest supplier with some 20,000 tonnes exported to the UK annually. Improved packaging, including gas flushing, has meant that chilled products will be able to extend their shelf life and also to become more tolerant of near ambient conditions.

Trade sources indicate that Aviko produce around 50,000 tonnes of the "traditional" short-life product each year for the Dutch market and export to Belgium and Germany. 50% of the gas flushed market in the UK is supplied by Dutch producers, 40% is British like Idwal Fisher, Everest Frozen Foods and some small local producers, the rest originates from Belgium.

Table 5.18:   Estimated Market Shares of Chilled Chips in the UK - 1991

Country of Origin	Company	Volume of UK Sales (tonnes)	Market Share (%)
Holland	De Fritesspecialist (Lords Chips)	20,000	21
	Kuibo Frites	15,000	16
	Boots Frites	10,000	11
	Bravi (since 1994 Farm Frites)	2,500	3
UK	Idwal Fisher (Aviko/Holland)	15,000	16
	Everest Frozen Foods	15,000	16
	Other Producers	6,000	6
Belgium	Farm Frites Belgium (100% Farm Frites Holland)	10,000	11

Source: Trade Sources

Figure 5.18 shows that of the main players, 52% of the UK market for chilled chips is directly in the hands of Dutch producers. Indirectly the Dutch had 79% in 1991, with their holding of Idwal Fisher in the UK and Farm Frites in Belgium. Trade sources are estimating that the UK market for chilled chips will grow to 125,000 tonnes in the 1990's

The Ambient Sector

This review of the Ambient Sector will deal mainly with crisps, but a general overview of the whole savoury snacks sector, covering extruded wheat and maize products, as well as those from potatoes, crisps and savoury biscuits etc. is given first.

Savoury Snacks

In the total market for bagged snacks (including own-label), KP Foods is overall market leader with a volume share of 39.7% in 1991, followed by PepsiCo with 38.7% and Dalgety with 11.2%. Table 5.19 shows that, in value terms PepsiCo leads the market, although it is not possible to derive its overall share as one cannot gauge its position in own-label sales. In 1991 PepsiCo brands accounted for 33.7% of market value, whilst KP brands claimed a 28.9% share. The top three brands account for c. 90% of the market in bagged snacks.

Both Smiths and Golden Wonder have lost share since 1990, probably due to the growing significance of own-label. Own-label's share of market value has risen from 15.7% in 1989 to 17.1% in 1991. The general expansion of multiple retailers has been a key factor. Furthermore, their tendency to offer a broader range of competitive multipacks and family packs has proved highly successful in a recessionary economic climate.

Table 5.19:   UK Market Shares in Bagged Snacks (% by value) - 1989-91

	1989	1990	1991
PepsiCo	35.4	34.1	33.7
Of which:			
Walkers	18.9	18.5	19.2
Smiths	14.7	13.9	12.6
Tudor	1.0	1.0	1.4
Planters	0.8	0.7	0.5
KP Foods	28.8	28.8	28.9
Dalgety	10.9	11.8	11.4
Of which:			
Golden Wonder	8.4	9.1	8.5
Sooner Snacks	2.5	2.7	2.9
Own-label	15.7	16.5	17.1
Other brands	9.2	8.8	8.9

Source: Trade Estimates

The savoury snack market was valued at £503m in 1991 and has been the most dynamic market sector over the past 12 years. KP and Smiths are the two main brands in the sector and have a combined share of 67% in 1991. KP's market share has risen from 37.6% in 1989 to 39.3% in 1991 and its four main products are Hula Hoops, Skips, Discos and Frisps. Launched in late 1990, Frisps has managed to claim 7.2% of the market.

PepsiCo's main brand in savoury snacks is Smiths, although Walkers also has a limited product range. Both brands have lost share but still hold a combined 30% slice of the market. Smiths core products are Monster Munch, Quavers, Square Crisps and Chipsticks. 1990 saw the launch of Tuba Loops and Cheetos; the introduction of the latter being an attempt to introduce a successful PepsiCo US brand to the UK market.

The principal Golden Wonder product is Wotsits which has seen a number of line extensions since 1988. Dalgety's acquisition of Sooner Snacks is expected to strengthen the company's position in the savoury snacks market. Sooner is particularly strong in the economy snacks segment.

In 1993 other brands accounted for 14.1% of the market. These other brands are a mixture of economy and premium labels. Redmill (Portfolio Foods) is Sooner's main rival in economy snacks. Derwent Valley (now part of KP Foods) controls the adult premium sector, and has an overall market share of around 3.5%. Bensons Crisps and Tucker Foods also market adult products, in particular snack products incorporating sauce dips. Cereal bar manufacturer, Jordans, entered the market in June 1991 with its oat-based Oatsters snack. Procter and Gamble also entered the snack market with Pringles, tube-packed crisps - this is a very similar product to Bahlsen's Stackers and both are aimed at the adult market. Table 5.21 shows the distribution channels for the savoury snacks market.

Table 5.20: Savoury Snack Market Brand Shares in the UK (% at RSP) 1988-93

	1989	1990	1991	1992	1993
KP	37.6	37.9	39.3	38.9	40.9
Smiths	29.0	28.0	27.6		
Golden Wonder	7.3	7.8	6.9	11.0	11.3
Walkers	3.9	3.3	2.7		
Other brands	13.9	14.5	15.1	14.0	14.1
Own-label	8.2	8.5	8.4	8.2	7.6
Total	100.0	100.0	100.0		

Source: Nielson/KP Snack Foods Review (various)
Note: Figures may not sum due to rounding.

The ethnic snack market essentially consists of Indian and Mexican snacks. Both types are encompassed in Derwent Valley's Phileas Fogg range (Punjabi Purris, Tortilla Chips). Oriental Kitchen, also from Derwent Valley, supplies Indian and Chinese-style snacks. KP's World Snacks range is second only to Phileas Fogg in adult premium savoury snacks. Other major manufactures entering the sector include Sharwoods (Ranks Hovis McDougall) and Shipphams, with its Old El Paso brand. There are also a variety of smaller manufacturers such as Bombay Halwas and Raj Foods. Although, ethnic-style snacks are evidently a growth market, these are probably best regarded as a subsegment of the bagged snacks market and that as the market grows, it will increasingly be dominated by the major brands.

Table 5.21:   Manufacturers' Brand Shares of the Savoury Snacks Market by Distribution Channel (% by value) - 1990 and 1991

	1990 Catering	1990 Licensed Grocery	1990 CTNs and other Trades	1991 Catering	1991 Licensed Grocery	1991 CTNs and other Trades
KP	31.9	40.5	32.3	53.8	36.4	58.3
Smiths	28.3	32.1	29.2	22.1	35.5	19.5
Golden Wonder	8.9	3.9	8.1	7.3	4.9	5.6
Walkers	30.9	23.5	30.4	16.8	23.2	16.6
Total	100.0	100.0	100.0	100.0	100.0	100.0

Source: KP Snack Food Review 1991
CTN's are Confectioners, Tobacconists and Newsagents

KP Foods is the snack food division of United Biscuits (Holdings) PLC. The company claims overall market leadership by tonnage in bagged snacks, including its share of own-label business. In branded terms, KP is the number two player in bagged snacks with a share of 28.9% by value in 1991. KP is market leader in both savoury snacks and nuts and is second in the crisps sector. It is also important to mention sister company, McVities, as its brand holds 30% of the savoury biscuit market. With the trend towards miniature varieties of savoury biscuits in bagged packs, these products are increasingly being considered as snacks. KP also has significant foreign operations and holds 22% of the European market. KP Foods purchased Derwent Valley in 1993 from Dalgety. Derwent Valley was created in 1982 and was one of the success stories of the 1980's being the chief pioneer of the premium adult crisp sector. The Phileas Fogg brand accounts for over 50% of the adult premium sector and Derwent Valley also supplies own-label products. In January 1991, the Baker's Street brand was launched, targeted at the 'dinner party' consumer. Economy and family snacks are marketed as Derwent Valley Family Snacks

PepsiCo's UK brands lead the market in value terms, as already stated. Whilst Smiths has lost market share since 1989, Walkers' share has grown, as has Tudor's. Walkers leads the crisp market and Smiths is placed second in savoury snacks. PepsiCo brands account for 10.4% of the nut market by value, although their share has dropped significantly since 1988. Since 1989, PepsiCo has introduced successful Frito Lay brands (Ruffles and Cheetos) to the UK, backed by strong media and promotional support.

Dalgety is a major UK-based food group which has expanded into the snack market via external acquisitions, initially through the purchase of Golden Wonder in 1986. If Sooner's share is included, Dalgety's overall market share in bagged snacks can be estimated at 11.4% in 1991.

Redmill Snacks is the group's snacks division and the company claims 62% of the economy snack market. Redmill also estimates that it holds around 60% of the pork scratchings market and 20% of own-label savoury snacks.

Established in 1980, Bensons has become the leading independent manufacturer of snacks in the UK. The company achieved a turnover of £26m in 1991, 19.5% higher than in 1990. The company is active in both crisps and savoury snacks but is stronger in the former. Bensons has expanded through acquisition and innovation. Its acquisitions include XL in 1984, Hedgehog Foods in 1987 and A K Snacks in August 1991. Following the purchase of Hedgehog Foods, the novel Hedgehog brand has been successfully transformed into a premium healthy crisp brand. The Hedgehog brand has also been extended into savoury snacks through the organic corn snack, Hoggits. Burton's Biscuits Ltd is essentially a manufacturer of sweet biscuits, such as the popular Waggon Wheels product. However, the company also markets some well-known economy, savoury snacks and savoury biscuits such as Snipp Snaps, Chicken 'n' Chips, Burger 'n' Chips, Cheese Pleesors, Pizza Pleesors and Potato Puffs.

Smith Weston has been one of the major raiders in the European snack market over the last few years with purchases in France and in the UK. In the UK, the company owns Forth Valley Foods Ltd and Tucker Foods Ltd. Both are well-established smaller players in the snack foods market.

There are a variety of other brands on the market, many of which are of foreign origin. These tend to be marketed by food brokers. Bahlsen is one of the leading snack companies in Europe and its product range consists of biscuits (eg Salzletten) and savoury snacks (eg Peppis and Stackers).

Finally two interesting recent market entrants, Procter and Gamble and Jordans, need a mention. Jordans is the undisputed leader in the UK cereal bar market and is also active in the breakfast cereal market. For Procter and Gamble, Pringles represents its first European food launch. Given Procter and Gamble's track record as a brand builder, the savoury snacks market should see significant competition over the coming years.

Crisps

In 1991, manufacturers' sales of potato crisps and sticks amounted to £493.7m, 31% higher than in 1988 - see Table 5.22

Table 5.22:   UK Manufacturer's Sales of Potato Crisps and Potato Sticks 1987-91

	1988	1989	1990	1991
£m	376.6	409.1	463.1	493.7
% change year-on-year	-1.5	8.6	13.2	6.6
Index (1987=100)	100.0	108.6	122.9	131.0

Source: Business Monitor PAS4239.

In terms of UK brand shares the market breakdown for 1988-93 is shown in Table 5.23. This shows that whilst Walkers have maintained sales growth, the Smiths brand has continued to decline. KP's share has also fallen and, like Smiths, this is principally attributed to the ever growing strength of own-label. Walkers does not have national coverage. In Scotland and north-east England, PepsiCo's principal crisp brand is Tudor. Tudor has a market share of 28% in north-east England and 14% in Scotland. Crisp and snack plants were reported by trade sources to be currently at or near capacity in 1993 and this may partly explain the increase in imports shown in Tables 5.7 and 5.8. There would therefore appear to be scope for new investment in this sector, particularly to produce premium adult crisps.

Table 5.23:   Crisp Market Brand Shares (% at RSP) - 1988-1993

	1988	1989	1990	1991	1992	1993
Walkers	27.7	30.7	31.3	33.1	32.8	35.9
KP	18.8	18.9	17.8	17.1	17.2	16.8
Golden Wonder	12.3	10.5	11.4	11.1	12.4	11.8
Smiths	9.2	8.3	6.6	4.5	3.5	2.5
Tudor	1.6	1.8	1.8	2.5	2.6	2.3
Other brands	11.8	11.7	11.3	11.2	10.1	9.7
Own-label	18.6	18.1	19.7	20.5	21.4	21.0

Source: Nielsen/KP Snack Food Review 1991
Note: Figures may not sum due to rounding.

The Commercial Performance of the Processing Sector

This section looks at the key ratios showing the comparative financial results of companies operating in the British potato processing sector using published data from company annual reports.

Comparison of Financial Performance

Table 5.24 presents the key financial ratios based upon UK company results. The sector, as a whole, has a very respectable profit margin of around 8%. The return on capital employed (ROCE) is also impressive with six of the twelve companies listed in Table 5.24 having an ROCE greater than 25%.

Table 5.24: Summary of Average UK Potato Company Results (three year average)

Company	Turnover £m	Profit £m	Profit/ Margin	ROCE (%)	Current Ratio	Debt Ratio	Years
Freezers/Chillers							
Bird's Eye Walls (Unilever)	625.57	50.94	8.14	29.23	1.18	0.60	90-92
Frigoscandia Ltd	79.60	3.46	4.36	12.05	0.60	0.69	91-93
HJ Heinz Company Ltd	486.67	40.33	8.29	31.72	0.71	0.71	90/91-92/93
Crisps and Snacks							
Golden Wonder (Dalgety Spillers Foods)	347.87	33.13	9.50	44.26	0.86	0.83	90/91-92/93
Smiths Crisps Ltd	202.49	4.61	3.35	17.42	1.11	0.56	90-91
Walkers Crisps Ltd	196.78	49.28	27.45	91.93	1.28	N/A	90-91
Sooner Snacks Ltd	46.23	-0.48	-2.85	3.75	0.62	0.92	90/91-92/93
Other							
UB (Ross Young's) Ltd	536.23	21.73	4.06	15.70	1.24	0.56	91-93
Gerber Foods Manufacturing Ltd	95.10	1.30	1.33	10.08	0.91	0.78	90/91-92/93
McCain Foods (GB) Ltd	212.05	22.46	10.62	29.26	1.65	0.63	90/91-92/93
Everest Foods plc	34.00	2.17	6.46	13.64	1.23	0.46	91/92-93/94
PAS (Grantham) Ltd	28.10	2.89	10.46	25.53	1.63	0.65	90/91-92/93
Average weighted by turnover		**31.34**	**8.23**	**30.66**	**1.08**	**0.65**	
Straight Average		**20.88**	**7.70**	**28.27**	**1.07**	**0.69**	
Total Turnover	**2,891**						

Source : Kompass, McMillans, Hambros Company Guide, Euro PA
Notes: Albert Fisher is a consolidated group and is not primarily concerned with potato products. Its results have not been used in the calculation of average performance. McCain(GB) and PAS(Grantham) Ltd are owned by the Dutch company McCain Europa B.V. This company is, in turn, own by the private company, McCain Foods Ltd (Canada). UB Group is part of United Biscuits covering the group of subsidiaries producing potato products.
          The figures shown above should be read in conjunction with the notes contained in the Appendix to Chapter One.

Analysis of the accounts of successful UK companies, such as McCain and Everest, reveals a policy of continuous investment in new plant which brings with it lower costs and the ability to extend their range of products. Investment has been based upon a trend of increased demand, technological developments in products and packaging.   These companies are also noted for a degree of secrecy concerning the technical aspects of their production. Trade sources suggest that there is a policy of not reselling redundant plant and not divulging technical details concerning how plants are run and their operating costs. Hence, the high capital cost of new technological investment coupled with the need for technical know-how may have acted as a barrier to entry at the quality end of the market.

Summary and Conclusions

In the period 1989/90-1993/94, British-based potato processing plants used 25% more domestically grown potatoes, and their total usage of potatoes increased by 21%. However, during this period, as consumption of potato products continued to grow strongly, increases in production have failed to match demand. The net result has been a growing UK trade deficit in processed potato products.

The growth in demand for potato products is seen in most key sectors including economy chips, oven and microwave chips, potato products, e.g. filled potatoes, potato shapes, waffles etc., premium/adult crisps, savoury snacks, and ready meals. Imported potato products include all these types but the most growth in recent years has been in chilled chips.

The increase in consumption of potato-based products has been largely due to changes in consumer tastes and preferences and in particular an increased demand for convenience food, snacks and an expansion in the number of meals eaten outside the home. It is likely that this trend will continue for the foreseeable future.

On the supply side, the chips market continues to be dominated by McCain, but Everest is gradually increasing its output. Most of the other processors of chips seem to have insufficient resources to make significant inroads against either imports or McCain's market share. These leading British-based companies demonstrate good trading records, with financial results comparing very favourably with those in other similar food processing sectors. There is also evidence of reinvestment being undertaken or being seriously considered by the major players. The growing market share of own-label brands has created the possibility for these companies to expand sales without taking on the 'branded might' of McCain.

In terms of crisps and savoury snacks, a number of relatively small manufacturers, e.g. Bensons and Forth Valley Foods, have proved that it is possible to operate successfully against the market dominance of PepsiCo, KP and Dalgety. The growth of own-label brands, plus the proven ability of a number of companies, e.g. Derwent Valley, Kettle

Foods, KP, to launch new brands in the premium crisp market, demonstrates the potential for a new entrant to develop niche segments of the market.

Perhaps the most important constraint for processors based in the UK is the procuring of ready supplies of potatoes in large quantities of even sizes, similar dry matter and sugar levels. The production of potatoes in the UK is characterised by many varieties, variable growing conditions and previously, the existence of intervention and quota schemes for potato planting. However, there seems no inherent reason why UK growers in the prime potato areas cannot produce potatoes to processors' standards. UK processors have certainly increased their uptake of domestic potatoes in the period 1989-94.

In 1997 the Potato Marketing Scheme will come to an end. After the termination of the PMS, growers will have the additional freedom to decide what quantity they wish to grow. However, in a more competitive unsupported market they will have to pay more attention to the variety preference and specifications of the leading buyers. This will emphasise the need for co-operation and development of a range of technical and marketing initiatives. For example, encouragement of the growing of a limited range of selected varieties for processing within easy access of the processing plant; efficient management of the crop from pre-chitting to storage, which optimises dry matter, sugar and colour. There will be a market need for the selection and grading of potatoes prior to storage to suit specific commercial requirements so that stocks of known quality and size can be built-up. Ambient and cold storage facilities will need to be in place to serve processors' needs. In the past it is the larger producers who have been able to supply processors like McCain with potatoes of the required quality. These producers invested in potato harvester, storage capacity and grading lines and irrigation equipment which were capable of providing potatoes of the required quality. However, scope exists for the further development of grower groups to develop long term supply commitments to processors and to share the costs of storage and harvesting.

And finally, research and development will be needed to develop products and processes which can use potatoes which are not of the current required size and hence to manufacture potato products alongside the processing of standard chips. Such an industry policy will give the processor and potato grower significant economies of scale and marketing opportunities whilst maximising the utilisation of available potatoes.

References

Collins, J.W.J (1989). *The Potato Industries of France, Belgium and Holland and their relevance to the UK.* The Potato Marketing Board, Oxford

Dennis, A.L. (1995) *A Comparative Structural Analysis of the UK and Dutch Frozen Potato Product Sector.* Continuing Doctoral research at the Department of Agricultural Economics, University of Newcastle-upon-Tyne.

EC (1992). *Proposal for a Council Regulation (EEC) on the Common Organisation of the Market in Potatoes.* Com (92) 185, Brussels.

ECOSOC (1993). *Proposal for a Council Regulation (EEC) on the Common Organisation of the Market in Potatoes (Com (92) 195 final).* AGR/472, COM/Potatoes, CES 218/93, Brussels.

Ennew, C.T. and Professor the Lord Peston, (1993) *An (Un)Common Potato Regime for Europe?* Occasional paper (1) School of Management and Finance, University of Nottingham, Nottingham

Euro Analysis (1992). Unpublished Report *The Potato Market*, R48, Euro PA & Associates, 11 Church St, Northborough, Cambs, UK

Euro PA & Associates (1994) *Investing in Processed Potato Production in Britain,* R 68A, Vols I & II, Euro PA & Associates, 11 Church St, Northborough, Cambs, UK

European Parliament (1993). *Report of the Committee on Agriculture, Fisheries and Rural Development on the Commission Proposal for a Council Regulation on the Common Organisation of the Market in Potatoes,* (COM (92) 0185 final - C3-0476/92) Rapportuer: Görlach, W. Brussels.

GATT, (1994) *Agreement Establishing the World Trade Organisation Agreement on Agriculture,* Cm 2559, Misc No 17, HMSO, London

HoL (1993). Select Committee on the European Communities Report 19. *The Common Organisation of the Market in Potatoes.* HMSO, London.

KP Foods (various). Snack Food Market Review, Heathgate House, 57 Colne Road, Twickenham, TW2 6QA.

NFS (various). *Household Consumption and Expenditure.* Annual Report of the National Food Survey Committee. HMSO, London.

PMB (1991). *British Potatoes in the Single European Market: Stability, Quality, Consumer Choice.,* Oxford

PMB (1991). *A Flow Chart for Potatoes in Great Britain.,* Oxford

PMB (1994). *Potato Consumption and Processing in Great Britain.,* Oxford

PMB (1993). *Historical Data Summary from 1960.,* Oxford

Chapter 6: Milk and Dairy Products

Barry Wilson, Bruce Traill and John Strak[1]

Introduction

The UK dairy industry is in the midst of a period of dramatic upheaval, which has seen the abolition of the Milk Marketing Boards (MMBs) and their effective monopoly over the marketing of milk and the creation of a 'free-market' in milk. The Boards have been replaced by farmer co-operatives which have a dominant share of the market (Milk Marque in England and Wales has around 65% of the market). These changes have brought an end to the formula pricing system which has been accused, in the past, of being anti-competitive and stifling innovation, with the result that the UK exports low-value products (such as skimmed milk powder) and imports high-value fresh products (yoghurts etc.).

It is too early to predict all of the ramifications of these changes in the markets for milk and dairy products but they are an important backdrop to the analysis presented in this chapter - especially with regard to how UK dairy companies will be affected. Continuing reform of the CAP and implementation of the Uruguay Round GATT agreement will add other dimensions of change to the dairy sector. And the adaptation of the industry to the European Single Market, which is already seeing the creation of giant European dairy multinationals, is another important driver of change.

The chapter begins with an overview of consumption trends for milk and dairy products and then goes on to consider the structure of production at the farm level including yields, farm numbers and, crucially, the impact of price policy and milk quotas. After this the aggregate market for dairy products is assessed, including an appraisal of the UK trade position and the position and performance of key dairy companies.

---

1   Barry Wilson is Editor of the publication 'Dairy Industry Newsletter', Cambridge. Bruce Traill is a Professor at the Department of Agricultural Economics, University of Reading. Dr John Strak is Principal at Euro PA & Associates, Cambs. The Editors would like to draw the attention of the reader to the caveat in the Appendix to Chapter One.

Consumption of Milk and Dairy Products

UK per capita consumption of dairy products, at 120 kilograms per annum, is equal to that of Denmark. Only the Irish Republic has greater consumption at 180 kilograms per head. However, consumption of milk and milk products has been declining since the early 1970's. In particular, per capita consumption of butter and liquid wholemilk has declined between 70% and 75% in this time. In contrast, the consumption of skimmed (low fat) milk has grown forty-five fold since 1980. Growth has also occurred in yoghurt consumption, with a two and a half fold increase in the last decade.

Doorstep delivery is traditionally associated with high liquid milk consumption. 50% of all liquid milk consumption in England is by doorstep delivery, but this proportion has been falling due to an increase in sales by supermarkets. The reason for the increase in the supermarkets' share is simply price. The price differential between a pint of milk bought at the supermarket and one delivered to the door has been as high as 10p.

Consumer prices for butter and the other milk products have also fallen substantially with discounters such as Kwiksave, NETTO and ALDI using butter as a loss leader to attract customers, charging prices for butter that are 60 pence per kilogram below the intervention price.

Cheese consumption in the UK, at 8.9 kilograms per head per annum, is low by EU standards. The UK is quite different from other members of the European Union in that the dominant cheese is a hard pressed variety, Cheddar. The major growth in the market is from the industrial and catering sector for cheeses such as Mozzarella.

Fresh dairy products, such as cream, yoghurts, fromage frais etc., are the most dynamic growing milk product sectors (except Mozzarella cheese). Sales of these dairy products grew by 12% in value in 1992 and was worth over £1 billion. There is great potential for this growth to continue as UK *per capita* consumption is lagging far behind other EU countries. Ice cream has 0.3 kilograms per head per annum consumption in the UK, in France this level is 6kg. Yoghurt *per capita* consumption is 5kgs in the UK in contrast to 21kgs in other EU countries.

The Markets for Milk and Dairy Products

Figure 6.1:   Consumption of Selected Dairy Products, 1945 to 1993

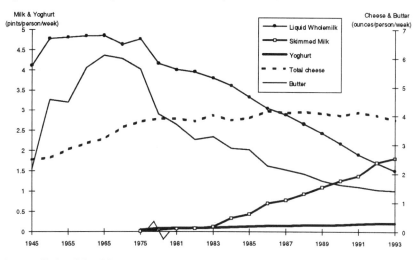

Source: National Food Survey
*Liquid wholemilk and skimmed milk and yoghurt in pints per person per week, cheese and butter in ounces per person per week.

Figure 6.1 above shows the long term trends in consumption against which the dairy industry is operating. These are discussed in more detail in the following pages but Figure 6.1 illustrates that the decline in the main markets, liquid milk and butter (largely on health grounds) is not compensated for by low growth rates in cheese and higher growth rates in yoghurt (and other fresh products).

The Liquid Market

About 86% of liquid milk sold is for household consumption. AGB market research suggests that this sector is currently declining by about 5% a year. Non-household sectors of the market include school milk (1% of total sales) and catering (11%). Flavoured milk and milk shake sales are expanding following several product launches but account for less than 2% of the market. Within the household liquid milk market, the most substantial trend has been from full fat to semi-skimmed and skimmed milks (see Table 6.1)

As Table 6.1 shows, liquid milk consumption in the UK is high relative to most of its European neighbours, only being surpassed in the EU by Ireland and Denmark.

Table 6.1:   Consumption of Liquid Milk (kg per capita per annum)

Country	Whole (Natural and Standardised)					
	1987	1988	1989	1990	1991	1992
Germany	53.9	55.1	52.9	52.0	46.7	48.1
France	30.5	28.0	26.7	23.9	21.9	21.7
Italy	43.0	42.8	43.0	43.2	na	na
Netherlands	37.0	32.9	30.5	28.4	27.9	25.2
Belgium	44.0	45.6	42.6	40.2	37.1	36.3
Luxembourg	70.4	69.2	59.4	57.2	64.6	na
UK	92.4	87.9	82.1	83.6	74.1	66.7
Irish Republic	172.5	168.9	168.7	165.9	159.2	157.1
Denmark	52.6	50.0	47.1	44.9	43.9	53.5
Total Nine	**55.2**	**53.7**	**51.3**	**51.0**	**47.7**	**45.7**

	Semi-skimmed					
	1987	1988	1989	1990	1991	1992
Germany	13.1	13.7	14.4	15.2	18.9	19.8
France	44.9	47.2	49.5	50.1	53.8	53.4
Italy	33.0	33.2	32.4	32.6	na	na
Netherlands	42.7	44.8	49.0	48.7	49.6	50.8
Belgium	19.0	18.7	19.6	22.0	23.2	26.6
Luxembourg	11.0	11.0	15.4	19.9	19.5	na
UK	16.9	20.1	25.2	27.6	33.5	41.0
Irish Republic	na	na	na	na	na	na
Denmark	51.4	52.5	54.8	56.2	56.4	56.6
Total Nine	**27.3**	**28.8**	**30.7**	**31.2**	**34.6**	**37.3**

	Skimmed and Buttermilk					
	1987	1988	1989	1990	1991	1992
Germany	3.1	3.1	3.4	3.6	3.7	3.8
France	2.7	3.1	3.3	3.1	3.0	3.0
Italy	3.5	3.6	2.7	2.8	na	na
Netherlands	11.5	11.8	13.5	12.9	12.6	12.7
Belgium	8.7	7.8	7.3	7.6	6.2	6.0
Luxembourg	1.4	1.4	2.1	2.0	2.0	na
UK	14.1	14.4	15.2	10.0	10.7	10.7
Irish Republic	10.2	15.1	15.9	18.2	22.4	23.0
Denmark	20.7	20.5	20.7	19.5	18.7	18.3
Total Nine	**6.6**	**6.8**	**7.0**	**6.6**	**6.6**	**6.6**

	Total Milk					
	1987	1988	1989	1990	1991	1992
Germany	70.1	71.9	70.7	70.8	69.3	71.7
France	78.1	78.3	79.5	77.1	78.7	78.1
Italy	79.5	79.6	78.1	78.6	78.0	77.4
Netherlands	91.2	89.5	93.0	90.0	89.1	88.7
Belgium	71.7	72.1	69.5	69.8	66.5	68.9
Luxembourg	82.8	81.6	76.9	79.1	86.1	86.2
UK	123.4	122.4	122.5	121.2	118.3	118.3
Irish Republic	182.7	184.0	184.6	184.1	180.1	180.1
Denmark	124.7	123.0	122.6	120.6	119.0	118.4
Total Nine	**89.1**	**89.3**	**89.0**	**88.8**	**86.0**	**86.4**

Source: EC Dairy Facts and Figures 1993 (MMB)

In the UK, doorstep delivery has always been held responsible for high liquid milk consumption levels. This has fallen substantially, but still accounts for over 50% of total liquid milk consumption. The price differential between doorstep and supermarket milk has widened from 2p-3p/pint in 1985 to 4p-6p in 1990 to nearly 10p in 1992. This growing price gap is held to be responsible for the decline in doorstep delivery but changes in lifestyle may also be relevant in considering what is the most appropriate distribution system for liquid milk in a modern society.

The Butter Market

Butter is part of what is generally known as the yellow fats market, which also includes margarine and more recent product developments, low and reduced fat spreads and dairy spreads. Consumption of butter in the UK has been in more or less continuous decline since the mid 1960's and is now only a quarter of its level of 30 years ago. At first, the switch was to margarine, but in more recent years that too has been in decline and the beneficiaries are the newer soft spread vegetable oil products and elements of vegetable fat and butter. Similar trends have been observed in other Member States (Table 6.2)

While health concerns have been a major factor in the long-term decline of butter consumption (although there is now some evidence of a reverse of this trend), lack of convenience is another issue and major producers have been trying to develop and market a product that is spreadable when cold. So far, only New Zealand has been successful, with 'Anchor Spreadable'. It sells at a premium of around 40%, but its availability is restricted.

Packet butter is priced at the retail level taking into account not only the cost of the raw material (bulk butter), but also the price of margarine. Butter is also a 'known value item' as far as retailers are concerned and, as a result, sometimes used as a loss leader to attract customers into stores. In 1993-94, butter was sold at 39p per 250 grams by discount chains such as Kwiksave, NETTO and ALDI for over a year. This represented a discount below the intervention price of up to £600 per tonne.

Manufacturing use of butter - ice cream, bakery, processed foods, etc. - now accounts for around 25% of total UK butter consumption. EC subsidies are payable on much of this usage: 48,000 tonnes in 1991 and 34,000 tonnes in 1992 were successfully tendered for under Regulation 570 in the UK; 1993 will be a year of record usage with 41,000 tonnes tendered for in the first nine months.

Table 6.2:   Consumption of Butter and Margarine kg per capita per annum)

Country			Butter			
	1987	1988	1989	1990	1991	1992
Germany	8.1	8.2	7.4	6.5	6.9	6.8
France	7.2	7.0	6.7	6.5	6.5	6.5
Italy	2.3	2.2	2.4	2.0	2.1	2.0
Netherlands	3.8	3.8	3.4	3.4	3.4	3.4
Belgium	7.1	8.6	7.9	7.8	7.0	6.8
Luxembourg	9.1	7.7	7.0	6.3	5.8	5.8
UK	4.5	5.1	3.8	3.5	3.4	3.5
Eire	5.8	4.6	3.8	3.5	3.4	3.9
Denmark	7.7	7.6	7.1	6.5	5.4	5.0
Greece	0.9	0.9	0.9	0.9	1.1	1.1
Total Ten	5.4	5.5	5.0	4.6	4.8	4.7
			Margarine			
	1987	1988	1989	1990	1991	1992
Germany	7.8	7.4	7.4	7.9	8.2	8.0
France	3.9	3.9	3.8	3.8	3.7	3.3.6
Italy	na	na	na	na	na	na
Netherlands	13.6	13.1	12.8	12.9	12.5	12.3
Belgium	12.7	12.8	12.6	na	na	na
Luxembourg	12.7	12.8	12.6	7.9	8.0	na
UK	7.5	7.2	7.1	6.5	6.6	6.5
Eire	4.2	4.3	4.5	4.3	4.1	3.9
Denmark	16.8	17.0	15.8	14.5	13.6	13.7
Greece	na	na	na	na	1.5	1.5
Total Ten	5.6	5.5	5.4	5.0	5.9	5.8

Source: Dairy Industry Newsletter

The Cheese Market

Consumption of cheese in the UK grew steadily between 1945 and the late 1980's, since when it appears to have stabilised, or, according to AGB research, be growing slowly. The household sector of the market, which absorbs just over 60% of total consumption, grew less than 1% in the past twelve months, according to AGB.

Consumption in the UK remains low by EU standards (Table 6.3), so in principle there is considerable scope for growth. The UK (with Ireland) is unique in the EU with its focus on traditional hard pressed cheeses (Cheddar still accounts for more than half the total cheese consumption in the UK).

It follows that UK cheese manufacturing is still very traditionally oriented. Cheese stocks statistics collected by the MAFF are a key statistic monitored by the UK cheese industry. Cheddar stocks attract the most interest since these are volatile, containing, as they do, both imported and domestic cheese, and cheese ready for sale and undergoing maturing. As the structure of demand changes, with rising mature Cheddar sales, so cheese has to be matured longer and stocks have to be larger.

Table 6.3:   Consumption of Cheese (kg per capita per annum)

Country	Total cheese					
	1987	1988	1989	1990	1991	1992
Germany	16.8	17.4	18.1	18.5	17.5	18.2
France	21.5	22.0	22.3	22.8	22.8	22.9
Italy	17.5	17.9	17.8	18.6	20.0	20.1
Netherlands	14.9	14.7	14.8	15.0	15.2	16.2
Belgium	15.7	15.8	16.5	17.7	18.0	18.9
Luxembourg	10.1	10.6	12.9	17.1	16.3	16.3
UK	7.5	8.2	8.1	8.6	8.5	8.9
Irish Republic	4.9	5.0	5.3	5.5	5.6	5.7
Denmark	12.6	12.7	14.2	14.8	15.3	15.5
Greece	22.0	22.1	22.1	22.5	22.0	23.0
Total Ten	15.8	16.2	16.5	17.0	17.1	17.5

Source: Dairy Industry Newsletter

The catering industry, which includes everything from five star hotels to burger bars, and hospitals to prisons, normally takes nearly a quarter of total cheese sales but this has declined slightly with the effects of recession. The food manufacturing industry, which absorbs nearly 15%, is the fastest growing market for cheese. This growth is being driven by the increased demand for prepared and convenience foods, particularly pizzas, quiches and vegetable grills.

The industrial and catering sectors used a total of 115,000 tonnes in 1992, or about a quarter of the total market (catering accounted for 70,000 tonnes and the industrial sector 45,000 tonnes). This market could grow by more than 20% to over 140,000 tonnes within five years.

Cheddar accounts for the biggest share (60%) of the UK catering and industrial market, followed by Mozzarella (nearly 25%) and processed cheese. It is forecast that the total UK market for Mozzarella will grow by 60% to nearly 50,000 tonnes by 1997. Trade sources suggest that this will be an under-estimate.

Fresh Dairy Products

Fresh dairy products comprise cream, yoghurts, drinking yoghurts, fromage frais, traditional desserts, cottage cheese, salads and (for definitional purposes) usually ice cream. This is the youngest sector of the market and the least well-documented.

Fresh dairy products are the most dynamic sector of the UK dairy industry (except for Mozzarella and industrial cheese). The total value of sales at the retail level (excluding ice cream) increased by 12% in 1992 to an estimated £1,045m, with total volume sold up 10% to 457,000 tonnes. The value of sales of yoghurt increased 9% last year, and this increase was a much lower than in the five years before. The value of sales of fromage frais increased 14% in 1993, and traditional desserts by no less than 33%.

Table 6.4:   Fresh Chilled Dairy Products - 1992 Market

		Total*	Yoghurt	Fromage Frais	Traditional Desserts
Total value of sales		£883m	£485m	£120m	£154m
change on year		+12%	+9%	+14%	+33%
MARKET SHARES					
	Northern Foods/ Eden Vale	28%	24%	20%	33%
	Unigate/St Ivel	17%	17%	12%	18%
	Müller (Germany)	12%	18%	-	6%
	Raines	8%	10%	5%	5%
	Yeo Valley	8%	12%	-	4%
	Nestlé/Chambourcy (Switzerland)	7%	2%	6%	28%
	Onken (Germany)	3%	5%	2%	-
	BG Foods	3%	4%	-	4%
	Danone (France)	2%	1%	7%	-
	MD Foods (Denmark)	1%	2%	-	-
	Yoplait/Dairy Crest (Fr/UK)	1%	-	17%	-
	Besnier (France)	1%	-	14%	-
	Sonoble (France)	1%	-	12%	-

Source Nielsen Audit, and estimates
*Excludes cream, cottage cheese and salads

Yoghurt

Yoghurt may be a lively and growing market but UK consumption of around 5kg per head is still well behind the level of consumption in the Netherlands, Germany, Denmark and France, where 12kg and 21kg per head levels are rising even faster.

Müller, with its 'Fruit Corner', 'Müller Light' and 'Müllerice' varieties, is shown by AGB research to be the current brand leader in the UK market. Second is Ski, followed by Sainsbury's 'Own Label'. Market shares are volatile in this innovative market, for example Ski moved from a 27%

market share in 1989 to 15.5% in 1992 while Müller moved from 4% to 18% (Müller, in fact, claim 22%).

Yoghurt imports to the UK grew sharply in the 1980's, but increased only marginally in 1992 to 93,000 tonnes. A significant factor here is the replacement of imports of Müller yoghurts by domestic production at the group's major factory in Shropshire. In 1992 imports of yoghurt represented 20% of the total UK market; this is now dropping sharply, as a direct result of devaluation, as local production replaces imports. But this has changed dramatically with a sharp increase in raw material milk prices following devaluation (and the abolition of the milk boards in late 1994). Major UK yoghurt manufacturers have, since then, experienced unprecedented competition from imports.

Ice Cream

Like yoghurt, UK consumption of ice cream lags well behind its continental neighbours. Estimated at 0.3 kgs/head per year in the UK, France has levels over 6kgs, Italy over 5kgs and Germany over 3 kgs.

In 1994 the total market was valued at £886 million, an increase of over 11% on 1993. The retail market can be split into three sectors; take home (£480 million and up 5.6% in 1993), impulse purchases (£289 million and up 20.0%) and soft scooping (£117m and up 14.0%).

Within the take home sector, own label accounts for 44% and Wall's 32%. Growth has been in Multipacks (£185.8 million - up 19% on 1993), premium/luxury ice cream (£110.1 - up 3%) and complete desserts (£41.2 million - up 9%). Standard type ice creams (i.e. vanilla tubs etc.) have fallen 8% to £142.4 million in 1994.

The impulse sector is made up of choc ices (£121.5 million in 1994), cones (£37.5 million), childrens (£66.5 million) and refreshment (£52 million). In total, including other types, the impulse market was worth £289 million, with Walls having a 66.5% share. Mars have 22% of the market and Nestlé have 8.6%. Own label products do not feature significantly in the impulse market.

Cream

With the falling EU value of butterfat, cream is now a by-product in the UK. Cream from low-fat milks (and standardising milk for manufacturing purposes) is used for the fresh cream market, butter-making, making desserts and for export. For butter-making there is a floor value linked to the intervention price of butter (i.e. around 1.10p to

1.20p per litre of 40% cream in 1993). Exported bulk cream is valued similarly as a commodity product. In the retail, catering and bakery markets varying higher prices prevail but packing and distribution costs are much greater.

Desserts

Trifles, mousses, cheesecakes and rice puddings - the list of dairy-based pot desserts is long and still growing. No accurate measure of the size of this market is available but it is probably between 30,000 and 40,000 tonnes a year or one-eighth the size of the UK yoghurt market. It is still growing but probably at a slower rate than the 15% to 20% per annum seen up to two years ago.

Fromage Frais

One of the success stories of the past decade is this quark-type cheese which, like yoghurt many years before, did not take off in the UK market until someone filled it up with fruit to make a product owing little to its origins. From virtually nothing in the mid-1980's, the market has soared to around 50,000 tonnes per annum at present. Sainsbury's, which gave the product lift-off with an own label product, is still the brand leader but there are now numerous brand imitators such as YOPLAIT's 'Petit Filous'.

The Policy Background for Dairying

Dairy farming in the EU has been among the most highly protected agricultural sectors, subject to the usual raft of support instruments e.g. intervention pricing, variable levies, export subsidies and, since 1984, production quotas. Additionally, individual sub-sectors have been subject to a complicated array of special measures such as Christmas and welfare butter payments, quotas on New Zealand butter imports, and regional *appellations* for the manufacture of certain cheeses. Many detailed descriptions of the support mechanisms exist so this section gives only a brief overview of the most important elements[2].

The principal price support mechanism in the EU is the intervention price, calculated for the two (non-water) milk components, butter and skimmed milk powder. Until 1987, intervention was an open-ended

---

2   For example, see CAP working notes, Milk and Dairy Products (Annual) European
     Commission, DG VI

commitment provided minimum quality standards and other specifications were met, but since March 1987, in order to reduce sales to intervention and to lower real price-support levels, strict limits for automatic intervention have been imposed, beyond which a tendering system operates. This has reduced effective intervention prices to around 90% to 95% of official intervention prices. Production purely for intervention has become less attractive than in the 1970's and 1980's. Nevertheless butter and skimmed milk powder buying-in prices maintain their considerable margins over world prices as a result of the operation of variable levies on imports. In 1992 they were respectively around 100% and 60% higher than world fob prices.

In the UK there has been another dimension to policy, namely the existence for over 60 years of the Milk Marketing Boards, and latterly, the dismantling of these Boards and new voluntary marketing structures created. With the demise of the statutory bodies, changes in the pricing of milk took place. Previously prices were worked out on an end-use basis. Milk used for low value-added products, such as butter, was priced lower than that used for higher value products such as yoghurt, fresh milk etc. For butter and skimmed milk, prices were worked out by formula which was based on average selling prices and costs. Trade sources suggest that this allowed inefficient processors to survive and gave no incentive to cost reduction. In the new system, brought in with the removal of the statutory Boards, dairy companies now have to buy their milk irrespective of end use. In theory this should encourage a shift in production towards higher value-added products and the implied restructuring of the dairy processing sector began in 1994.

One feature of the milk marketing reorganisation in the UK is that the new voluntary farmer co-operatives have obtained dominant shares of the market. 'Milk Marque' in England and Wales, 'Scottish Milk' in Scotland, and 'United Dairy Farmers' in Northern Ireland all have very large shares of their respective markets. The European Commission in Brussels made it clear it would have preferred to see a greater number of regional co-operatives, and was only prepared to sanction the new voluntary co-ops for a trial two-year period.

The unexpected success of the new co-operatives in signing up farmers and the prospect of an aggressive, market dominant milk selling co-operative encouraged the government to install new safeguards to inhibit the market power of Milk Marque. The government made clear that it expected the Office of Fair Trading, the Monopolies and Mergers Commission and the competition authorities at the European Commission in Brussels to ensure fair play.

Most milk processing companies, certainly all the bigger ones, wanted to source milk direct from farmers, to ensure security and continuity, and also so as not to have to rely on the Boards' successors, especially as Milk Marque made it clear that it would try to obtain the highest possible milk price for farmers. In their attempts to source milk direct, the dairy companies offered premium prices, up to 26 pence/litre and more, i.e. nearly 20% higher than milk producers were getting prior to deregulation. Other incentive bonuses were offered. By the summer of 1994 a number of milk producer groups had been set up to negotiate direct with processors. The feeling was that these groups would either be able to negotiate better milk prices than Milk Marque and the other successor bodies would be able to deliver, or that the competition authorities would ensure that the successor co-operatives would not be able to exploit their market power. There was also a widespread assumption that the successor co-operatives would not survive in the long run.

Milk Quotas

The introduction of EU quotas in 1984 had the most profound effect on the dairy sector, halting and reversing the upward trend in production and EU milk surpluses. Figure 6.2 shows the distribution of quotas among member states in 1993-94. In the UK the national quota was allocated first to dairies, then to individual farmers. Milk quota in the UK may be sold or leased within the country, but sale and leasing of quotas across national boundaries is not allowed, though the UK Government appears to be in favour of such transfers between Member States.

Figure 6.2:   EU Milk Quotas 1993-94

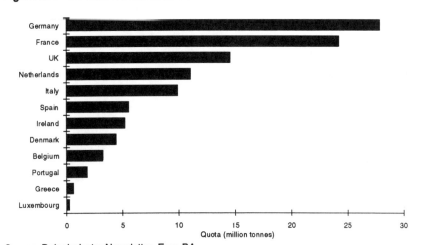

Source : Dairy Industry Newsletter, Euro PA
*extra quota for 1993-94 was awarded to Italy (900,000t), Spain (500,000t) and Greece (100,000t).

The overall EC milk quota was increased by 2.3% in 1993-94, mainly to accommodate significantly increased allocations for Italy, Spain and Greece. The Commission does not expect this to result in any actual increase in production because the allocations (to 'compensate' for initial 'miscalculation' of actual national milk production) have been provided only on condition that quota limitations are now policed. Large and subsidised quota buy-out programmes were announced in 1994 for Italy and Spain.

The Supply of Milk and Dairy Products

Milk Production

UK dairy farmers produced thirteen and a half billion litres of milk in 1993/94. Table 6.5 shows the steady reduction in production that quotas have induced in the UK over the last decade. Quotas were originally fixed at 1981 milk production plus 1%. In the event, a panic reaction by many UK milk producers resulted in production in the first year being 232m litres (1.5%) under quota.

Table 6.5:   UK Milk Production

Milk Year	Production	Compared with quota	
	(m litres)	+/- m litres	%
1983-84	16,435	-	-
1984-85	15,240	-232	-1.52
1985-86	15,289	+8	0.05
1986-87	15,363	+96	0.62
1987-88	14,448	+56	0.39
1988-89	14,023	+78	0.56
1989-90	14,133	?*	
1990-91	13,969	+35	0.25
1991-92	13,628	+15	0.11
1992-93	13,440	-11	-0.08
1993-94	13,570	+100**	0.74

Source : Dairy Industry Newsletter; *Never finalised ;**provisional.

Within two years of the quota regime being introduced, the system started to break down because the super-levy system was not an effective deterrent against producers exceeding their individual quota. But in that year the system was revised, and penalties significantly increased. Since then, production has stuck fairly close to annual quota, which has been progressively cut back. In all, since quotas were introduced, UK milk sales off farms have been reduced by about 18%. Quota reductions have had a clear impact on the milk processing sectors, particularly butter and skimmed milk powder. Together with tighter intervention conditions, quotas have reduced supplies and created excess capacity in some parts of the dairy processing sector.

A major problem for the UK milk processing industry has been the seasonal variation in milk production, from a peak supply in May to a trough in August or September (November in Scotland and Northern Ireland). Furthermore, the operation of the milk pricing formula has meant that there has been no incentive for processors to make their operations more seasonally efficient because if they remain 'inefficient', i.e. their costs remain high, dairy farmers have to pay the price of inefficiency via lower manufacturing milk prices. A consequence was that, for many years, the Milk Boards, especially the MMB (E&W), have resorted to extreme measures to iron out seasonal variations in milk supply.

Figure 6.3:   Milk Flows in the United Kingdom 1992-93 (million litres)

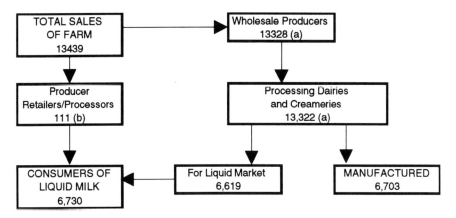

Source : MMB 1994, Euro PA

(a) Difference due to measurement adjustment

(b) Milk of own production sold liquid to consumers as whole milk

In the late 1980's the MMB (E&W) significantly increased milk price incentives and penalties to persuade producers to change calving patterns in order to improve the seasonal balance of milk supply. Producers were paid a bonus of more than 5p/litre to produce milk in the seasonal trough and received a penalty of more than 2.5p/litre for milk supplied in May, a price 'spread' of around 8p per litre. The scheme worked very well. In 1987, May milk production was 50% more than in the trough month; by 1993 that had dropped to under 5%.

Despite its success the scheme was abandoned. At the end of 1992 the MMB announced that as from April 1994 (when the statutory milk boards were due to end) the summer incentive would be halved, to 3p per litre, and the May 'penalty' would be slightly reduced, cutting the 'spread' from over 8p to under 6p. Presumably the MMB judged that such a wide spread of seasonal prices would leave it vulnerable in the 'free market'.

Seasonality of milk production is significantly less pronounced in the north of England than in the south. Hence, producers in the north are more likely to sell milk outside the confines of the MMB's successor - Milk Marque: northern producers are better able to meet the more level milk supply needs of the liquid milk companies. Also, neither Scotland nor Northern Ireland ever operated an influential seasonal pricing schedule.

Producer Numbers

There has been a steady decline in the number of UK dairy farmers since 1950, as shown by Figure 6.4. From a peak of 196,000 in 1950 numbers fell to under 37,000 in 1993, though the rate of decline is tailing off. Dairy farmer numbers fell 23% in the 1950's and 34% in the 1960's. The sharpest rate of decline was in the 1970's - down 44% over the decade. In the 1980's, numbers were down 27%, and in the 1990's the annual rate of decline is around 2% per annum..

Figure 6.4:   UK Milk Producer Numbers

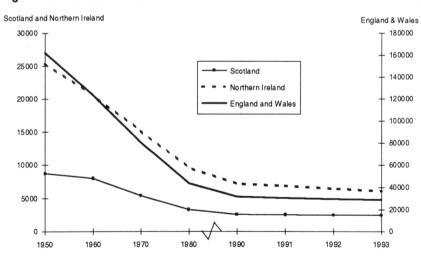

Source : Dairy Industry Newsletter, Euro PA

In addition to the 35,000 milk producers in the UK, probably up to 4,000 are 'non-producing quota-holders' (NPQHs) who do not milk cows but earn a living from leasing out the quota. The EU, in 1992, noted that NPQHs should be phased out but the UK authorities have told Brussels that NPQHs provide a pool of leased quota, especially for tenants who cannot buy quota without risking it being lost to their landlords.

Of the total number of registered producers, close to 1,400 are producer retailers or processors, nearly all of them in England and Wales; this number has dropped steadily, from over 8,000 in 1970.

The average size of UK dairy herds has increased steadily, even since the introduction of milk quotas (which was expected to stabilise the situation). Between 1982 and 1992, average herd size increased from 65 to 72 cows in England and Wales, from 88 to 92 cows in Scotland, and from 31 to 41 cows in Northern Ireland.

Milk Yields and Constituent Parts

A steady increase in average milk yield per cow was interrupted by the arrival of milk quotas, as can be seen in Figure 6.5 . Many farmers opted for less intensive production systems, with overall output 'capped' by quotas. However, with individual farmers now able to expand again, via quota buying and leasing, the average cow yield increase has resumed, and average herd yields reached record levels in 1993, and appear still to be rising.

Figure 6.5:   Milk Yields in the UK (kg per cow)

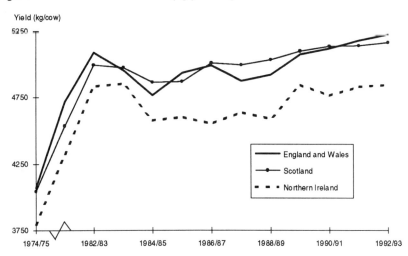

Source: Dairy Facts and Figures.
*Provisional

The average butterfat level in UK milk has also increased steadily, and is now close to 4.1%. Average protein content is close to 3.3%, and appears to move in line with butterfat levels, which makes it very difficult to breed for high protein and low butterfat levels. As the earlier part of this chapter noted, however, these product attributes are what the market demands.

Producer Prices for Milk

In the years before deregulation the Scottish MMBs have paid the highest milk prices to producers, primarily because virtually no butter is made in Scotland, and butter is usually the lowest-earning end product. Northern Ireland has traditionally paid the lowest price, mainly because only about 17% of milk in Northern Ireland goes into the higher priced liquid milk market. In the past ten years the Scottish MMB has paid an average milk price just over 4% better than the England & Wales Board, and the latter has paid an average of just over 7% more than the Northern Ireland Board (see Figure 6.6). However the difference between the payouts narrowed substantially in 1992-93, with the Scottish 'premium' dropping to 2% and the Northern Ireland 'discount' dropping to 3%. In the latter case a contributing factor might have been the growing element of competition in Northern Ireland, with Strathroy Milk Marketing accounting for nearly 10% of all milk in the province last year. Trade sources suggest that Strathroy Milk Marketing paid about 0.5p per litre more than the Northern Ireland MMB in 1992-93.

Figure 6.6: UK Milk Producer Prices (pence/litre)

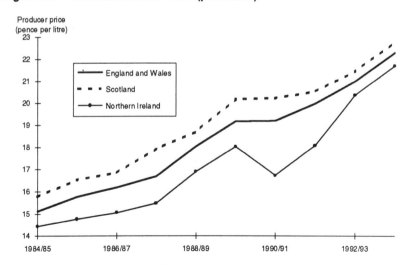

Source: Dairy Industry Newsletter, Euro PA
Note : 1993/94 figures are provisional

For several years UK milk producer prices were well below most of those paid in other EU Member States as shown in Table 6.6.

Table 6.6:   EU Milk Producer Prices (ECU/100 Kgs)

Country	1987	1988	1989	1990	1991	1992
Italy	32.85	33.00	34.53	34.48	33.72	33.47
Denmark	26.01	28.25	29.26	28.27	27.70	27.12
Netherlands	24.88	26.72	27.85	25.21	25.40	26.03
Germany (West)	24.58	26.47	28.65	26.43	25.42	25.71
Luxembourg	25.23	26.04	29.10	29.21	26.11	25.13
United Kingdom	23.49	24.55	25.05	23.95	23.41	23.72
France	23.44	23.81	24.72	24.09	23.24	23.62
Belgium	23.16	24.45	26.22	22.82	22.26	22.76
Irish Republic	21.50	23.61	26.06	22.46	21.30	22.54

Source: EC Dairy Facts and Figures 1993, MMB

With UK entry into the EC, and lately with the devaluation of Sterling, the liquid premium charged by the Milk Boards has narrowed substantially. Over 30 years ago, the premium reached as much as 400% but had been whittled away to 5% by mid-1993 (1.24p per litre over the higher manufacturing values).

The pricing policy that led to this is discussed in the next section. The position has been transformed since the autumn of 1991, when a new, informal system of pricing manufacturing milk was introduced. This gave producer prices a considerable boost. In addition, due to a variety of depressing market and price support developments, milk prices on the Continent have tended to decline in the past two years. The intense competition among processors to secure milk supplies and the restructuring of the milk pricing system is expected to give UK milk producer prices significant support in 1994-95, but whether this can be maintained in the face of declining EU milk prices is questionable.

Milk Pricing and Allocation Among Markets

Until 1991 the system which determined the allocation of raw milk among its alternative uses and established retail and producer prices has been far from a free market. Although that system has now been dismantled, its impact on the development of new products, investment and capacity of the dairy processing sector is still seen in the UK market. Prices to alternative end-users were determined by the Milk Boards first in 'consultation' with the Dairy Trades Federation, representing processors, through the 'Joint Committee'; later the Joint Committee became a decision-making body. These various bodies behaved in line with the principles of a price discriminating monopolist, setting the highest price in the market with least elastic demand (liquid milk).

Prices for butter and skimmed milk powder were set according to a formula-pricing scheme (CATFI - Common Approach To Financial Information) based on selling prices minus allowed costs (including a 'fair' return on capital). It was this system which permitted inefficient processors with excess capacity to remain in business, and placed the burden of adjustment on farmers, who are paid a pool (weighted average) price, and on consumers who were denied a range of dairy products at competitive prices.

Under the new milk marketing scheme, in theory, milk prices for all uses will be the same and "the market" will allocate product among alternative uses. This has significant implications for milk allocation in the UK and it would be expected that the range of dairy products and dairy processing companies will alter as producers and processors adjust to the new situation.

Trade in Dairy Products

The UK dairy trade deficit has been growing steadily in recent years(Figure 6.7). The large devaluation of Sterling between September 1992 and April 1993 (-23%; the biggest devaluation since the Second World War) may help to 'correct' the position although there are important constraints on UK processors reacting to the new set of exchange rates in terms of availability of capacity and raw milk supplies.

Figure 6.7: UK Dairy Trade Balance

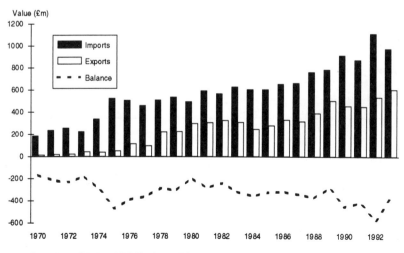

Source Food from Britain, CSO Business Monitors MQ20 and MM20, Euro PA

The UK had a negative balance of trade in dairy products with all countries in the EC except the Netherlands in 1992 (Table 6.7), and this negative balance of trade with the EC worsened by 38% in 1992.

Table 6.7:   UK Dairy Trade Balance with Main Trading Partners, 1992

(£m)	Exports to	Imports from	Balance
EC Member States	373	972	-599
Ireland	45	373	-328
Germany	44	160	-116
Denmark	6	115	-109
France	82	136	-54
Netherlands	130	81	+49
Rest of the world	155	165	+10
Total	528	1,137	-609

Source : Dairy Industry Newsletter

Whilst the UK's dairy trade deficit is increasing in value terms, it is decreasing in volume terms, which is even worse in a qualitative sense: i.e. this implies that the UK has been exporting low-value bulk commodities (often requiring the assistance of large, and increasingly vulnerable, EU export subsidies) and importing higher-value products. In 1992 the average value of UK dairy exports was £910/tonne whereas the average value of imports was £1,560/tonne.

Table 6.8:   UK Dairy Trade Balance by Commodity, 1992

(£m)	Exports	Imports	Balance
Butter	98	284	-186
Cheese	102	555	-453
Cheddar	47	230	-183
Other cheeses	55	325	-270
Milk powders	187	46	+141
Yoghurt	4	84	-80
Chocolate crumb	12	54	-42
Cream	45	5	+40
Condensed milk	31	7	+24
Liquid milk	16	29	-13
Other dairy products	34	72	-38
Totals	528	1,137	-609

Source : Dairy industry Newsletter

UK cheese imports come under three main categories: Cheddar; speciality (or Continental); and processed. Exports focus on Cheddar, either as table cheese or for processing. Total UK Cheddar imports in 1992 increased by 35% to 101,000 tonnes, while exports fell by 20% to under 22,000 tonnes. The average price of imports was close to £2,300/ tonne while the average price of exports was under £2,100/tonne.

Table 6.9: UK Cheese Imports and Exports, 1991-92 (tonnes)

CHEESE	Imports		Exports	
	1991	1992	1991	1992
Cheddar	75,600	101,000	25,000	21,718
Territorials	70	360	9,000	6,700
Blue Vein	5,700	5,700	1,200	1,100
Processed	29,100	33,300	5,200	5,200
Grated & for processing	7,300	7,400	2,200	2,900
Speciality	74,500	84,000	8,000	10,600

Source : Dairy Industry Newsletter

Ireland is the main Cheddar shipper to the UK and boosted its trade by some 20,000 tonnes to 66,000 tonnes as Sterling devalued, and prior to the disappearance of Monetary Compensatory Amounts on January 1, 1992. UK imports of German Cheddar totalled 12,000 tonnes in 1992, with small shipments from Belgium, Denmark and the Netherlands.

Australia (2,500 tonnes), Canada (4,000 tonnes) and New Zealand (7,500 tonnes) retain a toehold in the UK market under a previous GATT deal and these suppliers hope for more in the future under the increased market access agreed in the Uruguay Round.

Processed cheese imports (up 15% in 1992 to over 33,000 tonnes), overwhelmingly from Kraft, are mainly from Belgium and Germany, while speciality cheese imports are from a number of suppliers but with France, Netherlands, Germany, Denmark and Italy (in descending order of importance) dominating.

Cream imports are minimal but exports take about 10% of UK manufacture, and have grown relatively fast in recent years.

Table 6.10: UK Trade in Cream

	1991	1992
Imports	3,140	2,800
Exports	37,300	40,400

Source : Dairy Industry Newsletter

The majority of exports are in bulk, with fat content between 21% and 45%. They are mainly to France and Belgium, and are mainly used for making butteroil and in food manufacture. However, given the changes in milk marketing and pricing from 1994, the pattern of milk utilisation for cream, and the flows of cream for export, are facing a substantial shake-up.

Milk Processing

The Dairy Processing Industry

It is estimated that there are around 300 primary milk buyers in the UK, but some 'sell milk on', which means that there are probably nearly 400 primary milk processors in the UK (nearly 300 in England and Wales, 100 in Scotland and 25 in Northern Ireland) processing close to 13,500m litres of raw milk. Nearly three-quarters of these are small liquid milk dairies, including farm milk bottlers (producer-processors and producer-retailers). In addition, there are also probably more than 200 farmhouse cheesemakers who process only the milk from their own farms.

Table 6.11:   Utilisation of Milk by UK Processors, 1992-93

	England & Wales	Scotland	Northern Ireland	UK
Total (m/litres)	11,200	1,150	1,250	13,500
of which:				
Liquid milk	52%	54%	17%	48%
Cheese	20%	30%	26%	22%
Butter/SMP*	17%	3%	25%	16%
Condensed/Chocolate	3%	12%	-	3%
WMP	2%	-	26%	4%
Other	6%	1%	6%	7%

Source : Dairy Industry Newsletter
* Just over 40% of this is for the production of 'value-added' products made with the
SMP/protein element of the milk, with butter production being, in effect, the by-product.

There are only 22 companies which process more than 100m litres of milk a year, or just over 80% of the total, as shown in Table 6.12. Of the top 22, seven are controlled by non-UK interests (MD Foods, Nestlé, Avonmore, Waterford, Golden Vale, Müller and Dansco Tolona) which between them now control almost 20% of the total, a share which has grown very quickly in recent years.

The top 13 processors, Northern Foods, Unigate, Dairy Crest, MD Foods (Denmark), CWS, Nestlé (Switzerland), The Cheese Company, Avonmore (Ireland), Scottish Pride, Waterford (Ireland), Dromona (Northern Ireland), Golden Vale and the Midlands Co-operative Society, process between them just under 75% of the total UK milk supply.

Northern Foods is now the largest UK liquid milk processor by a significant margin, with about 24% of the total national market. The biggest change to UK liquid milk market shares in the past year was

Dairy Crest's disposal of about one-third of its total business for just under £50m (about one-third of the business it bought from Unigate five years before for £150m). This reduced Dairy Crest's share of the national liquid milk market from around 15% to 10%. The biggest part of the business was sold to Avonmore (Perry Barr/Hereford, 180m litres), the next biggest to MD Foods (Bamber Bridge, 110m litres) and a smaller part (Marshfield, just over 30m litres) was sold to Unigate, which has established itself firmly in number two spot, with 15% of the total UK market for liquid milk. MD Foods has 10% and Avonmore 6%.

Table 6.12:   Top UK Milk Processing Companies

Company	Milk Processed (m/litres)	Turnover* (£m)
Dairy Crest	1,500	800
Northern Foods	2,000	2,000
Unigate	1,600	1,600
ACC	750	600
MD Foods	650	350
Nestlé	500	1,800
The Cheese Company	620	300
Avonmore	650	200
Scottish Pride	350	150
Waterford	400	160
Midlands Co-op	220	600
Dromona (UDF)	200	80
Golden Vale	250	18
Fane Valley	160	60
Cricket St Thomas	150	100
Cadbury	150	1,600 est
Lord Rayleigh's	160	70
Raines	150	130
Müller	100	100
Robert Wiseman	220	100
Dansco Tolona	150	50
Lancashire Dairies	130	50

Source : Dairy Industry Newsletter
*Only in the UK

In anticipation of the 'free market' in milk in the UK the major processors have been rationalising and regionalising their operations at breakneck speed over the past two years. It should be noted, however, that there continues to be intense competition between the liquid milk dairies (and there remain many small operators, some of them extremely efficient and profitable), but increasingly that competition is for sales to supermarkets; local doorstep monopolies are more and more the 'norm'.

Dairy Crest, for example (as well as selling off parts of its operations to reduce its debts in advance of the flotation of the company) is concentrating its doorstep liquid milk business in East Anglia and London. Unigate now processes milk only south of a line across Pembrokeshire to north London. Northern Foods' liquid milk business cuts a swathe across Yorkshire and Lancashire and down to north-west London, to be served by its large new dairy at Ruislip, and into the south west. The ACC's liquid milk business is heavily concentrated in the north-east of England down to the north Midlands. MD Foods is also concentrated in the North and in north London. The main UK dairies are shown in Table 6.13.

Table 6.13:   Output of the main UK Liquid Milk Dairies 1994 (estimates)

Company	Million Litres
Total	6,600
Northern Foods (incl NI)	1,500
Unigate	950
MD Foods	600
Dairy Crest	600
ACC	500
Avonmore (Ire)	400
Waterford Foods (Ire)	230
Robert Wiseman (Scotland)	220
Midlands Co-op	200
Scottish Pride	180
Lord Rayleigh's	150
Cricket St Thomas	130
Lancashire Dairies	130
Southern Co-op Society	90
Golden Vale (Ireland)	90
Plymouth & South Devon	90
Others	600

Source : Dairy Industry Newsletter

Butter

The UK production of butter fell from over 250,000 tonnes in 1983 to 100,000 tonnes in 1991. The dramatic drop in butter manufacture has necessitated an enormous rationalisation of production, and many plants have been closed in recent years, mainly by Dairy Crest. This has largely been done via the 'Rationalisation of Facilities' programmes.

As described earlier, the old pricing system (CATFI) guaranteed processors a target rate of profit from manufacturing butter. This meant there was no incentive to close plants as they became less cost-effective; the price they paid for milk was simply reduced. To force greater throughput efficiency the MMB (E&W) had to subsidise plant closures (at a cost of £132m) in the past five years. The subsidy programme was widely criticised, but it did succeed in reducing buttermaking capacity and producer milk prices did benefit.

UK butter manufacture is now highly efficient, concentrated at little more than half a dozen major factories, with close to 90% of production in the hands of Dairy Crest (over 40%), Unigate, the CWS/ACC, Northern Foods and four manufacturers in Northern Ireland (a combined total of about 50%), as indicated in Table 6.14.

Table 6.14:   Capacity of the Main UK Butter Makers *

Producer	Tonnes/Year
Total	100,000
Dairy Crest	40,000
Unigate	15,000
ACC	12,000
Northern Foods	7,000
The Cheese Company	4,000
Dromona Quality Foods	4,000
Fane Valley	4,000
Golden Vale	4,000
Ballyrashane	4,000
Others	14,000

Source : Dairy Industry Newsletter

As butter is usually the 'product of last resort', butter manufacture by individual companies varies enormously from year to year. The above figures are therefore only approximations.

Imports are dominated by New Zealand whose quota in 1992 was 55,000 tonnes.   A further cut to 51,830 tonnes was implemented in 1993. Following the implementation of the Uruguay Round GATT agreement in mid 1995, New Zealand's EU butter quota will rise by 20,000 per annum. The other major exporters to the UK are Ireland, 35,000 tonnes in 1992, and Denmark, 24,000 tonnes.   Smaller quantities are shipped from Netherlands and France with nominal amounts also from Belgium and Germany.

New Zealand has the market's brand leader position with 'Anchor', which has a 31% brand share in 1993/94. This is about 3% up on a year earlier. Danish 'Lurpak' is the second leading brand with a steady 17% share while English 'Country Life' and Irish 'Kerrygold' rank fourth and fifth. Blends, an important element in the UK market, have a share of around 30%, though previous rapid growth has stabilised and in 1994 there was a slight decline.

Cheese

UK production of cheese has increased steadily and now totals just over 300,000 tonnes a year.   On top of which some 200,000 tonnes are imported. (These figures are rather unclear in that production figures include only 'natural cheese' whereas import figures include 'processed cheese'.)

UK cheese exports are currently running at around 50,000 tonnes, so domestic consumption ("availability" or "disappearance") is about 450,000 tonnes, and has increased steadily, by a total of nearly 50,000 tonnes in the past five years.

UK manufacture accounts for just over 50% of total consumption of cheese while imports, at record levels in 1992, are almost as important. The overall supply balance is shown in Table 6.15.

Table 6.15:   UK Supplies of Cheese ('000 tonnes)

	1991	1992
Opening Stock (mainly Cheddar)	145	125
UK Production	299	302
Imports	192	232
Total availability	636	659
Exports	51	48
Closing Stock	125	146
Disappearance	460	465

Source: Dairy Industry Newsletter

There are about 80 significant cheese manufacturers in the UK (the top 16 are shown in Table 6.16), and perhaps another 200+ specialist farmhouse producers.   But two manufacturers, Dairy Crest and The Cheese Company, account for 40% of total production, and eight manufacturers (Dairy Crest, Express, Unigate, Avonmore, Scottish Pride, Waterford, the ACC and Dansco) account for almost three-quarters of production.

Unlike the situation with butter there has been little rationalisation of the UK cheese industry in recent years. This is largely because consumer demand has remained buoyant, total sales have steadily increased, and manufacturers have benefited hugely from very low raw milk prices. This latter factor started to change in early 1992, and cheesemakers now face the prospect of having to pay competitive prices for milk, and even of being deprived of milk altogether in the forthcoming free market.

In the last 'Rationalisation of Facilities' programme Dairy Crest closed their cheese factories at Maelor (Clwyd) and Four Crosses (Powys) and Express closed their plant at Ruyton-XI-Towns (Staffs).

Around two-thirds (about 200,000 tonnes) of total UK cheese production is Cheddar, and most of the rest is long-life territorials. The main non-Cheddar types produced are   Mozzarella (35,000 tonnes), Cheshire (20,000 tonnes) and Leicester (19,000 tonnes).

Table 6.16:   Output of main UK Cheese Makers - 1994 (estimates)

Producer	Tonnes/Year
TOTAL	300,000
Dairy Crest	40,000
The Cheese Company	60,000
Unigate (incl. NI)	25,000
Avonmore	20,000
Scottish Pride	5,000
Waterford (NI)	16,000
ACC	15,000
Golden Vale	12,000
Dansco	15,000
Wyke Farms	7,000
A. J. & R. G. Barber	5,000
Horlicks	5,000
Unilever (British Creameries)	5,000
Joseph Heler	8,000
Augher Co-op (NI)	4,000
West Ulster Farmers	4,000

Source : Dairy Industry Newsletter

The most dramatic single trend in the UK cheese industry in recent years has been the explosion of Mozzarella production, clearly driven by the demands of the fast growing pizza industry. Mozzarella is now the second most-produced variety of cheese in the UK. It is perhaps ironic that the three biggest producers of mozzarella, Dansco (Canada), Avonmore (Ireland) and Waterford Foods (Ireland), who between them produce over three quarters of total UK production, are foreign controlled. It is a comment on the strategic decisions of the UK dairy industry that the first two of these produce Mozzarella at former Dairy Crest plants (Newcastle Emlyn in South Wales and Llangefni on Angelsey), which were closed down as part of earlier factory rationalisation programmes. Dairy Crest produces no Mozzarella.

Table 6.17:   Main Cheese Types Produced

Cheese	1987	1994	Change
Cheddar	186,000	210,000	+13%
Mozzarella	5,000	50,000	+1000%
Processed	19,000	21,000	+11%
Cheshire	17,000	20,000	+18%
Leicester	17,000	19,000	+12%
Double Gloucester	12,000	10,000	-17%
Stilton	8,000	8,000	nc
Lancashire	4,000	4,000	nc
Wensleydale	3,000	2,500	-15%
Soft & cream	500	2,000	+300%
Derby	1,000	700	-30%
Caerphilly	1,000	500	-50%

Source : Dairy Industry Newsletter

Nearly 20,000 tonnes of Mozzarella are produced in Wales (by Dansco and Avonmore), now more than 15,000 tonnes in Northern Ireland (mainly by West Ulster Farmers and Waterford Foods) and about 5,000 tonnes in Scotland (Dansco and Kingdom). The UK is allegedly the largest market in Europe, and it has become a significant exporter.

Table 6.18: Output of main UK Mozzarella Makers, 1993*

Company	Tonnes
Dansco	15,000
Avonmore	12,000
Waterford Foods (NI)	10,000
West Ulster Farmers (NI)	6,000
Kingdom	1,000
Olympic Foods	2,000
Carnevale	1,000

Source : Dairy Industry Newsletter
*being the most dynamic UK cheese sector these tonnages change fairly quickly, and are only approximate.

The UK processed cheese industry has hardly recovered from the decision by Kraft to shift production to Belgium ten years ago. This move cut UK processed cheese production by half to under 10,000 tonnes, while imports soared. But in the past five years the total market in the UK for processed cheese has grown from around 30,000 tonnes to over 50,000 tonnes, mainly in response to demands from the rapidly growing fast food industry, and domestic production has doubled to 20,000 tonnes.

Yoghurt

Initially much of the UK yoghurt market was served by imports, with one outstanding exception, Eden Vale's 'Ski' yoghurt range By the late 1980's, 'Ski' had 25% of the UK yoghurt market, far in excess of Europe's top-selling brands Danone (BSN), Chambourcy (Nestlé) and Yoplait (Sodiaal). Grand Metropolitan sold its Express dairy operations in the late 1980's and, at the same time, reduced 'Ski' advertising significantly. The brand lost its market share quickly. Almost exactly coinciding with this was the spectacular success of Müller yoghurts which, within 3-4 years, were not only the top-selling yoghurts in the UK, but they were also the top-selling branded dairy product. Northern Foods bought Eden Vale in 1991 and are now trying to revive the 'Ski' brand. Northern has been a substantial own-label manufacturer of fresh dairy products, as has Unigate.

Other significant suppliers of yoghurts are Südmilch (imported from Germany) and Bridge Farm Dairies (who manufacture in Suffolk). But both these companies make or market ambient or long-life yoghurts which do not fall into the category of chilled fresh dairy products.

Ice cream

Market analysts and companies have overestimated the taste of the British public in relation to ice cream. Many have tried but nearly all have failed to persuade the British to stop eating 'margarine' ice cream (based on non-dairy fats) and to switch to the 'real thing'. And it must be said that the opposition is formidable. Unilever spends a good deal more advertising its substitute dairy products than the whole of the dairy industry spends on promoting its wares. The power of the vegetable-fat industry was very clearly demonstrated in 1984 when the then chairman of the MMB, Sir Steve Roberts, convinced that dairy ice cream had a great future in the UK, set about launching a *'Campaign for Real Ice Cream'*. After considerable behind-the-scenes arguments, the campaign was quietly abandoned, and the reasons were never revealed. It was alleged that the giants Unilever and Allied Lyons had threatened to source their dairy ingredients purchases outside the UK if the campaign went ahead.

The MMB's Dairy Crest tried and failed to promote dairy ice cream, via acquisitions such as the ill-fated Morruzzi company. Hillsdown Holdings tried and failed, and ultimately sold out to Clarke Foods, the vehicle by which ambitious American Henry Clarke sought to change British ice cream eating habits (convinced he could copy the American experience). Clarke also bought the loss-making ice cream business from Allied Lyons, and announced the intention to switch the emphasis of this giant new group to dairy ice cream. Clarke Foods collapsed in the early autumn of 1992, owing £49m. Nestlé acquired what was left of Clarkes, but since then has been closing parts of the business and there has been no more heard of any major switch to milk-fat ice cream.

The most recent venture to shift the British consumer to dairy ice cream has been the campaign by Grand Metropolitan's US subsidiary Häagen Dazs. The campaign has been widely acclaimed, but very expensive and, according to some industry speculation, not hugely successful, although the makers vehemently deny this. The American-initiated New England ice cream company tried to compete with the Häagen Dazs advertising campaign with, apparently, little success. New England went into receivership in the summer of 1993 and has been acquired by a management buy out. Some people, with more modest ambitions, are doing well: Loseley, Thayers, Dayvilles, and many other small operations. Mars have, apparently, been a very substantial success. But they manufacture their dairy ice cream in France.

UK cream production is around 160,000 tonnes a year with up to two-thirds of this derived from low fat milks. This varies with the attractions of the export market, the profitability of putting cream into butter and the viability of buying milk at the 'cream' price to obtain supplies of skimmed milk.

Fresh Cream

Given fluctuating profitability, the use of milk for fresh cream varies annually. In England and Wales for example, production was as follows:

1989-90	496m litres
1990-91	594m litres
1991-92	592m litres
1992-93	464m litres

These variations are unrelated to fresh cream consumption which is growing by 5% to 8% per annum. This growth is partly in households, but also in other major sectors of the cream market. The household market only accounts for about one quarter of UK sales, with catering outlets and food manufactures each accounting for a further 25% to 30%. The bakery industry takes the balance of about 20%.

Industry Concentration and Financial Performance

The five firm gross output concentration ratio in the dairy industry is around 57%. Figure 6.8 displays the trends since 1981.

Figure 6.8:   Five Firm Concentration Ratios for the Dairy Sector (1981-1991)

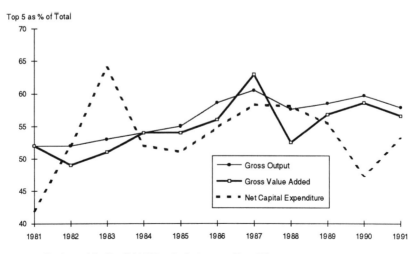

Source : Business Monitor PA1002 selected years, Euro PA

This concentration ratio has been rising steadily since the 1980's but seems to have levelled out in the early 1990's.

Table 6.19 shows company results for the major UK dairy companies. The gross value-added ratio has been, apart from one year, less than that of the gross output ratio. This indicates that the profit margins of the larger companies are less than those of the companies in the sector as a whole. This is in part due to specialist creameries producing higher value-added products such as cheese, whereas the larger companies have been involved, partially, in the distribution of fresh milk, which is lower value-added.

- The figures below include two companies that are not wholly milk processors.

- Unigate plc is concerned with all types of food processing and milk is just a subdivision.

- This is also the case with Nestlé Holdings (UK) Ltd, as it includes subsidiaries such as Rowntree's Mackintosh and as a whole is more concerned with confectionery for which milk is an important raw material.

- The weighted average has been calculated using estimates of the turnover of the dairy operations.

- In terms of the amount of milk processed Dairy Crest, Northern Foods and Unigate lead the way. Between them they accounted for 5.6 million litres of milk processed, just over 40% of the total.

- About half of the companies have profit margins (profit/sales) above 3% but the weighted average is 2.3%.

- The straight average for profit margin is higher than the weighted average. This suggests that smaller companies have a larger profit margin.

- This comment is supported by the observation that the averages for absolute levels of profit for companies of different size are very similar. This is in part due to the lower profit performance of the larger companies such as Dairy Crest and the Express Foods Group.

- Northern Foods with its two subsidiaries seems to have outperformed the sector in several respects.

- Dale Farm and Express Dairies have the greatest profit margin and ROCE.

Table 6.19 : Summary of Average UK Dairy Company Results (three year average)

Company	Turnover £m	Profit £m	Profit/ Sales(%)	ROCE (%)	Current Ratio	Debt Ratio	Years
Unigate plc	1975.33	89.67	4.54	17.30	0.84	0.63	91/92-92/94
Nestle Holdings (UK) Ltd*	1660.33	28.07	1.69	10.66	0.45	1.35	91-93
Dairy Crest (MMB)	1103.43	18.53	1.68	6.72	1.32	0.47	91/92-93/94
Avonmore Foods plc**	845.00	23.50	2.78	9.41	1.31	0.70	91-93
Express Foods Group Ltd****	488.05	-3.31	-0.68	-1.79	1.32	0.65	90/91-92/93
Dale Farm Dairy Group (Northern Foods)	678.87	31.15	4.59	9.17	1.01	1.08	90/91-92/93
Waterford Foods plc**	556.33	20.27	3.64	8.08	1.17	0.66	90/91-92/93
Express Dairy Ltd (Northern Foods)	280.25	15.81	5.64	34.09	0.77	0.57	88/89-90/91
Golden Vale plc	339.00	16.80	4.96	19.61	0.96	0.60	90/91-92/93
ACC (CWS)***	245.12	5.47	2.23	33.35	1.89	0.42	91/92-92/93
MD Foods	284.27	7.27	2.56	3.95	1.46	0.48	91/92-92/93
Scottish Pride Dairies Ltd	78.26	2.66	3.40		1.01	0.99	89/90-91/92
Kennerty Farm Dairies Ltd	41.75	0.06	0.17	1.14	1.05	0.91	90-92
Average weighted by turnover		**18.45**	**2.31**	**8.53**	**0.93**	**0.51**	
Straight average		**18.99**	**2.96**	**12.83**	**1.18**	**0.68**	
Total Turnover	**8,576**						

Source: Kompass, Euro PA

Note :   The figures shown above should be read in conjunction with the notes contained in the Appendix to Chapter One.

*   Nestlé's figures have not been used in the calculation of sector averages as their current and debt ratio are distorted due to the influence of their parent company.

**   These figures are in Irish pounds.

***   These figures are for Associated Co-operative Creameries Ltd. CWS's total milk businesses involves more than just ACC, thus the figures above do not tally with those given for ACC/CWS in Table 6.9. Reorganisation of the milk businesses has taken place at CWS which further complicates matters. In 1994 CWS milk businesses had total turnover of around £700m.

****   Later renamed The Cheese Company

Summary and Conclusions

This chapter has shown that long term changes in demand have had a profound effect on consumption of dairy products. Most seriously affected have been the traditional products, full-cream liquid milk and butter, whose consumption levels now stand at around a third and a quarter respectively of their post-war peaks, which occurred in the 1960's. Cheese consumption has been almost unchanged during the 1960's, and remains low by EU standards. Some growth areas have emerged during the 1980's and 1990's, low fat liquid milk, Mozzarella cheese, yoghurt, fromage frais and other fresh dairy products being the main beneficiaries. Health concerns have been a major driver for these changes and milk fat has become effectively a by-product of dairy production. Other changes have been in line with moves throughout the food sector towards differentiated 'fresh', value-added, and convenience food products, trends which can be expected to continue.

While demand for dairy products was contracting, UK entry into the EC was providing price incentives for farmers to expand production. This generated surpluses which had to be converted and stored as intervention products, and the processing industry expanded capacity to cope with the invervention demand. However, with the same process taking place throughout the Community, the situation became unsustainable and the policy response was to control milk production through the imposition of milk quotas in 1984. These have cut milk production in the UK by more than 15% in the last decade.

Superimposed on EU dairy policies has been the UK dairy marketing system, comprising the Milk Marketing Boards. Their system of formula-pricing of milk for use in producing alternative end-products has limited the responsiveness of the UK industry. Most notably this has been apparent in the butter sector, where substantial surplus capacity followed the cut-backs in milk production after quotas were introduced. Because returns were guaranteed under formula pricing, there was no incentive for manufacturers to cut capacity or respond to demand changes by moving production into the growing higher area of value products. The situation currently is that the UK market for these new products is, to a large extent, supplied by imports of production by foreign-owned dairy companies while the UK exports low-value intervention products.

Recent reform of the UK milk marketing system, assuming that the new dairy co-operatives are not allowed to exploit their near-monopoly positions, may be expected to promote more vigorous competition amongst dairy companies and increase their flexibility to respond to market changes. Continuing CAP and GATT reform might threaten increased competition from non-EU states, particularly from the CEECs,

Australia and New Zealand. However, these changes also open opportunities for expansion to EU companies in the value-added dairy sectors where they have a competitive advantage.

References

Colman, David (1992). The Breakdown of the Milk Marketing Schemes, *Oxford Agrarian Studies* **20(2)**, 129-138

Eden Publishing (Various), *Dairy Industry Newsletter*, 13 Hertford Street, Cambridge

DTI (1994) *The Uruguay Round of Multilateral Trade Negotiations 1986-94*, Cm. 2579 HMSO, London

DG VI (Annual). *CAP Working Notes, Milk and Dairy Products.* European Commission, DG VI, Brussels, Belgium.

GATT, (1994). *Agreement Establishing the World Trade Organisation Agreement on Agriculture*, Cm 2559, Misc No 17, HMSO, London

Henson, S. & Traill, B. (1993) unpublished report. *The CAP and Consumption of Yellow Fats: The Implications for Health.* Department of Agricultural Economics, The University of Reading.

MMB Dairy Facts and Figures (1993). MMB Residual Body, Giggs Hill, Thames Ditton, Surrey KT7 0EL

MMB EC Dairy Facts and Figures (1993). MMB Residual Body, Giggs Hill, Thames Ditton, Surrey, KT7 0EL

Pitts, Eamonn (1981). *A Comparison of Producer Milk Prices in EEC Countries.* An Foras Taluntais, Dublin

Ritson, C and Swinbank, A. (1991). *The British Milk Marketing Scheme - Implications of 1992.* Paper to 25th EAAE Seminar, Braunschweig.

Swinbank, A. (1986). Milk Pricing in England and Wales. *Food Marketing* 2.1, 34-54

Traill, B. and Henson, S. (1994). Price Transmission in the UK Yellow Fats Market. *Journal of Agricultural Economics* **45(1)**

Eden Publishing (October 1993). *UK Milk Report 93/94*, 13 Hertford Street, Cambridge

Wilkinson, G.A. (1984). *The UK Dairy Industry and the EEC*, in Swinbank and Burns (eds) *The EEC and the Food Industries.* Food Economics Study No. 1, Department of Agricultural Economics and Management, The University of Reading.

Williams, R.E. (1986). Perspectives on Milk Marketing. *Journal of Agricultural Economics*, **37(3)**, 295-309

Williams, R.E. (1993). The Future of Milk Marketing. *Journal of Agricultural Economics* **44(1)**, 1-13

Chapter 7: The Meat Industry

Mark Gunthorpe, Mike Ingham and Martin Palmer[1]

Introduction

The sale of finished livestock accounted for 37% of the value of the total UK farm output in 1993, UK household expenditure on meat was £10 billion in the same year, and the value of turnover in the meat slaughtering industry, also in the same year, was c. £3 billion. These three statistics are just part of the story of the meat industry but they are enough to demonstrate its significance. Clearly, meat production, processing and consumption are important but there have been significant trends and disturbances in the last decade. The UK meat industry has not had a quiet time.

Since 1985, apart from the vicissitudes of the Common Agricultural Policy, including major reform to the CAP and the GATT Uruguay Round agreement, UK meat producers have had to deal with EU regulations on animal growth hormones, UK laws on animal welfare, BSE (Bovine Spongiform Encephalopathy), and the agrimonetary system. Meat processors have seen demand for beef drastically affected by the publicity surrounding BSE at home and abroad. New meat hygiene regulations and a new system of administering meat hygiene inspections have also complicated their business decisions. The changing socio-economic environment as seen in the consumers' changing lifestyle, work and leisure patterns has resulted in a rapidly changing market for red meat. As a result of the severe competition in the food market, the share of red meat within the total meat market is under constant pressure.

Against this background, this chapter opens with an overview of meat consumption and demand, including catering. The policy context will be considered next and the overall meat supply balance, production and trade will be dealt with in the third main section of the chapter. Finally, the structure and key players within the slaughtering and meat

1   Mark Gunthorpe is a researcher in Euro PA, Cambs.; Mike Ingham is a financial journalist based in Cumbria; Dr Martin Palmer is head of the Industry Strategy Department at the Meat and Livestock Commission, Milton Keynes. The Editors are grateful for the data and information provided by the MLC that greatly assisted with the production of this chapter. Any opinions, ,errors or omissions in the chapter remain the sole responsibility of the Editors, but the Editors remind the reader of the caveat in the Appendix to Chapter One.

Meat Consumption

OECD data shown in Figure 7.1 illustrate that the UK has the lowest per capita consumption rate for meat of all western industrialised countries. Of the major countries in the world only Japan has a lower consumption level than the UK.

Figure 7.1: Meat Consumption in Major Economies - 1992

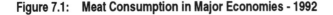

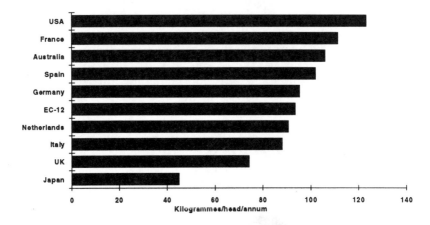

Source : OECD 'Meat Balances in OECD Countries'

Figure 7.2: UK Meat Consumption (Volume) by category

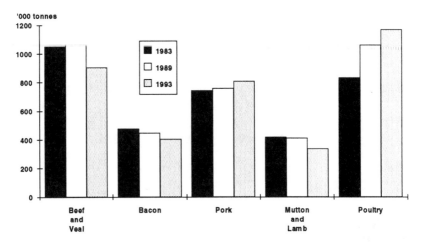

Source : MLC, Euro PA
Note :   In its availability calculations of meat consumption the MLC excludes imported processed products. OECD figures include imported processed products in its calculations.

Figure 7.2 illustrates the breakdown in total UK meat consumption by category. Many of the red meat categories shown have experienced falls in the level of consumption over the period 1983 to 1993. Beef and veal consumption has fallen 14% while bacon has fallen by 19%. Mutton and Lamb has also fallen, by almost 20%. Poultry (white meat), on the other hand, has seen strong growth of 40% between 1983 and 1993. Pork has shown an increase of 9% over the same period.

Household Consumption

Data from the National Food Survey provide a more detailed picture of how UK meat consumption in households has changed over time[2]. Table 7.1 shows consumer expenditure on meat and meat products in relation to total spending and spending on food.

Table 7.1: Household Consumers' Expenditure on Meat and Bacon

	1984	1987	1990	1993
		£ million at 1990 prices		
Total Consumer Expenditure	198,820	265,290	347,527	348,687
Of which:				
Spent on food	37,925	40,621	41,816	42,957
Of which:				
Spent on meat and bacon	9,589	10,063	9,832	10,111

Source: NFS, MLC
Note: excludes meat consumed outside the home

In 1993 UK consumers spent almost £43 billion on food for consumption in the home. In real terms this expenditure on food has increased 13% between 1984 and 1993, or approximately 1% per annum. This growth is against a 75% increase in overall consumer expenditure. This serves to highlight the income inelasticity of food demand. With such a growth in total expenditure the share spent on food fell from 19% in 1984 to 12% in 1993.

Of the household expenditure on food, meat and bacon (effectively all meat and meat products) accounted for over £10 billion in 1993. The real expenditure on meat and meat products has been around this level for most of the 1984-93 period. However, with food expenditure rising, the share of food expenditure accounted for by meat has changed from 25% in 1984 to 24% in 1993.

In addition to expenditure on food for household consumption, consumers also bought meat in the form of meals consumed in hotels, restaurants, canteens and other sectors of the catering industry.

---

2   See 'Meat Demand Trends', (various), MLC

In nominal terms, household expenditure on the carcase meats, (beef, lamb and pork) amounted to £3.4 billion and expenditure on poultry, £1.9 billion in 1993 (Figure 7.3). For both lamb and pork, expenditure in 1993 was below the 1990 level though higher than in 1985. In 1990/91 beef sales were badly hit by the BSE scare and beef consumption fell. It has since recovered but has not reached the level observed in the mid-1980's.

Figure 7.3:   Estimated Household Expenditure on Meat

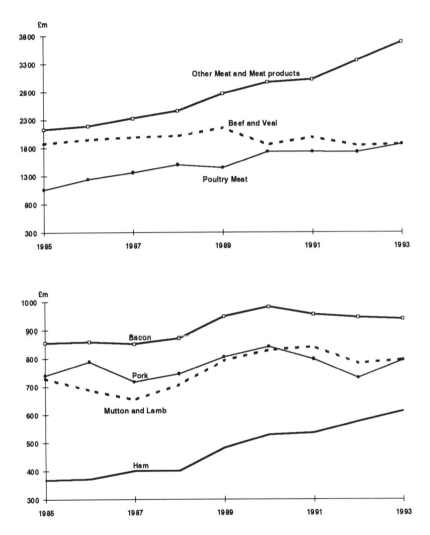

Source : MLC, National Food Survey

Consumption of poultrymeat and ham, in contrast, has increased consistently. Poultrymeat sales almost doubled from £1 billion in 1985 to £1.85 billion in 1993. Ham sales increased from £368 million to £612 million, an increase of 66% over the 9 years from 1985 to 1993 in nominal terms. These nominal sales increases are also reflected in volume figures as shown in Figure 7.2.

Total expenditure on meat products rose by 14%, in real terms (72% in nominal terms) over the period 1985-1993 and accounted for 35% of all meat spending by 1993. This shift in consumption away from meat purchased as fresh or frozen cuts to meat products and meat-based convenience foods tallies with the general trend in lifestyle and consumer demand whereby convenience and timeliness are an important part of food products. For meat supplying companies, this means extra preparation and pre-cooking before the act of consumer purchase.

There has been a significant shift in the purchase of red meat, bacon and poultry by households with regard to the retail outlet that purchases are made from. Figure 7.4 shows the dramatic fall in the share of sales made by butchers. In direct contrast to this there has been a marked growth in the share of household consumption that is being supplied by supermarkets. Over the 1979 to 1993 period the relative importance has completely switched. In 1979 independent butchers accounted for around 47% of all household meat purchases, whilst the supermarkets had a 26% share. In 1993 the supermarkets had over 55% of the market, the butchers have 25%.

This trend towards supermarkets is likely to continue and is linked to the general shift in consumption patterns towards convenience and prepared meats.

Figure 7.4: Household Purchases (by Volume) of Red Meat, Bacon and Poultry by Source of Purchase

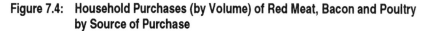

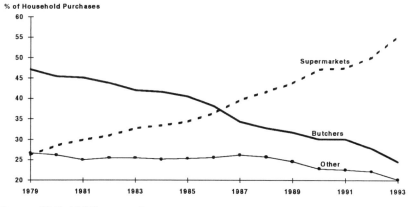

Source : MLC, AGB Superpanel
Other = Co-ops, independent grocers, freezer centres, farm shops and market stalls

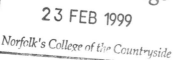

Catering Consumption

The consumption of meat in the catering industry is an important part of the description of meat consumption and demand in the UK. Especially because certain parts of catering demand have grown significantly (again linked with changes in consumer lifestyle and habit). There are also important consequences for the types and qualities of raw material that flow from this. Catering is defined as all outlets selling meals outside the home. Thus, this covers; hotels, restaurants, fast food cafés, takeaways, pubs etc. Table 7.2 shows the breakdown of catering consumption over the 1983-93 period[3].

Table 7.2 illustrates the 18% growth in catering consumption of red meat between 1983 and 1993. For all meats the volume sold to catering has increased. Even, mutton and lamb consumption has grown (from a low base) by 34.5% in the decade from 1983 to 1993. This equates to c. 3% growth per annum. This growth is in contrast to the fall in household meat consumption and overall red meat consumption.

Table 7.2:   Estimated UK Catering Consumption of Meat and Meat Products*

	1983	1993	1993/83
	'000 tonnes cwe		Change %
Beef and Veal			
Total Consumption	1,183	1,044	-11.7
Household	966	797	-17.5
Catering	217	247	+13.8
Catering as % of total	18	24	
Mutton and Lamb			
Total Consumption	413	339	-17.9
Household	355	261	-26.5
Catering	58	78	+34.5
Catering as % of total	14	23	
Pork			
Total Consumption	868	904	+4.1
Household	743	765	+3.0
Catering	210	254	+21.0
Catering as % of total	24	28	
Bacon			
Total Consumption	570	493	-0.5
Household	445	354	-20.4
Catering	125	139	+11.2
Catering as % of total	22	28	
Total Red Meat			
Total Consumption	3,034	2,780	-8.4
Household	2,424	2,062	-14.9
Catering	610	718	+17.7
Catering as % of total	20	26	

Source: MLC

cwe = carcase weight equivalent

* includes imported processed products

---

3   For example, 'Meat Demand Trends' (various), MLC

The importance of catering's share of total meat consumption has increased, from a fifth of total meat consumption in 1983 to over a quarter in 1993. Although the share of total consumption taken by catering is similar across all the different types of meat, being between 23% and 28%. the real gains have been for beef and pork, eaten either as fresh or processed products.

Figure 7.5:   Catering Demand for Individual Meats, 1992

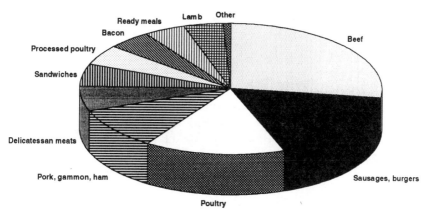

Source : GIRA

Figure 7.5 illustrates that beef is the meat most consumed in the catering sector with over 27% of the total market. In main courses offered by catering outlets, beef was present in 89% according to Marketpower research in 1994[4].

Sausages and burgers account for over 17% of the total catering market. The burger market has been one of the success stories of the catering industry as it has consistently seen increased sales, both in the home and in fast food outlets. National Food Survey results have shown that sales of beef burgers for household consumption rose from £179 million in 1989 to £188 million 1993. This rise was small but was in the face of the BSE scare of 1989, which weakened sales for household consumption. Euromonitor estimates that sales by burger bars in the same period rose from £785 million to £960 million.

---

4   Marketpower research is commissioned on a ad-hoc basis by the MLC. Some of this research on the catering market was published in the November 1994 edition of Meat Demand Trends.

The Policy Background for Meat and Livestock

The major policy influences on the UK livestock sector are all CAP regimes with a long history. UK national schemes are also important although not directly affecting prices. MLC publications[5] present full details of the history and development of these regimes and policy developments. This section of the chapter will cover only the essentials of the policy instruments that the UK meat industry has operated under but will present the reader with the key aspects of the institutional scene. It will also focus much more on the most recent changes to policy at an EU and national government level.

Beef

The beef sector is subject to the full gamut of policy instruments in the CAP, including automatic market intervention when prices fall below a given level (these conditions have recently become more restrictive). The 1992 CAP reform replaced several market support arrangements by direct producer premiums.

Premiums operate at the producer level and have a direct effect on incomes. Those currently available to beef processors include: the suckler cow premium, the special beef premium, the extensification premium and hill livestock compensatory allowances (HLCAs). Of these, the suckler cow premium and the beef cow premium, payable on male cattle, are operated on a restricted quota headage basis. The extensification premium is an additional payment to these two premiums, applicable only when stocking density is below a given level. Subject to a maximum stocking density and payment per hectare, hill livestock allowances are paid on breeding cattle in designated less favoured areas, which are difficult to farm and consequently experience higher production costs.

The EU market is also protected by variable import levies, import quotas and export refunds on products traded with third countries. These are various concessionary import schemes, the reduced levy and levy free quotas enabled over 80,000 tonnes of beef to be imported into the EU in the first half of 1995. From July 1995, new arrangements will apply when all trade protection measures will be the subject to the provisions of the 1994 Uruguay Round Agreement to liberalise trade in agricultural products.

---

5   For example see 'CAP Reform - The Challenge of Change' (1992)

It is also important to note that the beef industry does not operate independently of the dairy sector, which provides a large proportion of calves for finishing. As a result, many developments in beef production, such as the growth in the suckler herd since 1984 (when dairy quotas were introduced) have been a response to policy measures in the dairy sector.

Sheep

Currently, the sheep sector is supported mainly through direct producer premiums, the main one being the ewe premium. Until 1992, price support in Great Britain was also offered, in the form of a variable slaughter premium (the cost of which was deducted from the amount payable in ewe premium) but this was phased out before the introduction of the Single Market. Like its counterparts in the beef sector, the annual ewe premium is subject to a headage quota. In both sectors rights can be transferred between producers by sale or leasing agreements. HLCAs are also payable on breeding ewes held in less favoured areas, subject to a maximum stocking density and payment per hectare.

In addition, there is an automatic facility to introduce private storage aid schemes when market prices fall below a certain level. The EU market is also protected by variable import levies but there are concessionary arrangements that, in the past, took the form of voluntary restraint agreements (VRAs) or import quotas. The largest of the quotas is ascribed to New Zealand who, in the first half of 1995, is permitted to export to the EU a total of over 100,000 tonnes of fresh or frozen sheepmeat free of levy. From July 1995 these agreements will be covered by the provisions of the GATT Agreement. Since the EU is not self-sufficient in sheepmeat, export refunds do not apply in this sector.

Pigs

Unlike those for beef and sheepmeat, the pigmeat regime is a 'light regime'. In essence this means that the pig market is not subject to a range of support measures but that the European Commission relies to a large extent on the market to be self-regulating. The main means of market support is through temporary, EU-wide or regional, private storage aid schemes. These operate when market prices are particularly low or a disease problem arises, but are not introduced automatically.

The EU has a higher level of sufficiency in pigmeat and uses export refunds on a range of products exported to third countries. On imports there is a system of sluicegate prices and import levies, designed to prevent large quantities of pigmeat from non-EU countries being imported onto the EU market at low prices. The sluicegate price reflects the cost of pig production outside the EU and import levies are set to maintain an effective minimum import price level.

The pigmeat regime was introduced at the same time as for cereals in recognition of the close relationship between the two sectors. In modern pig production, compound feed, consisting principally of cereals, may account for more than two-thirds of production costs.

Agrimonetary Policy

In all sectors the agrimonetary system has a very important effect on the national level of support. Support prices are converted into Sterling at the 'green rate of exchange' and when this is devalued, Sterling support prices rise. Between September 1992 (when Sterling was removed from the ERM) and the beginning of 1995, the green rate for beef declined by 17%, resulting in a corresponding rise in premiums paid to UK producers.

The introduction of the Single Market in January 1993 necessitated the abolition of the system of cross border taxes and subsidies (MCAs) which applied to the intra-Community trade in beef and pig products of those countries, including the UK, whose currencies were not included in the 'narrow band' of the exchange rate mechanism. This meant that, without the offsetting effects of MCAs the full impact of currency movements is now felt in the beef and pigmeat trade flows between the UK and its EU partners.[6]

Animal Health and Meat Hygiene Regulations

By eliminating the distinction between domestic and international trade within the EU and removing border controls, the introduction of the Single Market impacted on the meat and livestock industry in several important ways. It meant that new procedures for controlling and monitoring trade in live animals had to be introduced; with controls at point of origin to ensure that stock conforms to disease status and health standards are maintained, and random checks at point of destination. There were also major implications for the abattoir sector. Prior to 1993, common standards (EU approved) were required only for export plants while those trading on the domestic market had to satisfy national requirements. The post-1993 arrangements are detailed in the section of the chapter dealing with the slaughter sector. In essence, the current

---

[6]   A more detailed account of the green currency or agrimonetary system is given in Chapter Nine.

negotiations mean that all plants will have to meet EU approval. This is causing a major investment programme in those UK and EU plants seeking to upgrade to EU approved standards. At the end of the transitional period, the only derogations available will be permanent derogations from the structural requirements for those plants which operate on a restricted throughput of 1,000 cattle units per year.

In addition, the harmonisation of meat inspection procedures has seen the introduction of a new centralised Meat Hygiene Service in the UK[7].

Consumer Concerns and Animal Welfare

The drive to improve standards to meet the concerns of the consumer has continued to have major implications for the industry. These are manifested in the legislation, such as that banning the use of growth promoting hormones in meat production throughout the EU.

Further major changes for the pig industry are imminent as producers in the UK are being required to phase out the use of sow stalls and tethers. In response to welfare concerns, the ban on sow stalls and tethers will be phased in earlier in the UK than in other EU States, and will involve producers in additional costs in a highly competitive industry.

Animal transport is another area where legislative changes are being considered in the EU on welfare grounds.

Food Legislation

In the last decade, major changes have also been made in food legislation, in both the EU and the UK. The Food Safety Act 1990 replaced and extended the provisions of the Food Act 1984 and placed particular emphasis on aspects of food safety. It covers all stages of commercial food manufacture and supply, including food preparation, storage, labelling, processing for sale, selling and transport. Its provisions control all businesses engaged in preparing, storing and handling food, including caterers and retailers. It also enables Community food legislation to be implemented in the UK.

This Act introduces the defence of 'due diligence' into food law. This enables an accused person (or company) to avoid conviction for an offence if it can be proved that all reasonable precautions were taken, and due diligence was exercised to avoid infringing a requirement. This has prompted many companies to consider introducing a 'due diligence

---

[7]   The new Meat and Hygiene Service became operational with the passing of the Statutory Instrument - Fresh Meat (Hygiene and Inspections) Regulations 1995.

system' and has been a major reason why many large supermarkets have become concerned with traceability. This concern is already having an effect on the structure of the animal distribution chain.

The Supply of Meat and Livestock

The figures in Table 7.3 show UK carcase meat balances.

On the basis of these availability calculations, the volume of beef consumed on the UK market has been falling almost continuously since 1980, largely as a result of declining supplies and increased meat exports.

Pork production has risen by 115,000 between 1980 and 1993. In the same period, exports have risen 15,000 tonnes more than imports. This has meant UK pork consumption has increased by 100,000 tonnes. Bacon, on the other hand, has seen production fall almost 30,000 and imports by 70,000, leaving consumption down by 100,000. From 1980-1993, the rise in consumption of poultry was met by increased production and imports.

Table 7.3:   Meat Balances ('000 tonnes dcw)

	1980	1985	1990	1991	1992	1993
Beef and veal						
Slaughtered production	1,102	1,155	1,001	1010	960	859
Imports	260	179	174	192	198	203
Exports	159	185	124	136	143	188
Consumption*	1200	1,132	997	1014	999	903
Mutton and lamb						
Slaughtered production	277	303	370	385	355	347
Imports	192	153	145	117	119	120
Exports	37	49	80	80	105	123
Consumption*	433	411	429	424	378	338
Pork						
Slaughtered production	685	718	740	778	781	801
Imports	39	34	77	71	80	102
Exports	17	43	49	73	91	94
Consumption*	707	709	768	775	772	807
Bacon						
Slaughtered production	209	203	179	175	167	181
Imports	303	264	260	254	234	228
Exports	4	6	5	5	5	5
Consumption	507	462	434	424	395	404
Poultry						
Consumption*	756	909	1110	1133	1198	1168

Source : MLC 'Market Trends'
* After allowing for changes in public stocks and private storage aid schemes
Note: Figures used in Table 7.3 are from an MLC source. In the availability calculations of meat consumption the MLC excludes imported processed products. OECD figures include imported processed products in its calculations.

Value of Livestock Production

Table 7.4 indicates the importance of livestock production within the UK agricultural sector. The sale of finished livestock accounted for 37% of the value of the total UK farm output in 1993.

Table 7.4: Value of United Kingdom Farm Output, 1993

	£ Million
FINISHED LIVESTOCK	
Cattle & calves	2,320
Sheep	1,258
Pigs	994
Poultry	985
Other	140
Total	**5,697**
TOTAL FARM OUTPUT*	15,164
Finished cattle, sheep, pigs and poultry as % of total	37

* excludes the value of animals sold for further fattening
Source: MAFF, Welsh Office, DAFS, DANI.

Structure of Production

Table 7.5 shows that more than half the 242,000 agricultural holdings in 1992 contained cattle or calves and 38% held sheep. The large number of holdings involved in cattle and sheep production indicates that much of it is quite small-scale in nature.   In contrast, however, only 7% of holdings contained pigs and 12% were poultry farms[8]. In the pig sector there has been a significant trend towards increased concentration and larger average herd sizes in recent years. The poultry sector is the most concentrated with 70% of production being controlled by 1% of producers. These are mainly large vertically integrated operations.

While the total cow herd has been relatively stable, there has been a reduction in the number of dairy cows accompanied by an expansion in beef cow numbers. Since 1990 ewe numbers have risen to a peak of over 17,000 in 1992 and then fallen back to 1990 levels in 1994. Breeding sow numbers have tended to follow a cycle, though less regular than in the past.

---

8   Derived from the number of laying fowl holdings.

Table 7.5:   Livestock Numbers, Holdings and Average Herd/Flock, June Census

	1985	1990	1993
Livestock numbers (000)			
Dairy cows	3,147	2,845	2,665
Beef cows	1,320	1,586	1,734
Total cattle and calves	12,792	11,995	11,648
Breeding ewes	16,020	19,337	19,614
Total sheep and lambs	35,461	43,359	43,614
Breeding sows	823	766	799
Total pigs	7,827	7,431	7734
Table fowls (including broilers)	61,311	73,588	79,504
Laying Fowls	39,556	33,489	32,416
Total poultry	128,590	124,615	130,175
Holdings (000)			
Dairy cows	54.0	45.1	41.5
Beef cows	71.9	73.4	73.0
Total cattle and calves	161.0	142.4	136.7
Breeding ewes	83.5	88.1	89.7
Total sheep and lambs	87.7	92.1	93.5
Breeding sows	17.5	12.6	11.8
Total pigs	23.3	17.1	16.6
Broilers	2.0	1.9	2.6
Laying Fowls	59.2	46.5	31.4
Total agricultural holdings	240.3	241.4	242.3
Average herd/flock size			
Dairy cows	58	63	64
Beef cows	18	22	24
Total cattle and calves	79	84	85
Breeding ewes	191	219	219
Total sheep and lambs	404	471	466
Breeding sows	47	61	68
Total pigs	336	434	465
Laying Fowls	668	848	1,031
Broilers (000)	31.0	37.9	30.5

Source : MLC
Note : Figures derived from source which has definitions that have changed over time.

Marketing of livestock

Tables 7.6 and 7.7 show the variation in livestock and poultry marketings since 1988. Supplies of cattle and sheep expanded up to 1992, but for both species there was a considerable reduction in supplies in 1992, largely as a result of changes in the support regime. Pig marketings also show a considerable degree of variation, but this is more cyclical in nature.

Table 7.6:   Cattle, Sheep and Pig Marketings 1988-94

	Slaughtered in the UK ('000 head)			Live Exports ('000 head)		
	1988	1991	1994	1988	1991	1994
Cattle	3,373	3,618	3,114	260	399	500
Sheep	17,102	20,918	18,918	498	879	1,100
Pigs	15,808	14,457	15,066	48	237	78

Source : MLC

Table 7.7:   Poultry Marketings 1988-94

	1988	1991	1994
Poultry Marketings	588	591	586

Source : MAFF

Poultry supplies and consumption have generally been stable, although the salmonella health scares of 1989 interrupted the pattern.

The most important factors in determining the volume of livestock sales have been:

- Policy changes - CAP measures and effects of reforms.

- Productivity changes - improvements in technology, husbandry, breeding programmes.

- Trade - live exports affected by fall in value of Sterling, removal of cattle MCAs, sheep variable premium and clawback demand from the Continent.

- Market forces - the role of demand and market forces in determining output levels is greater for pigs and poultry than for cattle and sheep where price support is more important.

The Quality Aspect of Meat Supplies

Table 7.3 illustrates the fall in the supplies of beef and veal. Cattle slaughterings fell from 3.8 million head in 1983 to 2.95 million head in 1993. However, as already stated, there has been a change in the composition of the British herd, with beef cattle increasing in prominence. This has led to an increase in the number of cattle slaughtered that are from the beef herd rather than dairy herd in origin[9].

Table 7.8 shows that there is little difference between 1983 and 1993 in the proportion of clean slaughtering (i.e. younger cattle) and cow/cull slaughterings (i.e. older cattle). Of the culled slaughterings there has been a move towards more beef animals being slaughtered and fewer dairy (due to the reduction in the dairy herd).

---

9   Dairy in this sense is defined to mean pure dairy cattle and cattle which are a cross between dairy and beef breeds.

Table 7.8:   Breakdown of UK slaughterings[10]

		1983	1993
Total slaughterings (million head)		3.811	2.953
% Cow/culled		20%	19%
	Dairy	(13%)	(11%)
	Pure Beef	(7%)	(8%)
% Clean		80%	81%
	Dairy	(52%)	(45%)
	Pure Beef	(28%)	(35%)

Source : MLC estimates

The importance of the breakdown is that it allows a closer examination of the quality issue. Beef cattle are regarded as having a superior conformation to those from the dairy herd. The average conformation of the dairy herd has been negatively influenced by the introduction of the Holstein breed which has a poor carcase conformation. Now, however, with a move towards a larger beef herd, and more pure beef cattle slaughtered, the average conformation of carcases produced in the UK should improve.

In total, slaughterings derived from dairy animals (including pure dairy and dairy/beef cross breeds) have fallen from 65% of the total in 1983 to 56% in 1993, representing a fall of some 820,000 head. The greatest movement has been in clean beef slaughtering, that is the production of the best quality meat from young beef cattle. Clean beef slaughtering has increased from 28% to 35%. In absolute terms, this represents a fall in clean beef slaughtering of 16,000 head, due to the fall in the overall level of slaughtering between 1983 and 1993. (Clean dairy slaughtering fell by over 600,000 head in the same period)

Table 7.9 displays classification results for clean cattle as a whole. Cattle carcases are classified according to fatness (scale 1 - 5, 1 leanest to 5 fattest, with classes 4 and 5 subdivided into H [high] and L [low]) and conformation (scale EUROP where E is excellent conformation and P poor conformation, classes O and P are subdivided into + and -).

Table 7.9:   Clean Cattle Classification Results

	1989	1990	1991	1992	1993
	percentage of classified carcases				
Fatness:					
4L or leaner	74.1	74	79.2	75.5	76.3
4H or fatter	25.9	26	20.8	24.5	23.7
Conformation:					
R or better	55.8	56.1	50.1	47.4	49.9
O or poorer	44.2	43.9	49.9	52.6	50.1
Average carcase weight	296.0	295.0	294.0	300.0	na

Source MLC

---

10   Proportion of meat derived from dairy and pure beef herds.

The results in Table 7.9 show an improvement in fat levels, as farmers produce carcases to more demanding market specifications, but a deterioration in conformation which has a great deal to do with the effects of increased Holstein breeding in the dairy herd where over half of British beef originates. Recent changes in the CAP have encouraged more beef from the suckler herd with the result that conformation grades improved in 1993. Producers are also finishing cattle to heavier weights, notwithstanding any price penalties for extra fat. Although requirements differ, supermarkets and the export trade generally demand carcases which are 4L or leaner and of R or better conformation.

A similar classification is used for sheep and results from MLC classification services, in Table 7.10, show an improvement in conformation and in fatness levels. Despite these improvements, supermarkets have complained of a shortage of carcases in the target range of R or better conformation and 3L or leaner. This is thought to result from increased demands for these grades from the export trade.

Table 7.10: Sheep Classification Results

	1989	1990	1991	1992	1993
		percentage of classified carcases			
Fatness:					
3L or leaner	67.7	65.5	69	66.1	67.7
3H or fatter	32.2	34.5	31	33.9	28.3
Conformation:					
R or better	65.7	65.9	68.2	71.6	72.5
O or poorer	34.3	34.1	31.8	28.4	27.5

Source MLC

Table 7.11: Pig Classification Results

Grade	Lean Meat Percentage	1990	1991	1992	1993
		percentage of classified carcases			
S	60+	19.9	25.2	28.4	31.8
E	55-59	58.3	57.3	55.8	54.2
U	50-54	18.2	14.8	13.6	11.9
R	45-49	2.8	2.2	1.7	1.7
O	40-44	0.5	0.3	0.3	0.3
P	<40	0.3	0.2	0.1	0.1
Average carcase weight (kg)		65	65.5	66.1	66.7

Source MLC

Table 7.11 shows a significant rise in the proportion of pigs classified as 60% or more lean meat. In addition, there has been a rise in average carcase weight although the British industry produces a much lighter pig than its competitors in Europe.

Eating Quality

A major focus of research and development in the red meat sector, in recent years, has been on producing meat that has better eating quality. This has seen the introduction by many abattoirs of process control specifications, in the form of MLC Blueprints for Eating Quality. In recent years this has had a major impact on meat quality throughout the industry. Over 60% of the high value cuts of beef are now produced to the blueprint specification, which forms the basis of the high quality cuts specification in the major multiple retailers such as Sainsbury, Tesco and Safeway.

A key part of the specification for beef is aitch bone hanging of the carcase (in contrast to the traditional leg suspension), and this is now widely used by all of the major abattoirs in Britain. Similar blueprints have now been launched for pork and lamb. Key components of the pork blueprint have now also been incorporated into the buying specifications of the major retailers, and a lamb blueprint in now beginning to be used which aims to improve the eating quality of older lambs (hoggets).

Links with Other Parts of the Chain

Linkages between producers and other parts of the chain have traditionally been weak reflecting the lack of concentration at the producer level. Livestock auction markets, of which there are some 300 operational in Great Britain, still account for over 50% of cattle sales and 70% of sheep sold liveweight. In the pig sector, over 95% are sold directly to abattoirs on a deadweight basis, with about two thirds of these being tied up in yearly supply contracts (the prices in these contracts, although often based on a formulae, are rarely fixed and fluctuate on a weekly basis).

The liveweight auction markets attract both buyers from large and small abattoirs, as well as a myriad of livestock dealers operating on behalf of others or on their own behalf as arbitrageurs in the system. Recent years have also seen the development, frequently by live auction companies, of electronic deadweight auctions, for cattle in particular. These have been in the form of both computer/video systems such as EASE, LEAN, DIRECT, BEACON and APEX, and the computer/video system operated by SLAM, although all of these still only account for a small proportion of the total market (estimates vary between 3% and 5% of cattle sales).

There is increasing interest in the industry at all levels to develop a more co-ordinated market approach in the meat chain, to give consistency of quality supply, traceability and assurance for the consumer. Outside of the auction market and direct sales by individual farmers to abattoirs, it was estimated that, in 1993/94, less than 10% of beef and lamb and 5% of pigs were produced, marketed and processed in 'co-ordinated/sectoral linked schemes. In addition, producer co-operatives accounted for 25% of pig marketing but have no major abattoir-processor linkages. It was estimated in 1993/94 that less than 6% of cattle and 8% of sheep were marketed through producer co-operatives (although many of these were in Scotland and they did have a direct link through ownership with abattoirs).

Historically, there was a growth of such co-operative activity in the 1960's, encouraged by grant aid, which also resulted in the development of a small number of co-operatively owned meat plants. The failure rate was high and only two co-operatively owned operations remain, both in Scotland - ANM/Scotch Premier and Buchan Meats. A further 25% of pigs in Britain are in the hands of commercial marketing companies, such as in the most completely integrated operation run by Cranswick and the feed based schemes of BOCM Pauls and Dalgety. Less than 1% of cattle are in such schemes, the only really developed one being the BOCM cattle scheme.

Both within and outside of these integrated schemes producers are also responding to consumer concerns over animal welfare and the environment by providing guarantees through a variety of farm assurance schemes. The most notable of these in England and Wales are the Farm Assured British Beef and Lamb Scheme (FABBL), the British Quality Assured Pig Initiative and the Farm Assured Welsh Lamb. In Scotland there is Scottish Farm Assured Beef and Lamb, and the Scottish Pig Initiative[11].

---

11   The 'farm assured' quality concept has been the subject of various experiments. See Euro Analysis (R57, 1993) for a review of the Farm Assured Scotch Livestock Scheme.

The Trade in Meat and Livestock

Figures 7.6 to 7.8 display the overall picture of the UK meat trade.

Figure 7.6:   UK Meat Industry Exports 1980-1992 (£m)

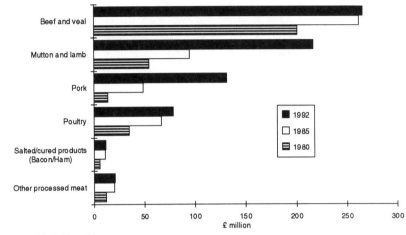

Source : MLC, Euro PA

Despite some improvement in export performance, there remains a negative trade balance in the meat industry largely due to the high value of the imports of imported cured and processed products. Up until 1992, lamb was the only sector in which the value of exports exceeded imports in these years (see Figure 7.8).

Figure 7.7:   UK Meat Industry Imports 1980-1992 (£m)

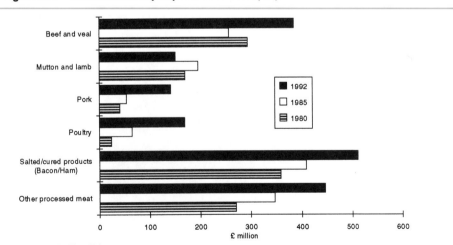

Source : MLC, Euro PA

In evidence given to a House of Commons Select Committee in 1992[12], the MLC stated:

"There has been a steady narrowing of the trade gap in meat and meat products since 1960 despite the fact that there have been fluctuations. The gap has halved over the last 30 years ... because of a reduction in imports" and *"because of an increase in exports"*.

However, this statement was made relative to volumes, indicating in real terms the gap has narrowed. Figure 7.9 shows that in nominal value terms the balance is getting worse. In 1992, the deficit was £1.08 billion as opposed to £860 million in 1980.

The improvement has continued in volume terms, however, helped by the devaluation of Sterling. Estimates for 1994 showing that for the first time the UK has become a net exporter of red meat (beef, lamb and pork) with 486,000 tonnes carcase weight equivalent, against 360,000 tonnes of imports[13]. There was still negative trade balance in total meat however, due to the high imports of processed meat products.

The processed products sector shows a particularly large imbalance, a large part of which is accounted for by imports of bacon and other processed products such as corned beef. In total processed products (includes salted/cured products) accounted for around £925 million of the deficit in 1992, according to MLC figures. Unprocessed meat accounted for around £155 million of the deficit.

Figure 7.8:   UK Meat Industry Trade Balance 1980-92 (£m)

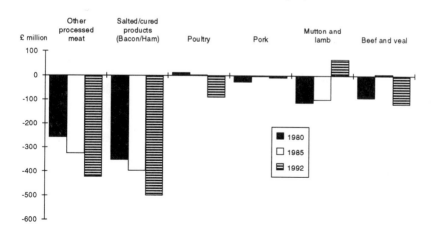

Source : MLC, Euro PA

---

12   See p184 in (HoC, 1992)
13   The export of quality beef from the UK has been a success story. See for example, Euro Analysis (R46, 1992)

Figure 7.9 illustrates the trend in exports of live animals for 1980 to 1992.
It can be seen that the main export, in terms of number of head of animal,
is sheep. Exports of sheep have risen dramatically since 1985 when
81,000 head were exported. In 1992, 1.42 million head were exported,
mainly for slaughter in French abattoirs.

Figure 7.9: UK Live Exports* 1980-92

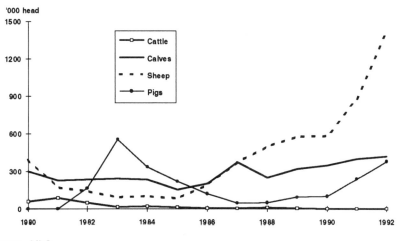

Source : MLC
* excludes exports of breeding stock

Calf exports have also risen from a low point of 152,000 head in 1985 to a
high of 420,000 head in 1992, most are destined for veal production on
the Continent. The Continental system of veal production in "crates"
was banned in 1990 in the UK. The continuation of this trade is under
threat and in 1995 protests at the export ports led to disturbances in the
trade and some switch of transport of animals to an air charter system.
Exports of fully grown cattle, on the other hand, have declined from a
high point of 85,000 in 1991 to being almost insignificant in 1992 (almost
entirely due to the ban on cattle exports as a result of BSE).

Pig exports have varied over the years with a peak of 555,000 in 1983,
followed by a decline to a low of 48,000 in 1988. Since 1988, exports have
risen again and 378,000 pigs were exported in 1992, mainly Northern to
Southern Ireland trade.

There have also been significant trends in live imports over the period
1980 to 1992.

Figure 7.10: UK Live Imports* 1980-1992

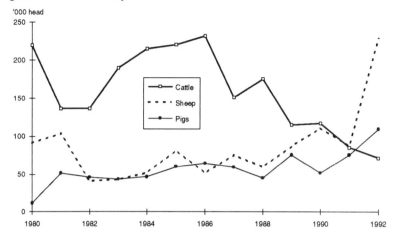

Source : MLC, Euro PA

Cattle imports have generally been falling (Note: there is very little importation of calves), having reached a peak in 1986 of 231,500 head. Pig imports have also declined to a very low level after being relatively stable between 1981 and 1987, though there looks to have been an upswing from 1989. However, imports of live pigs were 12,700 head against 50,000 head in the early 1980's.

The vast majority of all live imports originate from Eire, much of it being cross border trade with Northern Ireland.

In terms of live animals the UK has a significant surplus in the head of animals traded, as Figure 7.11 shows.

Figure 7.11: UK Trade Balance of Live Animals

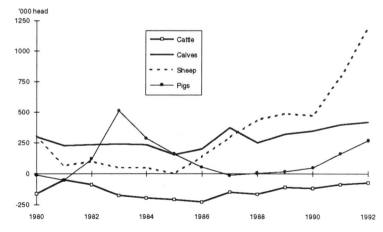

Source : MLC, Euro PA

Of the live trade the only negative balance is in cattle, and since 1986 this deficit has been falling, latest figures for 1994 show that live cattle imports have fallen to 20,000 head.

Public protests about live animal exports in 1995 have also affected the live sheep trade. The dramatic rise in sheep exports since 1985 illustrates that the UK from having a negligible net deficit in 1985 now has net exports of 1.2 million sheep. Most of these animals are fattened in France or Spain where the shortage of domestic production and relative overcapacity in slaughtering has underpinned the demand for these animals.

The Meat Processing Industry

This section includes all aspects of the processing of meat. It covers the slaughter, cutting and packing of meat for retail sale in the form of fresh or frozen cuts, and also further processing such as curing, smoking, cooking and canning. In addition, it includes the growing proportion of meat used as an ingredient in ready meals and other convenience foods.

The Abattoir Sector

The graph of slaughtered meat production (Figure 7.12) illustrates the downturn in supplies of beef, since 1985, and lamb since 1991 and continued growth of pork and poultry production.

Figure 7.12 : UK Slaughtered Production of Meat (1985-1993)
('000 tonnes dead carcase weight - dcw)

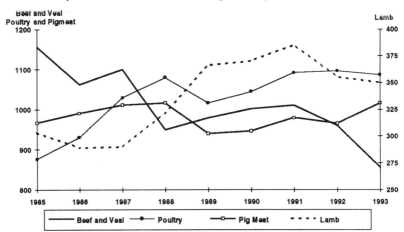

Source : SOEC, Euro PA

Figure 7.13 illustrates three important trends in the slaughter sector.

Firstly, the number of abattoirs has fallen dramatically, and consistently, since the early 1970's. This trend is almost certainly going to continue to the end of the 1990's.

Secondly, total throughput has increased slightly over the two decades[14].

This leads to the third point, the average throughput of a UK abattoir has tripled since 1972, rising every year. This point leads to the conclusion that there is a significant move to larger abattoirs in the UK industry.

Figure 7.13: Number of Abattoirs and Throughput 1972-1993

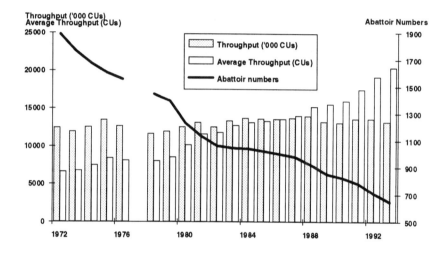

Source : MLC
Numbers refer to year ending March of the year shown
CU = Cattle Units. 1 CU = 1 cow or 3 calves or 5 sheep or 2 pigs

Table 7.12 illustrates the degree of rationalisation and concentration that has already taken place amongst the abattoirs slaughtering cattle, sheep or pigs. This table, however, breaks down the abattoirs into size groups.

52 abattoirs closed between 1991/92 and 1992/93. 37 of these were very small, processing fewer than 10,000 cattle units per annum. The other size group with notable losses was the medium sized 30,000-50,000 cattle

---

14   It is important to qualify this point by reference to the short and medium term fluctuations that occur. In the cattle and pig sector cyclical production trends are seen and time series trends are thus distorted. Beef production has declined, but not smoothly, since the mid 1980's. Currently, pig production is falling in a way that is similar to the traditional pig cycle.

unit group. The number of large abattoirs actually increased by 5 over the two years, increasing their share of the total throughput by 7% to 45%. It is very likely that this figure will exceed 50% in the next few years[15].

Many of the 242 small abattoirs that slaughter less than 1000 cattle units each year are left are connected to a retail butcher's operation. Though not independent slaughterhouses, these are still counted as abattoirs.

Table 7.12:   Abattoir Numbers and Throughputs, GB, 1991/92 and 1992/93

Cattle Units per year	Abbatoir Numbers		Throughput (Cattle Units)			
	1991/2	1992/3	1991/2		1992/3	
			'000	%	'000	%
1-10,000	466	429	959	7	901	7
10,001-20,000	76	71	1,110	8	1,028	8
20,001-30,000	38	31	961	7	773	6
30,001-50,000	52	40	2,059	15	1,606	12
50,001-100,000	47	41	3,398	25	2,904	22
100,001 +	30	35	5,501	38	5,991	45
Total	**709**	**647**	**13,588**	**100**	**13,205**	**100**

Source: MLC
1 cattle unit = 1 cattle beast or 3 calves or 5 sheep or 2 pigs

Despite the decline in the number of abattoirs there is still a degree of overcapacity[16] in the industry (estimated in 1993 at over 40% of peak kill) which exacerbates the problems of low profitability, which is common to all plants.

The introduction of the European Single Market has also meant a change in the regulations governing abattoirs. All plants are required to achieve EU approved status by 1996, whether they trade on a national or on an international basis. While making the necessary structural changes, plants can seek a temporary derogation from these requirements and very low throughput plants can obtain permanent derogations. These derogations apply only to the structural requirements of the legislation, all plants must meet EU hygiene standards. After 1996 there will be two types of abattoir, those that are fully EU approved and those small plants that have a permanent derogation to parts of the legislation as they slaughter less than 1,000 cattle units a year.

As meat companies have not wanted to modernise or upgrade plants without trying to ensure a consequent improvement in earning ability,

15   Compared to abattoirs in other EU countries the average size of these UK abattoirs is not very large.
16   As always the definition of overcapacity needs careful consideration. Plant capacity is not easily defined. It can be a reference to the speed of the killing line, boning hall throughput (which will vary according to customer specifications) and chiller capacity, or even unloading and despatch bay capacity.

this has often meant (informally or formally) an increase in slaughtering capacity. The need to develop additional value-added operations (boning, cutting, packaging) has also caused problems for the industry as potential conflicts in industry slaughtering capacity, sourcing unprocessed carcases and the due diligence provisions for the retail trade point the abattoir owner in different directions for commercial practice.

The importance of the 97 EU approved plants in 1993/94 in the industry is illustrated in Table 7.13. Plants with permanent derogations tend to be much smaller in size and represent only 4% of total throughput in the year to March 1994. If all those plants currently with temporary derogations achieve full EU approved status, 95% of throughput would be concentrated in these plants with the remaining 5% of throughput shared amongst over 200 small plants with permanent derogations.

Table 7.13:   Plant Status

		1993/94
	Plant Numbers	% of 1993/94 throughput
Closed during year	51	4
EU approved	97	63
Temporary derogations	198	32
Permanent derogations	206	1
Total	**552**	**100**

Source: MLC

Many of the larger abattoirs now deal direct with the large retailers. That is, they slaughter animals, cut and bone them, then pack them on site. Growth in direct transactions between abattoirs and large retailers has already contributed to the near-disappearance of traditional wholesalers. All the major supermarket groups are working to develop these bilateral trading relationships with slaughterers. The industry is starting to develop integrated procurement chains reaching right back onto the farms to ensure traceability and quality of livestock as consumer demand becomes more fastidious over food safety and animal welfare. This suggests the erosion of the wholesaling function will continue.

There are now two major national-scale non-slaughtering red meat wholesalers: Hillsdown's Tower Thompson, and Union International's Weddel, which in May 1995 is subject to management buyout bids as part of the Union International dismemberment by the receivers.[17]

---

17   There a still a large number of smaller national wholesalers, especially in the imported meat market for bacon, such as the Danish Bacon Company and agents for the Dutch Meat Board, New Zealand Lamb and Irish Beef.

However, there are reasons for believing the traditional wholesaling function will not vanish completely. Direct abattoir-retailer links depend on the ability of the slaughterers to provide the type of products the supermarkets require. Sales of red meat are shifting steadily away from beef and lamb as staple commodities towards products prepared and manufactured by specialist companies, although many of the larger and progressive abattoir companies are introducing cutting, packing and processing sections. There would, therefore, still seem to be a need for wholesale distribution channels linking slaughterers, meat product manufacturers and retailers. Furthermore, catering accounts for a growing proportion of meat sales, and the catering sector is mostly so fragmented as to make direct supply from abattoirs impractical in the majority of instances.

Further Processing Sector

The data in Table 7.14 cover the whole of the United Kingdom. The three sectors of the meat industry, slaughterhouses, poultry slaughtering and processing and bacon curing and red meat processing, consist of a large number of relatively small firms. Few companies are jointly owned and many operate with only one establishment. Over the period shown, there has been a considerable degree of rationalisation, which is particularly marked in bacon curing and red meat processing.

Table 7.14:   UK Meat Processing Sector

	1989	1990	1991	1992
Bacon Curing & Red Meat Processing				
Enterprises	722	655	617	605
Businesses	786	710	669	653
Slaughterhouses				
Enterprises	514	514	526	491
Businesses	525	526	536	502
Poultry Slaughter & Processing				
Enterprises	128	123	115	na
Businesses	142	139	135	na

Source: CSO
Definitions: An enterprise is one or more businesses under common ownership.
             A business is a company operating one or more establishments.

The number of enterprises involved in the production of different types of processed meats is shown in Tables 7.15 and 7.16. They relate only to those firms with at least 35 employees. Despite the large number of enterprises in the sector, many are specialist firms operating in only one area.

Whether bacon, and for that matter pork, can be called red meat is interesting. In some parts of the trade, and in some contexts, pork and bacon are seen as red meat, but in other contexts are called white meat. DBC does, at least, handle some beef and lamb.

Table 7.15:   Enterprises Producing Bacon and Meat Products

		Number of enterprises - 1991
MEAT PRODUCTS OTHER THAN FROZEN		
Bacon:	cured only	41
	cured and smoked	30
Not in hermetically sealed rigid containers:		
Ham and other meats, cooked		62
Meat puddings, pies, sausage rolls		86
Sausage meat		28
Uncooked sausages:	pork	55
	beef	29
	mixtures	34
Cooked sausages		19
Ready meat meals		14
Other products		21
Preserved meat in cans,bottles etc		
Canned meals without veg or pastry		9
Ready meals with veg or pastry		23
Other preserved meats		5
Meat pastes		6
FROZEN MEAT PRODUCTS		
Burgers		25
Sausages		20
Meat puddings, pies, sausage rolls		23
Other products		32

Source: Business Monitor

Table 7.16:   Enterprises Producing Poultry and Poultry Products

	No of enterprises 1991
POULTRY PRODUCTS OTHER THAN FROZEN	
Dressed poultry,fresh or chilled:	
Chicken (incl. capons)	20
Turkey	6
Other	3
Not in hermetically sealed rigid containers:	
Cooked chicken	13
Pies and ready meals	8
FROZEN POULTRY PRODUCTS	
Whole birds and cuts	
Chicken (incl. capons)	21
Turkey	5
Products, raw and uncooked	
(incl. offals, pies and meals)	16

Source: Business Monitor

When measured in terms of value of sales, meat puddings, pies and sausage rolls have the largest market of the red meat products, with bacon a close second. Apart from frozen puddings, pies and sausage rolls, where the demand seems to have switched to non-frozen varieties, sales of almost all meat products have expanded since 1989.

Table 7.17:   Sales of Bacon and Red Meat Products by UK Manufacturers

	1989	1990	1991	1992
MEAT PRODUCTS OTHER THAN FROZEN		£ million		
Bacon	435	464	478	549
Not in hermetically sealed rigid containers				
Ham and other meats, cooked	270	292	280	301
Meat puddings, pies, sausage rolls	487	511	551	591
Sausage meat and sausages	230	237	237	233
Ready meat meals	44	46	47	56
Other products	43	28	26	33
Preserved meat in cans,bottles etc.				
Canned meals without veg or pastry	35	39	45	42
Ready meals with veg or pastry	84	92	108	104
Other preserved meats	35	39	32	32
Meat pastes	28	25	30	17
FROZEN MEAT PRODUCTS				
Burgers	192	196	222	241
Sausages	68	77	84	88
Meat puddings, pies, sausage rolls	100	122	145	130
Other products	242	242	244	289
Total	**2,290**	**2,411**	**2,529**	**2,704**

Individual items may not sum to total shown due to rounding
Source: Business Monitor

The same trend is evident in sales of poultry and poultry products. Sales of dressed poultry were particularly depressed in 1989 due to the health problems that year.

Table 7.18:   Sales of Poultry and Poultry Products by UK Manufacturers

	1989	1990*	1991	1992
		£ million		
POULTRY PRODUCTS OTHER THAN FROZEN				
Dressed poultry,fresh or chilled				
Chicken (incl capons)	588	713	726	790
Turkey	33	74	55	76
Other	21	10	11	5
Not in hermetically sealed rigid containers				
Cooked poultry	108	142	139	147
Pies and ready meals	83	128	145	139
FROZEN POULTRY PRODUCTS				
Whole birds and cuts				
Chicken (incl. capons)	323	318	309	282
Turkey	91	108	143	166
Products, raw and uncooked				
(incl. offals, pies and meals)	147	143	151	166
Other	29	18	22	47
Total	**1,426**	**1,686**	**1,727**	**1,820**

* Sample base altered by raising reporting threshold
 Individual items may not sum to total shown due to rounding
Source: Business Monitor

Import/export penetration

An indicator of the international competitiveness of the UK meat industry is its market share at home and abroad. This can be illustrated by import penetration and export orientation ratios (imports expressed as a percentage of home consumption and exports expressed as a percentage of production).

Figure 7.14 shows that in all sectors trade has grown as a result of the introduction of the Single Market in January 1993. The lamb sector is the most open to trade with a high import penetration of New Zealand supplies, combined with the highest export orientation. Trade is least significant for pork and poultry, with both import penetration and export orientation low. The bacon industry appears to be the least competitive in terms of market share, with a high import penetration and low export orientation[18].

Figure 7.14: Export Orientation and Import Penetration Ratios in the Meat Industry

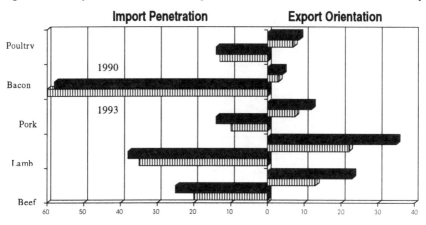

Source : MLC, Euro PA

Processed products

Because of the diverse nature of the products of this sector, it is impractical to calculate market shares and competitiveness measures on the basis of volume of meat used. Instead, value of sales is used to calculate import penetration and export orientation ratios. Because of the differences in the valuation method used for imports (measured cif)

---

18   However, a market for bacon scarcely exists in the EU except in the UK, and in the British tourist or expatriate communities abroad. The Danes and the Dutch do not produce bacon in significant quantities for any other market other than the UK. Technically, therefore, the question of competitiveness in the bacon sector is almost irrelevant.

and exports (measured fob), there is a bias towards overstating imports relative to exports.

There is a wide gap between the import and export performance of red meat and bacon products. Despite some gradual reduction in the negative balance, imports account for 26% of consumption, and only 1% of production is exported.

There is little trade in processed poultry products and both its import penetration and export orientation ratios calculated in Tables 7.19 and 7.20 are extremely low.

Table 7.19: Export orientation and Import Penetration of the UK Meat Processing Sector in Value

	1990	1991	1992
	£ million		
Value of sales by UK manufacturers	2411	2529	2704
Value of processed exports	30	30	32
Value of processed imports	932	933	946
	percentage		
Import penetration	28	27	26
Export orientation	1	1	1

Source: MLC, Customs and Excise, Business Monitor

Table 7.20 : Export orientation and Import Penetration of the UK Poultry Processing Sector in Value

	1990	1991	1992
	£ million		
Value of sales by UK manufacturers	1686	1727	1820
Value of processed exports	0.2	0.6	0.6
Value of processed imports	5	6	12
	percentage		
Import penetration	0.30	0.35	0.66
Export orientation	0.00	0.00	0.00

Source: MLC, Customs and Excise, Business Monitor

The Burger Market

The growth in the sales of burgers, both for consumption in the household and meals eaten outside the household, has been very significant in the past decade. In the UK, household expenditure on frozen beef burgers has risen from £140 million in 1983 to £190 million in

1993[19]. In the early 1990's consumption fell following the BSE scare but since 1992 has started to recover.

There has been corresponding rise in the sales through catering outlets i.e. burger bars. In 1979 the first McDonald's burger bar was opened in the UK and since then sales have rocketed. Table 7.21 illustrates the growth in value of sales in the UK in a five year period 1988-1992.

Table 7.21: The Fast Food Market: Sales by Type of Outlet

	1988	1989	1990	1991	1992
Burger bars	690	785	890	935	960
Pizza bars	495	580	650	665	695
Chicken bars	170	175	180	200	207
Hot potatoes	30	50	55	55	54
Other	25	28	30	30	28

Source : Euromonitor

Burger bar sales have risen 40% in 5 years (7% per annum). This growth has been matched by pizza bars which have also increased sales by 40% over the five year period.

Leading manufacturers

Birds Eye Walls leads the market for frozen burgers for home consumption and has a solid share of the grill steak market. Dalepak who deal only in grills, led that market with own-label products close behind.

Table 7.22: Brand shares of the burger and grill steak market 1993

	Burgers (%)	Grills (%)
Birds Eye Steakhouse	47.5	22.6
Ross	8.5	11.4
Dalepak	-	26.6
Own-label	12.4	23.1
Other brands`	31.6	16.3

Source : Bird's Eye Walls estimates, Based on AGB Superpanel data

Industrial structure and financial performance

Key meat industry characteristics are; the low 5 firm concentration ratios, participation of many small firms; and the decline in number of large stock-market quoted plcs. There is a predominance of small family firms organised

---

19   Beef burgers for household consumption are usually frozen. There has recently been growth in the fresh/chilled burger sector but as yet there is little quantitative data on this.

as limited companies often operating on a single plant basis. The five firm concentration ratios in Figure 7.15 relate to first-stage processing such as abattoirs and meat products. These do not include meat pies. Recent changes in ownership and changes in the meat processing sector structure are considered in the following section on profitability.

Figure 7.15: 5 Firm Concentration Ratios - Meat Processing[20]

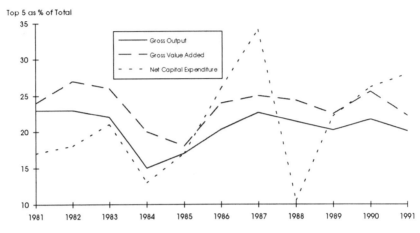

Source : Business Monitor PA1002, Euro PA

The meat sector has a low concentration ratio relative to others in the food industry, with a gross output concentration ratio of around 20%. The gross value-added line is continuously above the gross output line, indicating the largest firms have a greater profit margin. This is borne out by the table below.

The net capital expenditure ratio has been on a rollercoaster ride during the 1980's. In 1987 the ratio was almost 35% of the total; by the following year it was down to 10%.

Sector profitability

Over the past four years, the gross value of the output of the abattoir sector has fluctuated around the £3 billion mark. Gross value-added as a percentage of the value of output has remained at just over 10% while that for the UK manufacturing sector, as a whole, has been over 30%. The prevalence of low margins in this sector is a continuing issue.

___

20   Includes poultry.

Table 7.23: Profitability in the UK Abattoir Sector

	1989	1990	1991	1992
SLAUGHTERHOUSES		£ million		
Gross output	2936.0	3039.5	2964.6	3068.0
Gross value-added(a)	297.3	309.4	322.1	323.4
Net capital expenditure	30.6	34.5	41.9	34.1
Wages and salaries	151.6	173.0	180.9	192.0
		thousand		
Employment (head)	16.3	17.1	16.3	16.5
Gross value-added/hd (£)	18.2	18.1	19.7	19.6
		per cent		
Gross val add:gross output	10.1	10.2	10.9	10.5
Wages/sals:gross val added	51.0	55.9	56.2	59.3
Net cap exp:gross val added	10.3	11.2	13.0	10.5
UK MANUFACTURING INDUSTRY				
Gross val add:gross output	35.0	34.8	34.2	#N/A
Wages/sals:gross val added	51.2	53.8	57.8	#N/A
Net cap exp:gross val added	13.4	11.1	12.4	#N/A

(a) Factor cost
Source: Business Statistics Office

Net capital expenditure, expressed as a percentage of gross value-added, is comparable to that in other sectors of the manufacturing industry but the low rates of value-added mean that, in absolute terms, investment is relatively low.

Analysis of the structure of the further processing industry is hampered by a lack of data and the difficulties of integration of activities. Table 7.24 shows that gross value-added as a percentage of the value of output in the further processing of red meat and bacon is more than double that in the slaughter industry, although it still remains below the average for UK manufacturing. The value of output rose by almost 8% over the period and capital expenditure was higher than that of the abattoir sector, both in absolute terms and when expressed as a percentage of value-added. Comparing the number of employees and the value-added per employee with that of the abattoir sector shows that the firms involved in further processing are generally more labour intensive.

Figures on the processing of poultry are included in Table 7.25. These show that gross value-added per head is similar to that in the red meat industry, but the gross value-added as a percentage of the UK volume of output is nearly three times that of the abattoir sector.

Table 7.24: Profitability in the UK Meat Processing Sector

	1989	1990	1991	1992
	£ million			
BACON CURING & MEAT PROCESSING				
Gross output	3534.9	3601.8	3858.2	4158.7
Gross value-added(a)	886.4	940.3	1061.0	1008.2
Net capital expenditure	146.8	147.3	177.7	202.0
Wages and salaries	549.6	566.0	633.5	646.0
	thousand			
Employment (head)	64.4	61.0	61.4	60.0
Gross value-added per employee (£)	13.8	15.4	17.3	16.8
	percentage			
Gross val add:gross output	25.1	26.1	27.5	26.1
Wages/sals:gross val added	62.0	60.2	59.7	64.1
Net cap exp:gross val added	16.6	15.7	16.7	20.0
UK MANUFACTURING INDUSTRY				
Gross val add:gross output	35.0	34.8	34.2	#N/A
Wages/sals:gross val added	51.2	53.8	57.8	#N/A
Net cap exp:gross val added	13.4	11.1	12.4	#N/A

(a) Factor cost
Source: Business Statistics Office

Table 7.25: Profitability in the UK Poultry Sector

	1989	1990	1991	1992
POULTRY SLAUGHTERHOUSES & PROCESSING		£ million		
Gross output	1600.3	1869.9	1924.8	2055.7
Gross value-added(a)	445.9	597.5	519.7	572.2
Net capital expenditure	48.8	77.1	70.0	74.9
Wages and salaries	263.1	316.0	350.0	352.0
			thousand	
Employment (head)	33.8	35.6	36.1	35.5
Gross value-added per head (£)	13.2	16.8	14.4	16.1
Gross val add:gross output	27.9	32.0	32.0	32.0
Wages/sals:gross val added	59.0	52.9	67.3	61.5
Net cap exp:gross val added	10.9	12.9	13.5	13.1
UK MANUFACTURING INDUSTRY				
Gross val add:gross output	35.0	34.8	34.2	#N/A
Wages/sals:gross val added	51.2	53.8	57.8	#N/A
Net cap exp:gross val added	13.4	11.1	12.4	#N/A

(a) Factor cost
Source: Business Statistics Office

Table 7.26 below summarises the financial position of the major UK owned abattoirs and meat manufacturers

It is crucial to note that many meat companies have interests in other industries, e.g. farming, transport and other sectors of the food industry, and this creates problems when trying to separate out and analyse the profitability of activities in the meat sector. Thus, the overall value of a company's sales is not necessarily a good guide to its importance in the meat sector.

Table 7.26: Summary of Major UK Meat Company Results (three year average)

Company Name	Type	Turnover £m	Profit £m	Profit/ Sales (%)	ROCE (%)	Current Ratio	Debt Ratio	Years
Bird's Eye Walls Ltd	PR	625.57	50.94	8.14	28.41	1.10	0.60	89/90-91/92
Brake Bros.	PR	286.00	16.83	5.89	26.75	1.08	0.57	90/91-92/93
Sims Food Group	A/PR	264.00	4.82	1.83	14.27	1.02	0.62	90/91-92/93
Sun Valley Poultry	PPR	203.68	2.36	0.98	12.77	0.83	0.84	90/91-92/93
Marshall Food Group	PPR	156.74	2.83	1.71	5.70	1.01	0.63	90/91-92/93
Grampian Country Food Group	A/PR	141.79	1.69	1.19	7.55	1.18	0.94	90/91-92/93
G.W. Padley (Poultry) Ltd	PPR	130.98	3.05	2.35	16.57	0.26	0.52	90/91-92/93
F.W.Baker	A/PR	124.24	3.34	2.69	17.44	1.31	0.43	90/91-92/93
British Beef Company Ltd	A	119.37	0.30	0.25	5.05	0.93	0.84	91-93
Favor Parker Ltd	PPR	116.75	-1.40	-1.20	-3.52	0.97	0.58	89/90-91/92
Newmarket Foods	A/PR	114.57	2.57	2.25	12.37	1.11	0.38	90/91-92/93
Barretts and Baird (Holding) Ltd	A/PR	112.78	-1.00	-0.89	-6.62	0.75	0.78	90/91-91/92
Faccenda Chicken Ltd	PPR	115.10	1.41	1.23	10.13	1.06	0.43	90/91-92/93
Cranswick plc	A/PR	92.97	1.76	1.90	23.66	1.37	0.57	90/91-92/93
Dalehead Foods (Holdings) Ltd	A/PR	83.93	1.21	1.44	9.64	0.93	0.62	90/91-92/93
Aberdeen & Northern Marts (ANM)	A/Auc	71.17	1.05	1.47	7.06	0.78	0.54	93-94
St Merryn Meat Ltd	A/PR	50.71	0.99	2.10	20.02	1.17	0.84	90/91-92/93
Beck Food Group	A/PR	35.82	0.31	0.98	4.34	1.19	0.66	90/91-92/93
Average weighted by turnover			14.10	3.23	15.70	1.01	0.63	
Straight Average			5.17	1.91	11.76	1.00	0.63	
Total Turnover		2,882						

Source : Kompass, Euro PA

Note : The figures shown above should be read in conjunction with the notes contained in the Appendix to Chapter One

A = Abattoir; AUC = Auctioneer, P = Processor, PPR = Poultry Processor

There are some major meat processors that are not listed in Table 7.26. These are the UK companies owned by Grand Metropolitan Foods, Hazlewood Foods, Unigate (which with its abattoir at Malton is a very large pig slaughterer and processor) and Northern Foods, in particular. This is because their accounts make it difficult to separate out and analyse the profitability of activities in the meat sector.

Hillsdown Holdings still has a large number of companies operating in the meat and poultry processing sectors, its main divisions are listed in Table 7.27 along with other major independent companies with turnovers above £35 million in 1992/93.

Table 7.27 : Other Meat Processing Companies (1992/93)

Company	Type	Turnover (£m)
Henry Hargrave	A	88.1
Geo. Adams	A/PA	83.3
Cavagham & Gray	PR	81.9
Roach Foods	PR	72.1
B. Brooks (Norwich)	PR	69.6
McKey Holdings	PR	66.9
Hygrade Foods	PR	66.6
Lloyd Maunder	A/PR	66.0
Buchan Meats	A/PR	59.0
David A. Hall	A/PR	52.3
D T Duggins	A	44.8
Cheale Meats Ltd	A	42.9
G.D. Bowes & Sons Ltd	A/PR	41.7
Dalepak	PR	41.2
Beni Foods	PR	40.6
Borthwicks	PR	38.9
AJ & RG Barber	A/PR	38.8
Alec Jarrett	A	38.4
Cherry Valley Farms	PPR	36.5
Hillsdown Holdings:		
Towers Thompson	Wholesaler	209.0
Premier Poultry Ltd	PPR	125.4
Moorland Foods	PPR	80.4
C&T Harris (Calne) Ltd	PR	63.5
Buxted	PPR	53.4
Harris (Ipswich) Ltd	A/PR	43.3
Farm Kitchen Foods	A/PR	41.3
Ross Poultry Ltd	PPR	22.4

Source : Kompass, Euro PA

Note :   The figures shown above should be read in conjunction with the notes contained in
           the Appendix to Chapter One
           A = Abattoir; AUC = Auctioneer, P = Processor, PPR = Poultry Processor

- The information in Tables 7.17 and 7.18 shows that the value of sales by UK processors, over the period 1990-92, was just under £4.3bn. The companies in Tables 7.26 and 7.27 have total turnover of over £3.0bn. The financial information above therefore accounts for the majority of the total UK processing capacity (but not abattoirs).

- The profit margin (profit/sales) shown in Table 7.26 is low in this sector, compared to other food sectors.

- The weighted averages (by turnover) show an improvement on the simple averages for all indicators. They suggest that larger firms are achieving higher margins or returns than the smaller companies in the sector. This would generally be expected due to economies of scale or size.

- There is a large disparity in the calculated profit/sales averages.

    - This suggests that profit margins for smaller companies are low in comparison to larger companies.

    - The majority of companies are operating with a margin of less than 3%.

    - Some of the companies have made losses (on average) over the three year period their results cover. Not only that, but companies such as Ross, Premier Poultry and the British Beef Company made losses in two of the three years over which the average was calculated.

- However, the overall debt ratio for the sector is low compared to that of other food sectors. This is, in part, due to the greater labour intensity of the sector. As such, there is less borrowing required in order to purchase machinery.

- The ROCE is high, both on average and for particular companies. This is in part due to the fact that meat processing, especially in the cutting up of the carcase, is more labour intensive than that of other sectors.

- The situation in the red meat industry is contrasted with that of poultry in Table 7.20. The poultry data includes enterprises involved in further processing as well as slaughtering, but illustrates the higher returns in this sector.

Notwithstanding the comments made above and the comparison in Table 7.26, the ownership pattern of the meat industry, particularly the slaughtering/primary processing sectors, has altered significantly during the late 1980's and in the 1994/95 period. Companies which once dominated the sector have now faded from the scene, with a new generation of large multi-plant operators together with several smaller but high-profile independent firms taking their place. Several of these changes have taken place since 1993 and 1994. Hence, some these will not be shown in Table 7.24, which depends on publicly available accounts and, reports financial activity in 1992/93 at best.

Most dramatic of these recent changes was the withdrawal of Hillsdown Holdings from the sector. This diversified food conglomerate had been by far the biggest British slaughterer, through its FMC subsidiary, but publicly expressed dissatisfaction with red meat margins for several years. After a large number of plant closures failed to bring profitability, Hillsdown pulled out of the sector through a series of disposals including sales to management. Other, formerly significant operators have also abandoned the sector. Borthwicks, which was a company of similar size to FMC through its trading operation in imported meat, disposed of its three British abattoirs after running into severe financial problems a decade ago. More recently, the privately owned Union International, which like Borthwicks had been a major trader in imported meat, also encountered serious financial difficulty. Early in 1995, Union's slaughtering subsidiary, The British Beef Company, was put into receivership. Three of its four plants were sold to Kepak, an Irish meat company.

Some of the groups now coming to prominence based their expansion partly on the purchase of FMC plants. Perhaps the most notable example is the Scottish producer co-operative ANM, until recently best known for its big livestock auction business, trading as Aberdeen and Northern Marts. In 1993, it bought Hillsdown's Inverurie and Edinburgh abattoirs, closed the existing ANM plant at Banchory, and has emerged claiming to be the biggest red meat processor in Scotland, with nearly 20% of the Scottish kill.

Hillsdown's other major Scottish plant, at Perth, was sold to the Lincolnshire-based Beck Food Group. Beck is another relative newcomer to the industry gradually establishing a significant presence, though so far on the second tier. A more high profile new group is West Country based St Merryn, now believed to be the biggest beef supplier to Tesco. St Merryn's expansion has included the purchase of Hillsdown's North Devon Meat killing plant.

Other noteworthy disposals include the sale to management of the Hillsdown Lamberhurst lamb exporting plant which now trades as Invicta. The theme of newcomers basing their businesses on purchasing from outgoers or reviving financially crashed plants is pervasive.

Almost certainly the biggest beef and lamb slaughtering operator in Britain is now Anglo Beef Processors (ABP), controlled by Irish entrepreneur Larry Goodman. This group has nine plants (not all of which are slaughterers) and partly originated in the former red meat facilities of Dalgety. Estimates of ABP turnover for 1994 are around £250 million. In Table 7.24 there are companies with larger turnovers, but ABP is almost a pure cattle and sheep slaughtering operation (but includes two frozen meat plants).

Irish interests in the British industry have expanded steadily over the years, largely because meat companies in Ireland have wanted to forge closer links with UK supermarkets to replace their traditional opportunistic and weaker priced wholesale carcase trade.

The themes merge in the recent (1995) purchase by the Irish group Kepak of three of the four British Beef Company plants. These slaughterhouses were part of the Vestey family's huge Union International meat empire. Unlike the Hillsdown disposals, however, Union was forced into the sale by being pushed into receivership. Another notable recent transaction involving the Irish has been the sale of West Bromwich slaughterer Barretts & Baird to the dairy co-operative Avonmore. Barretts and Baird had been one of the biggest and best known family controlled livestock slaughter and meat processing companies in Britain.

Perhaps the most striking example of the new generation taking over the industry is the rapid expansion of the Scottish company, Grampian Country Foods. From a £1 million turnover, 15 years ago, Grampian claims to be on track for sales of more than £320 million in 1995. It is basically a poultry processor but is also strong in pork. Grampian's strategy has been to spread horizontally across the meat sector, as well as vertically (its activities include animal feed). The latest of its acquisitions is the McIntosh Donald beef plant at Portlethen, Aberdeen and the Anglesey sister company McIntosh Reynolds.

The overall effect of these ownership changes has been some fragmentation of the meat industry, particularly through management buyouts resulting in new single plant operations taking over parts of large company red meat activities. The only remaining quoted public company with major red meat killing interests is Sims Food Group plc (although Unigate still have major pig slaughtering interests at Malton as do Sainsbury with Newmarket Foods). The emergence of a new generation of large-scale privately owned red meat plant operators is a key feature of the sector.

Summary and Conclusions

Most British consumers still regard meat as the basis for a main meal, despite the wide media coverage of reports suggesting the meat-eating habit is fading. Correspondingly, the production and slaughtering of livestock and the processing of meat remain central pillars of the UK food industry. This does not mean that the industry can relax, however, as there are clear challenges, particularly for red meat, that have to be

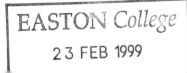

addressed if meat is to remain at the centre of the British diet, both as an individual food and as a major ingredient of many meals. In answer to these challenges the red meat industry, through the MLC, is devoting major resources to both generic and species promotion campaigns[21] to maintain and wherever possible increase consumption in the domestic market by enhancing the image of meat.

In addition, there are clear structural changes occurring both within the meat industry and its market. Some of the shifts are trends that have been under way for many years; others are recent developments which seem likely to alter the profile of the livestock and meat sector quickly and dramatically. No single influence is dominant. Instead, pressures are evident at each stage of the production and marketing chain, in some instances for quite independent reasons but in others as effects of natural distortions in other sub-sectors. In some cases, they are peculiar to the British industry; in others reflections of EU or even worldwide trends.

For example, the BSE epidemic has provoked recurrent, seriously destabilising backlashes in the consumer market for beef. This has been mostly a British problem, although since 1993 it has also emerged in the German retail and catering sectors. It is of negligible significance in most consumer markets elsewhere, even in neighbouring France, though several Member States banned imports of British beef or cattle, although these are now gradually being relaxed.

On the other hand, signs of a weakening in demand for carcase beef were visible in Britain well before the BSE crisis erupted. Demographic shifts, altering lifestyles, heightened awareness of health issues and changing shopping habits have been suggested as the causes for many years. Similar, though less severe erosion of demand has been apparent in most advanced western societies, even in Australasia and North America were the beef eating culture has been more deeply entrenched than in Britain. Likewise, a shift towards white meat, particularly poultry, is almost a worldwide phenomenon.

The strategic challenges facing the British meat industry include a need to respond to trends such as these, while adapting to national pressures which in some cases amplify the trends in the UK but in others diminish their significance, though perhaps just temporarily.

For instance, by far the most dramatic structural change throughout the British slaughtering industry over the past 20 years or more, involving all species, has been the reduction in the number of abattoirs and the sharp rise in average plant throughput against a background of broadly stable total slaughterings. This has not simply been the manifestation of a quest

---

21 These campaigns are funded by industry levies but the costs are effectively borne by consumers, see Euro PA (1994) for a fuller explanation of the incidence of producer levies.

for better net margins through economies of scale. More subtle factors are at work, and there is some evidence of increasingly sophisticated investment approaches being adopted by a new generation of plant operators which have begun emerging as the main players during the past few years.

The concentration of retailer power, allegedly more extreme in Britain than in most countries, has been a spur to restructuring partly because processors have sought the commercial strength to match the buying muscle of supermarket chains. There are signs of a reaction against this approach among processors and a desire to limit their vulnerability by broadening their customer base. A consequence of this desire is that attention has turned back towards independent retail, catering, secondary wholesaling and further processing/manufacturing outlets which some feel have been unwisely neglected in the clamour to win supermarket business. This slight change of emphasis appears vindicated by MLC estimates which imply, that even after any foreseeable further restructuring, the processing sector will still be too fragmented for individual companies to negotiate on an equal basis with supermarket chains.

Similar thinking partly explains the growth of exports, although it is not the main cause (which has more to do with agrimonetary factors, diminishing EU trade barriers, and the greater purchasing power in major Continental retail markets). Several of the biggest processors say privately that they have sought export business, particularly in Continental markets, specifically to reduce their reliance on revenue from the small number of major UK retailers. This has been apparent in the beef and lamb sectors for several years, but is now also visible in the clean pork trade. This strategy, built with a great deal of help from MLC may have to change in the future, however, from one based on primal product alone to one based on more value-added, cut and packaged meat as the Continental retail industry develops towards the UK model.

If three powerful structural themes can be isolated from among all the influences on the industry's current development, they are probably these. First, the end market is steadily shifting away from the business of selling traditional cuts of meat to consumers, towards the sale of more value-added meat and meat as a food product ingredient. Secondly, despite the increasing concentration of slaughtering and processing capacity, the industry will remain highly competitive with persistently narrow margins. Thirdly, the red meat industry is seeking to develop structures that will lead to more integrated production and marketing throughout the meat chain, in order to deliver the consistent quality of product required by the market.

References

DTI (1994). *The Uruguay Round of Multilateral Trade Negotiations 1986-94*, Cm 2579, HMSO, London

Euro Analysis (1993) unpublished report R57. *Farm Assured Scotch Livestock - A Strategy for 1993-97*, Euro PA & Associates, 11 Church Street, Northborough, Cambs, PE6 9BN.

Euro Analysis (1992) unpublished report R 46. *The Scotch Beef Club in Italy*, Euro PA & Associates, 11 Church Street, Northborough, Cambs, PE6 9BN.

Euro PA (1994). Levies on Farm Products: Who Pays and Who Gains?, R74, Euro PA & Associates, 11 Church Street, Northborough, Cambs, PE6 9BN.

Euromonitor (Oct 1993). *Retail Sector Review, Fast Food*. Euromonitor, 87-88 Turnmill Street, London.

GATT (1994). *Agreement Establishing the World Trade Organisation Agreement on Agriculture*, Cm 2559, Misc No 17, HMSO, London.

GIRA (1992). *Meat Usage in Catering*, Grilly, France.

HOC (1992). Agricultural Committee Report on *The Trade Gap in Food and Drink*, Volume II, HMSO, London.

MAFF (selected years). *Agriculture in the United Kingdom*, HMSO, London.

MLC (1994). *The abattoir industry in Great Britain*, MLC, Milton Keynes.

MLC (May 1994). The continuing success of the United Kingdom burger market, *Market Trends*, MLC, Milton Keynes.

MLC (November 1994). The UK catering meat market, *Meat Demand Trends*, MLC, Milton Keynes

MLC (1992). *CAP Reform - The challenge of change*, MLC, Milton Keynes.

NFS (selected years). *Household Food Consumption and Expenditure*, HMSO, London.

OECD (1986 and 1992). *Meat balances in OECD countries*, OECD, Paris.

Chapter 8: The Fruit and Vegetable Industry

Rosie Simpson, Ian Farley and David Hallam[1]

Introduction

This chapter deals with the fruit and vegetable industry and it should be noted at the outset that this particular sector of the UK food and drink industry is the least involved of all sectors in processing. Fruit and vegetable consumption in the UK is predominantly in fresh form rather than processed. However, this comment must immediately be qualified by the acknowledgement that prepared fruit and vegetables are a significant growth area in the market. This preparation is often done by processors or distributors e.g. cutting/slicing, cleaning, packaging, etc. but the final product competes directly on the supermarket shelf with fresh products. It also competes indirectly with frozen and processed products.

In this chapter the description and analyses of the fruit and vegetable markets are separated into sections dealing with fresh and prepared products, and processed products. Potatoes are a major item of vegetable consumption but are dealt with in Chapter Five. Amongst the remaining fruit and vegetable products the fresh/prepared section is easily the largest category of consumption and is dealt with after the initial demand section. The involvement of UK companies in fruit and vegetable trade and distribution (including those dealing with prepared fruit/vegetables) is mainly considered in the final, processing section of the chapter. These distinctions provide a structure for the chapter and the reader. This is intended to allow the commercial and economic factors operating in the fruit and vegetable industry to be disentangled.

---

1 Rosie Simpson is a researcher at Euro PA and Associates, Ian Farley is Research Manager at Geest International Produce, Spalding, Lincolnshire, Dr David Hallam is Senior Lecturer at the Department of Agricultural Economics, University of Reading. The Editors are grateful for the help provided by Kathryn Florey, a visiting research student at Geest plc and Doug Henderson, Chief Executive at the Fresh Produce Consortium, and the comments of Professor John McInerney on an earlier draft of the chapter. The Editors also wish to acknowledge that the opinions expressed in this chapter and any errors or omissions are their sole responsibility and draw the reader's attention to the caveat in the Appendix to Chapter One.

Consumption of Fruit and Vegetables

The total retail market for fresh and processed fruit and vegetables in the United Kingdom[2], is estimated at £5.3 billion over the three years 1991 to 1993 (see Table 8.1)[3]. £4.3 billion worth of produce is consumed fresh, accounting for 82% of the market. Approximately 24% of vegetables and 12% of fruit are consumed in a processed form.

Table 8.1: The UK Fresh and Processed Fruit and Vegetable Market 1991-93 £million at RSP

	1991	1992	1993	Average 91-93 (% of market)
Vegetables				
- Fresh	2082	2244	2310	2212 (76%)
- Frozen	391	409	421	407 (14%)
- Dried	4.7	4.7	4.5	4.6 (0.5%)
- Canned	272	278	272	274 (9.5%)
Total Vegetables	**2749.7**	**2935.7**	**3007.5**	**2898 (55%)**
Fruit				
- Fresh	1965	2145	2252	2121 (88%)
- Dried	85	88	89	87 (4%)
- Canned	207	193	182	194 (8%)
Total Fruit	**2257**	**2426**	**2523**	**2402 (45%)**
Total Fruit and Vegetables	**5007**	**5362**	**5530.5**	**5300**

Source: Datamonitor 1994

Note :   Calculated by surveying companies in the UK fruit and vegetable industry. The sum of production (plus net trade) multiplied by retail prices (obtained from a price survey) gives total market value. National Food Survey (NFS) figures are higher than those shown.   The NFS calculates its total market value by aggregating from the results of a household survey. The estimate of the fruit and vegetable market based on this (shown in National Accounts data) is c. £6.8 billion in comparison with the Datamonitor value shown here of £5.3 billion.

The market for fruit and vegetables is the fourth largest in the UK food industry; after meat, dairy and cereals & bakery products. The fruit and vegetable sector has seen little overall volume growth in recent years, although, there have been significant changes within this relatively static total market.

---

2.   Excluding potatoes which are dealt with separately in Chapter five

3   The data sources used in this chapter are not strictly comparable. Fast Facts provides data grossed up from the National Food Survey. Data from Datamonitor are from primary sources, i.e information direct from the companies involved in the processing of fruit and vegetables.

Figure 8.1:   Change in Household Consumption in the UK Fruit and Vegetable Sector 1982-93

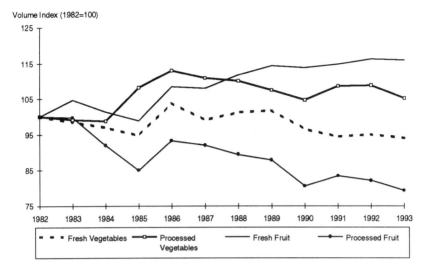

Volume Index (1982=100)

Source: CSO 'Annual Abstract of Statistics', NFS, Euro PA
Note: Processed fruit excludes fruit juices.

Figure 8.1 shows that in volume terms the fresh fruit sector grew by around 15% between 1982 and 1993., whereas for fresh vegetables there was a fall of almost 5% over the same period.

The processed fruit sector has fallen greatest in the fruit and vegetable industry, down 20% over the period shown. This, however, excludes the largest growth area - that of fruit juices.   Consumption of processed vegetables, has increased by approximately 5%.

Despite an increase in the range of fruit and vegetables offered to the UK consumer, 'traditional' fruit and vegetables remain the biggest sellers. In the vegetable market this includes carrots, cabbage and onions (See Figure 8.2), although salad vegetables have grown in popularity among UK consumers.

Similarly 'traditional fruits', apples, bananas and oranges still dominate the fruit market. In the past decade bananas have overtaken oranges as the second most popular fresh fruit with the UK consumer, after apples (see Figure 8.3).

Figure 8.2:   UK Main Fresh and Processed Vegetable Consumption, 1991-1993 av.

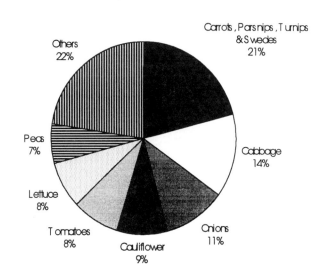

Source : MAFF, Euro PA

Figure 8.3:   The Growth in per capita Fresh Fruit Consumption - main categories

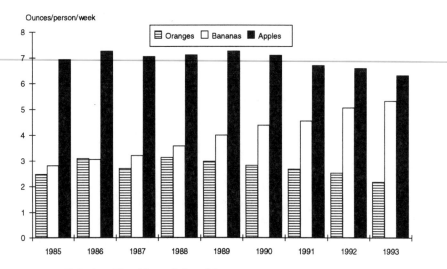

Source : MAFF 'National Food Survey', Euro PA

The fruit market is almost totally dominated by imports which averaged 2,249,000 tonnes (90%) over the period 1991-93 out of a total consumption of 2,504,300 tonnes. Obviously the UK cannot produce fruit such as bananas, citrus fruit, grapes, peaches and other tropical fruit, because of its climate. Demand for these fruits has grown considerably over the past decade, led by a more than doubling in consumption of bananas from 300,000 tonnes imported in 1984 to 655,000 tonnes in 1993.

The growth in the consumption of bananas per capita has been in contrast to the stable nature of apple consumption and the decline in the volume of oranges consumed (Figure 8.3).

Figure 8.4 provides a breakdown of the fresh and processed fruit market. It shows that apples are the most popular fruit consumed, with bananas in second place. Citrus fruit account for 30% in total with oranges taking half of this.

Figure 8.4:   UK Main Fresh and Processed Fruit Consumption 1991-1993 (av.)

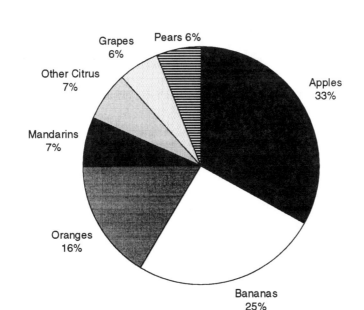

Source : MAFF, Euro PA

Figure 8.1 illustrated that the volume of processed fruit consumed fell between 1982 and 1993. Figure 8.5 shows that the canned fruit sector fell by almost 40% in this period.

Figure 8.5: Changes Houshold Consumption in the Fruit and Vegetable Processing Sector 1982-93

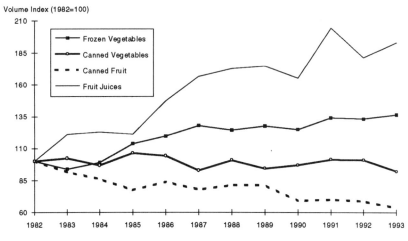

Source : MAFF 'National Food Survey' selected years, Euro PA

The UK market for tomatoes and other salad vegetables has shown strong growth over the last decade. The winter market for vegetable imports is lucrative and is being driven by an increased demand by UK consumers for fresh, high quality, 'healthy' produce all year round.

These changes in the structure of demand for fresh fruit and vegetables have been encouraged by income and lifestyle changes, and facilitated by improvements in transportation, distribution and packaging. Improvements in (global) transport and distribution links have reduced travelling times, allowing the sourcing of fresh produce from further afield. Chilled food distribution and gas flushed storage systems have been an important part of transporting fruit and vegetables over long distances[4]. Thus UK consumers enjoy a wider choice of produce almost all year round for most fruit and vegetables. A growing number of consumers seem content to pay price premiums for out of season and imported produce. Also the large multiples have introduced a wider range of the more expensive produce, such as salad vegetables, to take account of an increased demand for convenience and prepared foods.

Organic vegetables are now available in a number of the large grocery multiples in recognition of the apparent growth in demand for organics over the past five years. The higher prices charged for organically grown produce and their non-uniform appearance, may have prevented a more rapid growth in consumption. However, organic vegetables are

---

4   See Irving (1992)

produced on a relatively small scale in the UK and this availability factor may also be part of the explanation for apparent lack of consumer interest.

An increasingly health-conscious UK consumer has probably boosted demand for fruit and vegetables in all forms, but particularly fresh. A recent report by the Committee on Medical Aspects of Food Policy[5] highlighted the 'healthy' characteristics of fruit and vegetables relative to products that are highly processed. This and other media coverage of the issue have supported this tendency.

On the other hand, the increase in the size of the workforce has shifted demand for food towards the more convenient foods, with a decline also in the amount of meals eaten at home. These demands for "convenience" and "snacks" are satisfied in the fruit and vegetable sector by the use of supermarkets' chilled and prepared foods' shelf space mentioned earlier. New pre-prepared fruit and vegetable products are a feature of the market. Improvements in the packaging of fresh produce have increased its shelf life and satisfied the demand for pre-prepared fresh produce. New snacks based on fruits (e.g. apple chips, stoned prunes, dried fruits) are in evidence and may have the same impact on consumers as the introduction of prepared salads have had on the salad market (Euro PA, 1994).

The Influence of Price and Income on Demand

The demand for fruit and vegetables is affected by price, although own-price and cross-price elasticities are typically less than one. Prices can increase sharply in years of bad weather as supplies are restricted. In such circumstances, consumers switch more to alternative fresh produce or to frozen products rather than to other food groups (Datamonitor, 1994). This intra-sectoral substitution leads to overall fruit and vegetable consumption being relatively price insensitive compared to other food groups. In normal circumstances, consumer awareness of price levels appears limited, and quality seems a more important concern than price in influencing decisions to buy.

Price elasticities of demand for fruit are typically greater than those for vegetables. The NFS estimates for price elasticity of demand show that a 1% increase in price results in, respectively, a 0.4% decline in quantity of fresh green vegetables purchased, a 0.8% decline in fresh fruit purchased and a 0.5% decline in frozen vegetables purchased (Household Food Consumption and Expenditure, 1989). These figures reflect UK

5. See Coma (1992) and Euro Analysis (1993)

consumers' attitudes towards fresh vegetables as 'necessities' as well as their typically small budget share. Consumption of staples, such as beans, show no significant response to price changes. Fresh fruit, frozen vegetables and fruit juices are considered a lesser part of the staple diet and consumption falls more when their prices rise[6]. Sales of frozen vegetables also appear to be sensitive to changes in the price of fresh vegetables. Elasticities of demand are greater for individual fruit and vegetables than those for fruit and vegetables as a group, reflecting substitution possibilities within these broad groupings. Elasticities for individual products can be greater than one, significantly so in the case of exotic fruits and vegetables (Hallam, 1988).

NFS data also indicate that increases in per capita income have a positive effect on consumption of all fruit and vegetables with the exception of processed vegetables. Processed vegetables tend to increase in popularity in times of recession when they are used as substitutes for fresh produce Consumption of all fruit is particularly sensitive to income changes and tends to be significantly reduced when incomes decline.

Differences in the income elasticities of demand for particular fruits and vegetables go some way to explaining the changes in their relative levels of consumption discussed in the previous section, although the influence of income is difficult to separate out from the effects of social class and taste changes. For some traditional root vegetables, the income elasticity of demand is not significantly different from zero, and for traditional fruits such as oranges it is not more than 0.3 to 0.4. Less traditional fruit and vegetables such as pineapples, courgettes and aubergines, and prepared products have significantly higher income elasticities of demand and so will advance their market share as incomes grow.

Policy Background for Fruit and Vegetables

EU Fruit and Vegetable Regime

A CAP regime exists for fruit and vegetables. The vegetables which are excluded are potatoes, beans and peas for fodder and olive oil grown in Community countries. The CAP regime for the fruit and vegetable sector (Regulation 1035/72) consists of import protection, quality standards and internal market support through intervention[7]. The current regime is

---

6   Hinton (1991)
7   For a more detailed description see Hinton (*op cit*) or Ritson (1977) or CAP working notes for the fruit and vegetable regime.

under review and a "Reflections" document was released by the European Commission in July 1994 which set out ideas on reform. A Commission proposal for reform is expected to be discussed by the Council of Ministers in 1995[8].

Guarantee spending (under FEOGA) for the fruit and vegetable regime is c. 1.6 billion ECUs each year. Intervention is designed to provide a safety net in years of poor production and to stabilise prices in a market characterised by perishable produce and large price fluctuations.

The two principal vegetables that are withdrawn from the European market are cauliflowers and tomatoes. European Commission forecasts are that 80,000 tonnes of cauliflowers and 70,000 tonnes of tomatoes will be withdrawn in 1994/95. The quantity of fruit withdrawn from the EU market through Intervention has varied considerably from year to year. The largest quantity is of apples - 950,000 tonnes in 1994/95 (Commission estimate). Peaches and nectarines are the other main withdrawals with 800,000 tonnes and 195,000 tonnes respectively in 1994/95.

UK vegetable withdrawals are mainly cauliflowers and are not significant proportions of the total crop. In 1993/94, 9,003 tonnes of cauliflowers were withdrawn from the UK market under intervention, which is lower than the ten year average of 10,830 tonnes. Tomatoes have also been withdrawn in the past in very small quantities, only 3 tonnes last year (1992/93) and none in 1993/94. These figures disguise a considerable amount of produce deemed to be sub-standard quality which is ploughed back into the ground.

In the UK market 23,276 tonnes of apples were withdrawn in 1993/94, which is above the average for the past decade of 14,431 tonnes (the largest quantity withdrawn under intervention was 34,213 tonnes in 1988/89 and the lowest of 881 tonnes in 1991/92). Pears have also been withdrawn from the market but in much smaller quantities, 751 tonnes of UK production in 1993/94.

Intervention prices are set within 30% to 40% of basic prices for tomatoes, cauliflowers and aubergines, and within 40% to 55% for other vegetables. Processing is encouraged as an alternative to intervention through aids from the Management Committee to processors who agree to pay producers a minimum price. This aid is a fixed amount with adjustments made according to the level of the minimum price. Export refunds are also available for exporters to third countries.

The regime for fruit and vegetables was the subject of a Commission working paper in July 1994. The proposals for reform within that document have yet to be presented to the Council of Ministers in the

---

8   See "Development and future of Community policy in the fruit and vegetable sector" European Commission, Brussels, July 1994.

form of firm Commission proposals. The working paper's suggestions for reform included;

- an increased role for producer organisations (POs)
- elimination of surpluses by redrafting intervention prices
- redefinition of quality standards

Whether or not these suggestions are translated into firm proposals and then supported by Ministers will not be clear until the end of the French Presidency in the Council in June 1995, or even until the end of the subsequent Spanish Presidency in December 1995. Most commentators view the suggested reforms as being insufficient to reduce the chronic surpluses of the CAP regime for fruit and vegetables. Another influence on parts of the European fruit and vegetable market may be the implementation of the Entry Price System for fruit and vegetables agreed as part of the GATT Uruguay Round.

Fruit and Vegetables in the GATT

The Entry Price System for fruit and vegetables in the GATT is described in various publications[9]. The essence of the system is the change from a reference price system where a levy or countervailing charge is made on all products from a particular origin that attempt to enter the EU if at a lower level than the reference price. The new Entry Price System sets a minimum import value (the entry price) for each consignment of a specific product from each country of origin. If the import value falls below the entry price a tariff equivalent is charged. In the EU, 15 products will be brought into the scope of the Entry Price System during 1995[10]. The entry price and maximum tariff equivalents for the various products will be reduced (up to a maximum of 20%) over a 6 year period under the provisions of the GATT Uruguay Round.

EU Banana Regime[11]

An EU banana regime was introduced in July 1993 (Regulation 404/1993), allocating import quotas to traditional African Caribbean and Pacific (ACP) States and third countries (primarily Latin American "dollar" bananas). The most interesting aspects of this regime are not

---

9   See, for example, the publication by the Fresh Produce Consortium (April, 1995)

10   Tomatoes, cucumbers, courgettes, cherries, apricots, lemons, nectarines, plums, apples, pears, grapes, artichokes, clementines, mandarins, oranges.

11   The Editors are grateful for the assistance of Geest and the CBEA in preparing this section.

those concerned with EU production but those that concern external trade. Because several member states had traditional suppliers of bananas and there was a commitment to these suppliers enshrined in the Lomé Convention (the Fourth Lomé Convention was signed in March 1990) the banana regime adopted a distinct "partnership" approach to dealing with the import trade in dollar and ACP bananas. This partnership concept divides the EU import quota on dollar bananas and distributes it between ACP suppliers and banana operators in such a way as to ensure that quota rents are transferred to less competitive (more costly) ACP suppliers. Hence, the CAP regime maintains the benefits received under the Lomé banana protocol. An amended regime which included the Framework Agreement on export quotas for certain Latin American banana producers was incorporated into the GATT agreement signed in April 1994.

The banana regime has come under attack from some member states, especially Germany, and has been the subject of a European Court of Justice ruling (which upheld the regime), a GATT panel (which found against it) and in late 1994 was the subject of a USTR 301[12] investigation which was still pending in May 1995. In April 1995 an application to the German Constitutional Court was made by a German banana distributor alleging that the regime was "anti-competitive". Detailed references to the history and various analyses of the EU banana regime are given at the end of this chapter[13].

Supply of Fruit and Vegetables

Production and Trade

Table 8.2 and figure 8.6 outline the value and volume of fresh fruit and vegetables available for consumption or produced in the UK.

---

12 The United States Trade Representative's office is empowered to recommend trade sanctions against another country under Article 301 of the Trade Act 1974, as amended. Hence the term USTR 301 action. A USTR 301 investigation can be undertaken if trade practices of other trading nations is deemed to be detrimental to US businesses. If a trade practice is found to be harmful the US Trade Representative's office can initiate trade sanctions against the offending country. In 1994, Chiquita, a major US banana operator, and the Hawaian Banana Producers's Association put forward representations to the USTR that the EU regime was damaging their business.

13 See, for example, Bananarama III (1994), McInerney and Peston (1992), Chapter Three in Pedler *et al* (1994), and Euro PA (1995).

Table 8.2:   Value and Volume of Fruit and Vegetable Output Produced and Traded in the UK 1991-93 av. (£m)

	Production		Value of trade £m		Total Supply £m
	'000 tonnes	£m farmgate	Imports (c.i.f)	Exports (f.o.b.)	
Vegetables					
field	2930.8	654.6			
protected	408.2	326.4			
Total	3339.0	981.0	552	21.9	1,511
Fruit					
field	460.8	265.4			
protected	n/a	0.38			
Total	460.8	265.7	1,104	29.9	1,340
Total Fruit and Vegetables	3,800	1,246.7	1,656	51.8	2,851

Source: MAFF Basic Horticultural Statistics for the UK, 1984-93

At the farmgate and port of entry level the fruit and vegetable market in the UK is valued at around £2.85 billion per annum (Table 8.2). 58% (£1.65 billion) of fruit and vegetables are imported Domestic production is worth £1.25 billion and exports and re-exports of fresh and dried fruit and vegetables amount to £51.8 million.

The UK produces two thirds of its fresh vegetable requirements but only a fifth of the total fresh fruit consumed. Imports are sourced increasingly from the EU which provide around three quarters of all the UK's vegetable imports and about two-thirds of fruit, the rest originating from non-EU countries.

Figure 8.6 :   Breakdown of the Fruit and Vegetable Output Produced in the UK, 1991-93 average farmgate value

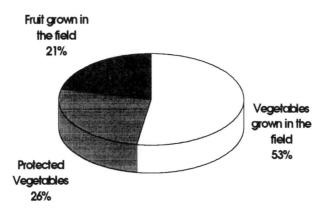

Source : MAFF, Euro PA

Vegetable Production and Trade

The market for vegetables in the UK is estimated by Datamonitor to be worth £2.9 billion (1991-93 average) at the retail level. Over 3.3 million tonnes of vegetable are produced annually, this is seven times the amount of fruit produced. Vegetable production covers 192,000 hectares (average 1991-93), four and a half times the area devoted to fruit production in the UK. The breakdown of vegetable supply is given in Table 8.3 and illustrated in Figure 8.7.

Just under 3 million tonnes or c. 90% of the total of vegetables are grown in the field on average each year (1991 - 1993 average). The remainder, 408,200 tonnes over the same period, is grown under protection, that is, glasshouses or other forms of protected environment.

The traditional vegetables, carrots (631,000 tonnes), cabbage (580,300 tonnes), cauliflowers (324,300 tonnes), peas (287,200 tonnes) and onions (267,700 tonnes) dominate the tonnages produced in the field in the UK. Tomatoes (126,200 tonnes), mushrooms (121,700 tonnes) and cucumbers (101,500 tonnes) dominate the vegetables grown in the UK under protection. Despite amounting to only 12% of the tonnage produced in the UK, protected vegetables account for 33% of the value.

Figure 8.7: UK Production and Imports of Fresh Vegetables, 1991-93 av., '000 tonnes

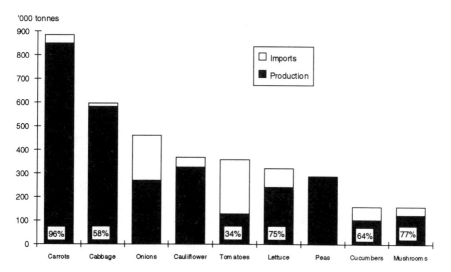

Source : MAFF 'Basic Horticultural Statistics for the UK, Euro PA

Annual domestic production is valued, on average, at £981 million at the farm gate (MAFF, 1994)[14]. Of this £655m is accounted for by field vegetables and protected vegetables account for £326m.

Table 8.3:   Total Supply of Fresh Vegetables in the UK, 1991-1993(av.) '000 tonnes

Vegetable	Production, field and protected	Imports	Exports and Re-Exports	Total Supply
	'000 tonnes marketed	('000t)	('000t)	('000t)
Beetroot[f]	82.2			82.2
Carrots, Parsnips, Turnips & Swedes[f]	847.7	37.0	(13.1)	871.6
Onions[f]	267.7	193.0	(6.1)	454.6
Brussel Sprouts[f]	105.9	2.2	(0.4)	107.7
Cabbage[f]	580.3	15.1	(1.3)	594.1
Cauliflower[f]	324.3	43.3	(3.0)	364.6
Calabrese[f]	38.2			38.2
Beans[f]	56.8	8.5	(1.8)	63.5
Peas[f]	282.2	5.3	(9.1)	278.4
Asparagus[f]	1.6			1.6
Celery[fp]	61	26.5	(1.2)	86.3
Leeks[f]	70.6			70.6
Lettuce[fp]	239.4	81.0	(1.7)	318.7
Rhubarb[f]	23.2			23.2
Watercress[f]	4.4			4.4
Tomatoes[p]	126.2	232.6	(6.3)	352.5
Cucumbers[p]	101.5	5-5.7	(0.6)	156.6
Mushrooms and Truffles[p]	121.7[c]	35.3	(1.2)	155.8
Sweet Peppers[p]	4.3	44.1	(0.1)	48.3
Aubergines and Courgettes		26.9	(0.1)[d]	29.8
Sweet Corn		5.9	(0.15)	5.75
Sweet Potatoes		3.0	(0.1)	2.9
Others		71.8	(11.9)[e]	59.9
Total	**3339**	**890**	**(58)**	**4171**
Farmgate Value	**£981m**			

Source : MAFF 'Basic Horticultural Statistics for the UK, Euro PA

c   In the UK, mushrooms are grown only under protection and no truffles are produced. These figures also exclude Northern Ireland for which figures are not available.

d   includes marrows and pumpkins

e   includes garlic, asparagus, artichokes, olives, capers, gherkins, spinach, chicory, fennel, celeriac, shallots and other onions, leeks and chicory.

f   grown in the field

p   grown under protection

The cost of transporting relatively bulky vegetables has meant that imports have been dominated by the higher value salad vegetables in the

---

14   Average of 1991 to 1993.

UK off-season. The 890,000 tonnes of vegetables imported on average each year over 1991-93 are sourced largely from within the EU. Salad vegetables and onions (70%) constitute the bulk of this trade. Tomatoes (232,600 tonnes) and onions (193,000 tonnes) are the largest single categories of imported vegetables into the UK. Spain, France and the Netherlands are the main sources of these fresh vegetable imports from within the EU. Africa, the Canary Islands, Israel and the USA are the most important sources of vegetable imports from outside the EU.

Glasshouse vegetable production is very much larger than that for fruit, covering 2,700 hectares.   Virtually all the tomatoes, cucumbers, mushrooms and sweet peppers grown in the UK, and 18% of the lettuce and celery, are produced in glasshouses.

Carrots, peas, tomatoes and onions are the only significant vegetable exports from the UK. These comprise 13,000 tonnes, 9,100 tonnes, 6,300 tonnes and 6,100 tonnes respectively out of a total export tonnage of 58,000 tonnes per year on average for the period 1991-93.

98% of peas grown in the UK are grown under contract for processing. Of the 691,000 tonnes of carrots produced annually in the UK, 66% come from East Anglia with the remainder being grown in Lincolnshire and Nottinghamshire, the North West and West Wales. Carrots are marketed for close to nine months of the year, peaking in September and falling away to almost no marketings in May and June. No significant amount of carrots are grown under protection.   The area devoted to carrot production has been increasing and yields per hectare were the highest in 1993/94 for more than a decade.

Only 37,000 tonnes of carrots were imported, on average, over the period 1991-93, representing 4% of the total UK carrot supply.   Monthly marketings averaged between 82,000 tonnes in the peak months of September, January and February down to 27,000 tonnes in May. Thus imports represent one to two months production, imported in the months of May and June when domestic marketings are at their lowest. These imports are largely from France, Spain and The Netherlands.

The salad vegetables, in particular lettuce, tomatoes, cucumbers and celery, have seen a growth in production over the past decade in response to an increase in UK household demand for healthy fresh produce which is no longer purely a seasonal demand. The UK produces 33% of its total supply of tomatoes, equivalent to 126,200 tonnes of tomatoes a year (average over 1991-93). Imports of tomatoes, 232,600 tonnes, come from the Canary Islands outside the EU and from the Netherlands and Spain within the EU.   In value terms, tomatoes dominate consumer spending on salad vegetables with 54%, compared with 19% for lettuce, 14% cucumbers and the remainder (celery, spring onions, radishes etc.) at 13%.

Approximately 9,150 hectares of lettuce was grown in the UK of which 1,386 hectares was grown under protection year round, in the period 1991-93. An increase in demand for lettuce has been met by domestic production which has seen a 34% increase over the past decade. The majority of lettuce is grown in the field in the summer with imports being primarily during the winter when domestic production falls. Imports have also seen a 115% increase, albeit from a low base, over the last decade, driven largely by the extended demand for lettuce by UK consumers in the winter.

The UK provides nearly two-thirds of its total consumption of cucumbers from domestic production which are grown wholly under protection. Imports come primarily from The Netherlands in summer and the Canary Islands in winter.

Mushroom production, which is all under protection in Great Britain (figures for Northern Ireland are not available), doubled from 56,000 in the mid 1970's to a peak of 123,300 in 1990 and has since levelled off at around 119,000 tonnes. This is due to a rapid growth in yields per hectare over this time.

Half of the UK's mushroom production comes from a few very large holdings whilst the other half is produced by over 200 small family farms. The sector is very competitive and both large scale and the smaller holdings have been under pressure. Economies of scale have contributed to larger mushroom producers profitability whilst smaller farms have benefited from intensive use of family labour and management (Hinton, 1991). However, the English mushroom industry has claimed that it has been disadvantaged by the favourable tax treatment given to Irish mushroom producers in recent years. This was the subject of formal complaints to the European Commission and in 1994 the Commission advised that this tax treatment should not be continued.

Despite a 60% increase in UK production, the increase in demand for mushrooms over the past decade has outstripped domestic supply. Growth in demand has been matched from increased imports, not from domestic production. This has also been the case for leeks, beef tomatoes and radishes where domestic production is apparently unable to meet domestic demand (Datamonitor, 1994).

As noted earlier, the fresh produce market has become more and more dominated by the grocery multiples during the 1980's. This has eroded greengrocers' market share and put major pressure on the highly fragmented produce wholesale structure in the UK[15]. Fresh fruit and vegetable distribution is characterised in the UK by a large number of small independent operators who have not in the past been able to supply the large multiples with a regular supply. This has led many of the large grocery multiples to source directly from UK producers and independent retailers preferring to buy imports where available (Datamonitor, 1994).

Fruit Production and Trade

Table 8.4:   Supply of Fruit in the UK, 1991-1993(av.)'000 tonnes

Fruit - fresh and dried	Production ('000 tonnes marketed)	Imports ('000t)	Exports and Re-Exports ('000t)	Total Supply ('000t)
Apples	316.6	444.5	(28.7)[d]	732.4
Bananas[a]		563.0		563.0
Oranges[a]		363.6		363.6
Mandarins[a]		150.7		150.7
Other Citrus[a]		145.2		145.2
Grapes		127.5	(2.4)	125.1
Pears	32.2	99.6	(2.2)	129.6
Pineapples[a]		20.6		20.6
Cherries	2.4	8.6	(0.2)	10.8
Plums	19.0	29.5	(0.8)	47.7
Peaches		82.3		82.3
Figs		0.6		0.6
Dates[a]		11.2		11.2
Strawberries	42.8	20.3	(0.23)	62.9
Avocadoes[a]		15.2		15.2
Other Fresh Fruit[ac]	47.8[b]	166.0	(33.7)	180.1
Total Supply	**460.8**	**2249.0**	**(68.23)**	**2641.0**
In Value terms	**£266m**			

Source: MAFF Basic Horticultural Statistics for the UK, 1984-1994, HMSO

a   includes dried fruit
b   Other fruit includes mostly berries i.e. raspberries, blackcurrants, red and white currants, gooseberries, blackberries and loganberries.
c   includes melons and kiwi fruit among others.
d   1993 figures for apple exports are only a quarter of what they have been in previous years, hence this figure is low.

The value of UK produced fruit that is marketed is around £266 million on average over 1991-93, i.e. a quarter of that for vegetables. Protected fruit, which is all soft fruit such as strawberries and raspberries, accounts for less than 1% of the total value of all fruit production and is grown on only 41 hectares.

---

15   See Shaw *et al* (1994) for an analysis of the long term trends affecting the UK wholesale markets for fresh fruit and vegetables.

Fruit grown in the open covers nearly 43,000 hectares in the UK, concentrated in the South East of England and in East Anglia. 80% of all fruit consumed in the UK is imported. Of these imports, three quarters are of non-indigenous fruit, i.e. bananas, citrus fruit, grapes, pineapples, peaches, figs, dates and avocados. Remaining imports are of indigenous fruit such as apples, pears and cherries.

Figure 8.8:   UK Main Fruit Supply, 1991-93 average, '000 tonnes

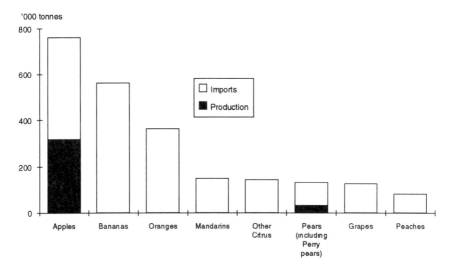

Source : MAFF 'UK Basic Horticultural Statistics of the UK' 1994, Euro PA

Glasshouse fruit production has undergone considerable structural change. The area devoted to production has doubled since the late 1970's, reflecting the high returns to intensive protected fruit production. For example, in 1993 strawberries and raspberries were selling at between £1,500 and £2,000 per tonne compared with £275 per tonne on average for apples and £350 per tonne for pears.

In the past, the market for strawberries has been heavily influenced by the jam-making industry in the UK, despite a gradual decline in this sector and an increase in fresh strawberry sales (Hinton, 1991). Glasshouse production, improvements in packaging and increased availability of chilling space in supermarkets have extended the season for UK produced soft fruit. The UK is the largest producer of raspberries in the EU, producing almost 20,000 tonnes per annum on average (1989-93).

Two thirds of the UK's fruit imports are sourced from other European Community countries. With the important exception of apples, the amount of UK fruit exports is negligible.

Apples

Apples are the most popular fruit in the UK and are also produced in the largest quantities. UK grown apples cover around 20,000 hectares, producing close to 360,000 tonnes a year. Despite this level of production, close to 60% of apples consumed in the UK are imported.

The UK apple sector has faced considerable competition from French imports since the formation of the EU, due largely to the French extended growing season and the strong demand in the UK for French Golden Delicious apples. As a result of this competition, the area of apples grown in the UK has declined by 2% a year since the mid 1970's. However, production has been stable over the same period with yields increasing by a third. The sector is characterised by low profitability, the lowest of all UK fruit sectors which is exacerbated by a fall in domestic apple consumption.

Bananas

The single largest category of fruit imported into the UK is that for bananas. 563,000 tonnes per annum on average (1991-93) worth £239 million (including plantains and dried bananas). Greece, Portugal and Spain produce bananas (the last two from their North African annexes and the Canary Islands), France re-exports bananas from its Caribbean annexes, Martinique and Guadeloupe. The UK has traditionally sourced its bananas from the Windward Islands and Jamaica in the Caribbean, and Belize and Surinam, and other members of the ACP. These traditional suppliers have increasingly been supplemented by South and Central American "dollar" bananas. Direct imports into the UK come primarily from the Caribbean states (62%), the Central American countries of Costa Rica, Guatemala, Belize and Honduras (23%) and the remainder from South America and Africa.

There are a number of large companies involved in the importation of bananas who have ripening centres in the UK and the rest of Europe. Banana ripening centres are also owned by independent companies who have a varying degree of autonomy in different parts of the EU. The largest UK companies involved in banana imports include Geest, which has 40% of the ripening business in the UK, and Fyffes, an Irish owned company which has a major part of its operation in the UK but is based in Ireland. Since the introduction of the banana regime Geest and Fyffes have started a programme of partnership and acquisition with other smaller banana shippers and ripeners in other parts of the EU. The North American multinational banana companies, Chiquita, Dole and Del Monte, are estimated to hold a share of about 70% of the European banana market.

Citrus Fruit

The UK imports all its citrus fruit, totalling 660,000 tonnes per annum, valued at c. £226 million at the port. The main source within the EU is Spain (30%). Other sources of imports include Morocco (13%), Israel (11%), South Africa (11%), Uruguay (4.5%) and Turkey (4%). The key imports of citrus fruit by category are oranges (55%), followed by mandarins (24%), grapefruit (12%) and lemons and limes (9%).

Soft Fruit

The production of berries and currants has been one of the more profitable UK fruit enterprises which has, in the past, faced no substantial in-season competition from imports due to the highly perishable nature of the produce. The jam making industry used to be a major market for domestic strawberry production, but improvements in packaging/transport have increased fresh/prepared supplies especially off-season. Imports of cheaper strawberry pulp from Poland and Third countries in the late 1980's encoraged a restructuring and a large number of producers went out of strawberry production. Total imports of strawberries into the UK almost doubled, from 10,000 tonnes in 1984 to 19,700 tonnes in 1989. Growth of strawberry imports has continued but at a slower rate since 1989. This increased competition has led to a halving of UK strawberry acreage from 1984 to 1993, although yields have doubled over the same period maintaining production at around 50,000 tonnes per annum. At this level of production, UK strawberry production is relatively profitable, enhanced by an extension to the harvest period as growers increase the area of strawberries grown under protection and increased marketing through PYO operations.

Processing companies such as Ribena who produce a high vitamin drink for the dilutable soft drinks market using blackcurrants have encouraged UK blackcurrant production, which has increased 38% to 23,000 tonnes over the past decade, valued at close to £15 million (MAFF, 1994). Blackcurrant production is regionally concentrated on a number of large arable farms in East Anglia, with 18,000 tonnes a year produced, on average, worth £32 million per annum. Over 80% of raspberries grown in the UK are located in the east of Scotland. 2,000 tonnes of raspberries (just over 10% of production) are exported from the UK.

Developments in the Marketing and Distribution of Fresh Fruit and Vegetables

The marketing and distribution system for fresh fruit and vegetables has seen a number of important changes in recent years. The most significant and influential of these has been the growth in the retail market share of the supermarkets. These outlets now account for more than half of retail sales of fruit and vegetables. Traditional channels of supply from growers or importers through wholesale markets have proved ill-equipped to meet the supermarkets requirement for consistency and continuity of regular deliveries of high class produce. The supermarket trade by-passes the wholesale produce markets, such as New Covent Garden in favour of direct purchasing from selected growers or from the specialist distribution companies such as Geest and Saphir which undertake not only wholesaling and distribution but also transportation, pre-packing, labelling, bar-coding and preparations to the supermarkets; requirements. Production even where the produce is imported is to a given specification calling for efficient vertical co-ordination of all stages from production through to retail sale. Cool chain distribution is necessary to ensure quality standards are met. The volumes traded and the necessary investments to achieve the required specification favour large companies, and concentration in the marketing and distribution system has increased.

As the distribution companies have grown in importance, so the wholesale markets have declined (Shaw *et al, op cit*). The major clients of the wholesale markets, the traditional greengrocers have lost market share to the supermarkets. Throughput of the markets has now diminished so that they handle variable residual quantities of produce. Their role in price determination for the fruit and vegetable market has lessened as they become increasingly marginal to the overall demand and supply situation.

Processing of Fruit and Vegetables

This section deals with fruit and vegetables primarily as an input into processed produce which is defined as freezing, canning or drying. Fresh/prepared produce refers to that which has not undergone any such transformation, including the grading, cutting and packing of fruit and vegetables. The ripening of fruit such as bananas, which is often carried out in the UK on imports of green bananas, is also not considered as processing here.

Within the fruit and vegetable processing industry a breakdown by value indicates that canned vegetables account for 40%, frozen vegetables 59%

and dried vegetables less than 1% of total vegetable processing. 70% of fruit consumed in a processed form is in cans with the remainder dried. There is relatively little freezing of fruit. This analysis does not include either potato products or fruit juice.

Figure 8.9: UK Market for Processed Fruit and Vegetables (£m RSP)

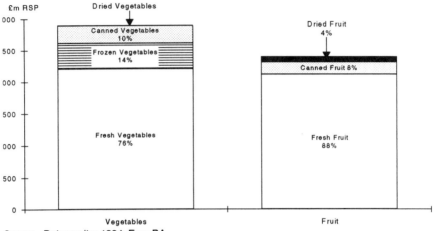

Source : Datamonitor 1994, Euro PA

Concentration ratios in most processed fruit and vegetable markets are relatively low, with the exception of frozen potato products and dried vegetables. All other processed fruit and vegetable products are dominated by own brand labels with concentration ratios less than 50%.

Table 8.5 shows the share of the total value of the market that the top three manufacturers have in each sector. This varies from 24% for frozen vegetable processors to 68% for dried vegetable processors with the average being close to 40%. The second column in Table 8.5 is relative market share of the top manufacturer. This is calculated as the share of that leader divided by the share of the next largest manufacturer. The average is close to 4 with canned fruit and frozen vegetables processors being low, reflecting the fragmented nature of the market, as opposed to dried vegetable processing which is a highly concentrated industry.

Table 8.5:   Fruit and Vegetable Processors Competitive Structure, 1993

	% Value for the Top Three Manufacturers	Relative Market Share of the No. 1 Manufacturer
Canned Vegetables	42	3.94
Canned Fruit	39	1.62
Dried Fruit	25	4
Dried Vegetables	68	7.5
Frozen Vegetables	24	2.43

Source: Datamonitor 1994

Processed Vegetables

The processed vegetable market in the UK is worth c. £700m annually. A breakdown of this market is given in Table 8.6.

Canned Vegetables

393,000 tonnes of canned vegetables were consumed on average over the period 1991-93 (Datamonitor 1994). The canning market had an average value over these years of £274m. Growth in this area has been small or negative in the past decade as other forms of vegetables have been perceived as more convenient and healthy and an increase in the number of households with freezers and microwaves has made storage and preparation of frozen and fresh fruit easier. Innovations in offering products with low salt and sugar contents and a wider range of vegetables available, such as asparagus, have somewhat stemmed this decline. In terms of relative size, the frozen potato products market in the UK is larger than the canned vegetable market as a whole.

Tomatoes, peas and sweetcorn dominate the canned vegetable market with the most growth occurring in canned tomatoes and asparagus while sales of traditional vegetables such as peas, beans and carrots in cans have declined. The market for canned tomatoes is worth £84 million in the UK and is very price competitive, being dominated by the Napolina brand (£26m). Vegetable canning in the UK has a concentration ratio for the top three manufacturers of 42%. This is low in terms of other food sectors representing a mature market as well as the dominance of own-label sales which comprise about 40% of the market.

Table 8.6:   Consumption of Processed Vegetables in the United Kingdom 1991-93 av. RSP

Product	£m RSP
Total Frozen Vegetables -	**407.0**
Frozen Peas	150.0
Mixed Vegetables	64.0
Frozen Beans	46.0
All Other Frozen Vegetables[1.]	147.0
Total Canned Vegetables -	**274.0**
Canned Tomatoes	83.7
Canned Peas	83.3
Canned Sweet Corn	44.3
Other canned vegetables	62.7
Dried Vegetables	**4.6**
Total Processed Vegetables	**685.6**

Source: Datamonitor

Hillsdown are a major company operating in canning with their brands as well as supplying the own-label market. Green Giant are a major supplier at the top end of the market, dominating sales of canned sweetcorn, and HL Foods (part of Hillsdown) have released vegetables in sauces under the Morton brand aimed at increasing the convenience of canned foods. Other major canners include Anglia Canners and Brooke Bond Batchelors.

Frozen Vegetables

This sector is dominated by the large retailers own brands and has become more fragmented as an increased number of vegetables become available in frozen form. The sector was worth £407 million on average over 1991-93 and has been static during much of the 1990's after considerable growth in the 1980's (Datamonitor, 1994).

The frozen vegetable sector has grown largely at the expense of canned vegetables, with the concept of freshness being desirable to consumers and associated with frozen rather than canned vegetables. In turn, frozen products are suffering at the hands of increased availability of chilled and pre-packaged fresh produce.

The frozen vegetable sector is dominated by frozen peas which have 34% of the market, followed by mixed vegetables (19%). Mixed vegetables are the only type of frozen vegetable product to have experienced an increase in demand since the mid 1980's.

Table 8.7:   Market Share for Frozen Vegetables, % value of market, 1987-93

% Value	1987	1988	1989	1990	1991	1992	1993
Ross Young	8	9	7	7	7	7	7
BEW[a]	21	20	19	19	18	17	17
Own-label[b]	50	52	55	57	59	60	60
Other	21	20	19	17	16	16	16
Total	100	100	100	100	100	100	100

Source: Datamonitor 1994
a   Birds Eye Walls

The sector is dominated by Ross Young (owned by United Biscuits) and Birds Eye Walls (owned by Unilever) with sales of own-label being the fastest growth area. Own-label is dominated by Froqual which is now part of Albert Fisher plc since its acquisition in December 1990 of Campbells UK vegetable division (Datamonitor, 1994).

Frozen peas is the largest sector of frozen vegetables worth an average of £150m from 1991-93. Demand has declined in the past two years but is otherwise relatively stable. Frozen beans is a much smaller market, £46m, while the market for mixed vegetables has grown from £44m in 1987 to £80m in 1993 (£64m average over the last three years) in response to consumers continued search for quality convenience foods. There has also been an increased fragmentation of the market as an increasing number of frozen vegetable products have become available.

Dried Vegetables

This is a declining market in the UK which has faced increasing competition from rice and pasta products. Dried vegetable products include mushrooms, onions, mixed vegetables and mixed peppers. The top three manufacturers of dried vegetables hold 68% of the market with Whitworths accounting for 60% of the market. Own-label has the second largest market share at 27% (Datamonitor, 1994).

Processed Fruit

Canned Fruit

Consumption of canned fruit has fallen by 13% in volume terms over the past decade, from 211,000 tonnes in 1982-84 to 183,000 tonnes on average from 1991-1993 (Datamonitor 1994). However, the value of this market has increased 15% (from £171m in 1982-84 to £194m in 1991-93 - Table 8.8).

Canned peaches, pears and pineapples are the largest consumer items in this area, averaging £116m (1991-1993). Canned products are very price sensitive and strong growth in own-label brands in canning as well as in frozen fruit and vegetable products has led to some very competitive pricing (Datamonitor, 1994).

Table 8.8   Value of Processed Fruits in the UK, 1991-93 average RSP

	Product	£m RSP
Total Canned Fruit -		**194.0**
	Peaches	50.0
	Pineapples	41.8
	Pears	24.3
	Fruit Salad	31.7
	Mandarins	14.5
	Grapefruits	10.8
	Other	21.6
Total Dried Fruit		**87.3**
	Sultanas	32.0
	Currants	12.7
	Raisins	22.0
	Other	20.7
Total Frozen Fruit[16]		**11.0**
Total Processed Fruit		**292.3**

Source : Datamonitor

---

16 Figure for frozen fruit from Fast Facts, the rest from Datamonitor. Due to the different methods of producing the data these sources do not complement each other exactly.

Canned fruit has also faced strong competition from a number of other areas. The frozen sector has grown with the increase in home freezers in the UK. The increased popularity of yoghurts and prepared desserts has taken demand away from canned fruit as a dessert. The fresh fruit market has also eroded the canned fruit market share. Within the canned fruit sector consumers have moved away from fruit in syrup towards a preference for fruit in juice which has been a complementary rather than a competitive shift and as such has added value to the sector.

The top three fruit canners in the UK accounted for 39% of the canned fruit market in 1993. Own-label products dominate the canned fruit market and have dramatically increased their market share from 34% (£67m) in 1988-90 to 42% (£82m) in 1991-93. Some of the large food processing companies in the UK, such as Albert Fisher, provide canned fruit to the supermarkets' own-label brands. The largest canners based in the UK are HL Foods which is a subsidiary of Hillsdown Holdings based in Spalding, Lincolnshire.

Table 8.9:   Market Shares for Canned Fruit in the UK, 1988-90 and 1991-93

Brand	1988-90 £m RSP	% market share by value	1991-93 £m RSP	% market share by value
Del Monte	36.5	19.0	39.1	20.0
Princes	24.8	12.7	23.0	11.7
Australian Gold	6.5	3.3	5.4	2.7
John West	4.5	2.3	4.4	2.3
Dole	2.0	1.0	3.0	1.7
Gerber Pride	7.2	3.3	9.8	5.0
Own-label	66.6	34.0	82.0	42.3
Other	47.4	24.3	27.7	14.3
Total	**195.5**	**100.0**	**194.0**	**100.0**

Source: Datamonitor (1994) p. 171-72

Frozen Fruit

The frozen fruit market is much smaller (excluding frozen fruit pies) with 7,300 tonnes being consumed on average over the past three years. This has increased from 3,000 tonnes (on average) in 1985-87 but, like the average price for these goods, fluctuates widely year on year.

Dried Fruit

The dried fruit market in the UK is worth £87m with 67,500 tonnes being consumed on average for 1991-93. This market is growing steadily with an average annual growth rate of 2.7% over the past decade. Growth in the last three years has slowed to 1% per annum.

Industry Structure and Financial Performance

In comparison with other sectors, the fruit and vegetable sector is not very concentrated, whilst within the sector itself, the processing sector is far more concentrated than the fresh produce sector.

The five firm concentration gross ratio overall is estimated at 45% as Figure 8.9 illustrates. Unfortunately this data from CSO Business Monitor includes potatoes which has the effect of increasing the ratios.

Figure 8.9: Five Firm Concentration Ratios - Fruit and Vegetable sector

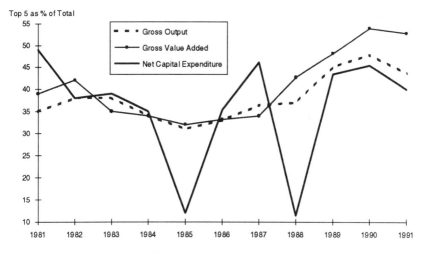

Source : Business Monitor PA1002 selected years, Euro PA
Note: Figures include potatoes

The five firm concentration ratios shown above are interesting. The fruit and vegetable sector as a whole has a gross output five firm concentration ratio of around 40%. This is a rise from 1981, yet from 1981 to 1985 the ratio fell. Since then the ratio rose till 1990 when it began to fall again.

The gross value-added ratio has closely followed the gross output ratio indicating that that the top five firms have had a stable profit margin over the ten years shown. It would appear that increases in profit have come due to increases in sales.

The net capital expenditure five firm ratio is the most spectacular especially between 1985 and 1989. For the ratio to fall to 10% of the total when the five firms have 30% of the sales implies that most of the top 5 companies have reduced capital expenditure severely.

Table 8.10 displays a summary of the average performance of UK fruit and vegetable companies over a three year period.

These companies are coded by reference to their primary activity as:

FRFV - handling, importing and distribution of fresh fruit and vegetables
FRV or FRF - as above but for vegetables or fruit respectively
PROC - fruit and vegetable processing, includes chilling, canning, freezing and drying.

The average ROCE is relatively high, being almost 17%, with most companies having a 10% plus figure. The companies that have achieved this are those that have focused on the growing market for further processed fresh goods such as prepared salads and chilled produce as well as frozen vegetables. The sectors have higher value-added products and opportunities for higher profit margins.

Within companies there is a wide divergence of results. Of the larger companies Hazlewoods seems to have done paticularly well achieving a high profit margin, high ROCE and satisfactory current and debt ratios. Brooke Bond (a Unilever subsidiary) has good overall figures, including an ROCE figure of over 50%.

- The figures in Table 8.10 for United Biscuits are for the Ross Youngs subsidiary which covers UB's frozen foods operations.

- Of the smaller companies Smedleys appears to have performed well along with Henry Telfer, its fellow Hillsdown Holding subsidiary.

- Several companies have profit margins less than 3%. This applies to both large and small companies alike.

The Albert Fisher Group plc is a multinational company which is involved in the UK in importing, processing, packing, storage and distribution of fruit, vegetables and seafood. Group turnover for the UK fresh fruit and vegetable division was £478 million in 1994 which equates to 54% of the European Divisions £891 million turnover and 34% of total group turnover. 39% of this was sales of citrus fruit, 8% bananas, 14% potatoes, 13% other vegetables, 11% apples and pears and 15% other fruit.

Turnover in processed food (primarily fruit and vegetables) was £247 million in 1994 in the European market. Albert Fisher invested in canning capacity in the late 1980's but found the canned market dwindling. It is likely that Albert Fisher has spare canning capacity.

Table 8.10: Summary of Average UK Fruit and Vegetable Company Results (three year average)

Company and Primary Activity	Turnover £m	Profit £m	Profit/ Sales(%)	ROCE (%)	Current Ratio (%)	Debt Ratio	Years
Dalgety (FRFV- by Dalgety Produce)	4,469.00	114.67	2.58	24.65	1.00	0.62	91/92-93/94
The Albert Fisher Group (FRFV and PROC)	1,302.00	29.20	2.23	9.49	1.76	0.61	91/92-93/94
UB (Ross Young's) Ltd (PROC)	536.23	21.73	4.06	15.70	1.24	0.56	91-93
Hazlewoods (PROC)	731.33	51.47	7.12	16.51	1.55	0.64	91/92-93/94
Geest (FRFV & PROC)	640.33	8.50	1.35	10.08	1.02	0.65	90/91-92/93
Birds Eye Walls (Unilever)	625.57	50.94	8.14	29.23	1.18	0.60	90-92
Fyffes (FRFV)*	581.00	29.13	5.03	11.92	1.48	0.57	90/91-92/93
Perkins Foods (PROC)	332.00	20.67	6.56	39.28	1.10	0.76	90/91-92/93
Princes (PROC)	224.78	3.84	1.63	14.04	1.17	0.87	89/90-91/92
HL Foods (HH) (PROC)	179.56	10.76	5.91	70.78	0.94	0.93	92-93
Campbells (PROC)	179.30	-6.64	-3.33	**	0.71	0.68	89/90-91/92
M. & W. Mack (FRFV)	136.48	2.87	2.10	25.78	0.98	0.59	90/91-92/93
Fairfax Meadow Farm Ltd (HH) (PROC)	72.80	4.73	6.49	17.07	1.43	0.57	91-93
Smedleys (HH) (PROC)	33.32	3.53	13.53	17.88	4.01	0.51	90-92
Average weighted by turnover		**61.64**	**2.72**	**18.22**	**1.04**	**0.87**	
Straight Average		**24.69**	**4.27**	**22.84**	**1.33**	**0.65**	
Total Turnover	**10,057**						

Source :   Kompass, McMillans, Hambro Company Guide, Euro PA
Note :   The figures shown above should be read in conjunction with the notes contained in the Appendix to ChapterOne
*   Figures for turnover and profit are in millions of Irish pounds
**   Campbells ROCE figure omitted as very high and negative due to high losses and low capital employed. Insertion of this figure would severely distort sector averages.

80% of Geest's turnover is in its fresh produce division.   Another division, Geest Foods, is heavily concerned with preparation and marketing of chilled convenience foods for Marks and Spencers, Sainsburys and other retailers under their own-labels.   In April 1995 Geest Wholesale Services (GWS) - the part of its fresh produce division concerned with wholesaling was sold for £4.4m.   A substantial proportion of the remaining fresh produce turnover is the importation, ripening and sale of bananas under the 5 Isles brand of those bananas which originate from the Windward Isles.

Fyffes are an Irish based group who import and distribute fresh fruit and produce, principally bananas, into Ireland, the UK and the rest of Europe under the Fyffes brand. Warehousing and distribution is provided under the Vangen name. However, Vangen was sold in April 1995.

Hazlewood Foods Plc are involved in the marketing and distribution of imported and domestically-grown produce (40% in 1993) as well as the preparation of bakery and meat products, ready meals, bottled and convenience foods. Of the figures quoted in the above table, 60% on average is attributable to their entire UK operations, not just fruit and vegetables, and this percentage is growing.

M & W Mack Ltd are one of the largest independent companies operating in the fruit and vegetable sector, based in West Sussex. The company deals primarily with the marketing, distribution and sale of fresh fruit and vegetables as well as flowers, and increased its banana ripening facilities by 75% in terms of volume-handled, in 1994.

26% of Perkins Foods Plc is attributable to their UK operations of fresh produce sales and manufacture of frozen and chilled foods.

Summary and Conclusions

Recent years have seen relatively little change in the overall volume of the fruit and vegetable sector, though this static overall picture conceals significant changes in the balance between the different products offered, and the means by which they reach the consumer.

As with other sectors the fruit and vegetable sector has shared, though to a lesser extent, in the trend towards increasing provision of 'convenience foods' with prepared fresh produce. However, the market is still primarily for fresh rather than processed products, and more than other fresh food sectors, fruit and vegetables reach the consumer in much the same form as they leave the grower. Processed products account for a relatively small part of fruit and vegetable consumption, and consumers seem to regard processed, especially canned, fruit and vegetables as a rather inferior substitute for the fresh item.

While still accounting for the biggest shares of consumption, the traditional vegetables and fruits, such as roots and brassicas, and apples and oranges, have lost market share. Salad vegetables, and 'Mediterranean' vegetables, such as aubergines and peppers, and bananas and more exotic tropical fruits have all benefited from changing consumer preferences, while the higher income elasticities of demand for these products has meant that they have gained more than the traditional fruits and vegetables from income growth. The same factors lie behind growth in year round consumption of traditionally seasonal fruits and vegetables made possible through imports. The substitution of these higher value products for the traditional cheaper fruit and vegetables, and increasing sales of prepared fruit and vegetables have increased the value of the sector in spite of its static volume.

Equally significant changes have taken place in the marketing and distribution system. The driving force behind these has been the growth in the importance of the supermarkets and they are now the major retail outlet for fruit and vegetables. The increasing retail market share of the supermarkets and the commensurate increase in their buying power together with plentiful supplies of produce has allowed them to impose their requirements in terms of quality, price and delivery on the marketing and distribution system producing far-reaching changes. There is no shortage of fresh fruit and vegetables, and in such a buyers' market and in spite of the resulting pressures on prices and margins, suppliers must meet the stringent quality requirements of the supermarket chains if they are to survive. The supermarkets' requirement for consistency and continuity of the highest quality supplies has extended vertical co-ordination right back to the growers both in the UK and abroad, and has promoted the growth of large specialised fresh produce distribution companies. These companies have provided the necessary investment in new technology such as cool chain and gas flushed distribution systems. The result has been the shortening of the marketing chain through vertical integration and the by-passing of the traditional wholesale produce markets, and increasing horizontal concentration in the marketing and distribution system.

References

Coma (1992). *The Health of the Nation,* Cm 1986, HMSO, London

Coma (1992). *The Coma Report: Dietary Reference Values for Food Energy and Nutrients for the United Kingdom,* HMSO, London

Datamonitor (1994). *UK Food Reports, Fruit and Vegetables.* Datamonitor, 106 Baker Street, London, W1M 1LA

DTI (1994). *The Uruguay Round of Multilateral Trade Negotiations 1986-94,* Cm 2579, HMSO, London

Euro Analysis (1993) unpublished report R58, *A Review of Health and Nutrition Policy,* Euro PA & Associates, 11 Church Street, Northborough, Cambs, PE6 9BN.

Euro PA & Associates (1995) unpublished report R79. *The US and European Markets For Apple Chips*. Euro PA & Associates, 11 Church Street, Northborough, Cambs, PE6 9BN.

Euro PA & Associates (1995). *Commentary and Analysis on the EU Banana Regime*, R81a, Euro PA & Associates, 11 Church Street, Northborough, Cambs, PE6 9BN.

Fast Facts (April 1994). *Food Trends (1985 to December 1993)*. Fast Facts Ltd, Walgrave, Northants, NN6 9RW

Fresh Produce Consortium (Sept 1994). *The CAP: Proposals for the reform of 1035/72*. Fresh Produce Consortium, 103-107 Market Towers, 1 Nine Elm Lane, London, SW8 5NQ

Fresh Produce Consortium (April 1995). *A guide to the Entry Price System*. Fresh Produce Consortium, 103-107 Market Towers, 1 Nine Elm Lane, London, SW8 5NQ

GATT, (1994). *Agreement Establishing the World Trade Organisation - Agreement on Agriculture*, Cm 2559, HMSO, London

Hallam, D. (1988). The UK Market for Fresh Exotic Fruit, *ODNRI Bulletin* **No.13**, ODNRI, London

Hinton, Lynn. (1991). *The European Market for Fruit and Vegetables*. Elsevier Applied Science, London

Irving, W.R, (1992). *The Distribution of Food in Europe*, paper presented at the conference for the International Food and Drink Industry, London

KeyNote Report (1994). *Fruit and Vegetables, A Market Sector Overview*. Keynote, Field House, 72 Oldfield Road, Hampton, Middlesex, GW12 2HQ

MAFF (1994) *Basic Horticultural Statistics for the United Kingdom, Calendar and Crop Years 1984-1993*. MAFF Statistics Division, Branch B, London.

McInerney, J. and The Lord Peston (eds) (1992). *Fair Trade in Bananas?* Report No. 239, Agricultural Economics Unit, University of Exeter, Exeter

NFU, (1994). *Real Choices*, discussion paper by the Long Term Strategy Group., London.

NFU, (1994). *GATT Settlement in Agriculture*, London.

Pedlar, R.H. and Van Schendelen, M. (1994). *Lobbying the European Union*. Dartmouth Publishing Company, Aldershot

Ritson, C. (1977). *Agricultural Economics: Principles and Policy*. Granada Publishing, St Albans

Shaw, S.A., Gibbs, J. and Gray. V. (1994). *The Strathclyde Wholesale Markets Study - Summary Report*, University of Strathclyde.

Chapter 9: Further-Processed and Branded Products, and Alcoholic Drinks

Mark Gunthorpe, Wyn Morgan and John Strak[1]

Introduction

The preceding chapters have focused on individual sectors of the UK food industry and have generally followed the approximation of first-stage processing discussed in Chapter One. However, a great proportion of the food and drink industry's products do not fit into this category - many food products and virtually all drink products are produced after a second-stage transformation i.e. they are further-processed goods. Branded goods, created by the marketing efforts of food and drink companies (and through the own-label products of the retail sector) are, typically, also further-processed products. Alcoholic drinks are, perhaps, the best example of these two observations and, accordingly, are dealt with here. The commercial companies that produce further-processed and branded products are spread along the size spectrum but the major brands recognised by most UK consumers are mainly owned and produced by large food and drink companies. Indeed, many major food and drink brands in Europe are produced by firms based in the UK. Hence, this chapter offers the reader the opportunity to consider the market shares and production of many further-processed products that are not dealt with in earlier chapters. It also offers the chance to examine the structure of the food and drink sector from the perspective of major companies.

The chapter begins with a brief note on the definition of further-processed goods and lists the categories covered therein. The chapter goes on to discuss one particular aspect of agricultural policy that affects all of the food and drink industry but which is especially relevant to the further-processed sector because of its complexity - the agrimonetary system in the EU. The chapter then identifies and tabulates the largest UK food and drink companies and moves on, through the categories of further-processed goods and discusses their market characteristics one by one. Alcoholic drinks is the largest section within this listing and its coverage concludes the chapter.

---

[1] Mark Gunthorpe is a researcher in Euro PA & Associates, Cambs.; Dr Wyn Morgan is a lecturer in Economics in the Department of Economics at the University of Nottingham Dr John Strak is principal at Euro PA & Associates, Cambs. The Editors are grateful for the information provided by; Birds Eye Walls, Geest plc, The Gin and Vodka Association, Mars, The SWA, and Zenith. Any opinions, errors or omissions in the Chapter are the sole responsibility of the Editors subject to the caveat in the Appendix to Chapter One.

Defining Further-Processed Food Products

The Treaty of Rome Non-Annex II Goods list includes food and drink products which are, "a combination of two or more agriculturally based raw materials, or are processed beyond first-stage transformation"[2]. The Non-Annex II products, which are classified as food, do not have a rationale presented with them for the inclusion of one product or another - beyond that given in the previous sentence. A selected list of these "further-processed" product categories is:

- Confectionery - chocolate and sugar (including chewing gum)

- Biscuits

- Breakfast Cereals

- Margarine

- Infant food

- Pizza

- Ready-to-eat meals

- Pasta

- Rice

- Non-alcoholic beverages - this includes soft drinks, mineral water, fruit juices, tea, coffee and maté.

- Alcoholic drinks.

The Food Industry and Agrimoney[3]

As noted in the Chapter One and all subsequent chapters, the food and drink industry is directly affected by agricultural and trade policies. These policies are generally implemented with the production and trade of raw materials in mind, but their indirect effects on the food manufacturing sector can be very significant.   In first-stage

---

[2]   See EC (1994) for the latest revised list of Non-Annex II products.
[3]   The Editors wish to acknowledge the help of the FDF and Sinon Harris of British Sugar in the preparation of this section but readily accept full responsibility for any opinions, errors or omissions herein.

transformation processes the availability and cost of raw materials may be affected through quotas, intervention standards, import/export restrictions, etc.. In second-stage transformations the effective protection[4] (or taxation) of value-added processes because of these policies can be very significant. It would be surprising if these direct and indirect effects on the protection of the domestic food and drink industry did not affect production and investment decisions of food companies. In this chapter, several categories of further-processed goods will be examined and it is often these value-added product areas that endure disguised, but the greatest, effects from agricultural and trade policy. One specific example of agricultural policy in the EU that deserves special mention, and supplements the references in earlier chapters, is the agrimonetary system of the CAP[5].

The EU's agrimonetary system (or "green" currency system) came into being in 1969 as a temporary measure with the aim of reducing the effect on German farmers' prices as the German currency was revalued. The agrimonetary system is an artificial exchange rate system used to convert CAP prices for farm products, which are set in ECU, into national currencies. Before the Single Market, "green" exchange rates were effectively fixed against the ECU and trade between member states required monetary compensatory amounts (MCAs) to be levied or granted on imports and exports. These import taxes or subsidies allowed the "common support price" aspect of the CAP to be maintained at the national frontier and hence maintained free trade in agricultural products within the European Community. Without MCAs, the common support price to farmers in conjunction with green currency rates, could have allowed distorted trade flows of agricultural raw materials and semi-processed products within the Community.

Although MCAs reduced or removed these potential trade effects farmers in individual member states were still being more or less protected from exchange rate fluctuations. In general, German farmers obtained the most benefit from the green currency system because the strengthening German mark was not reflected in a cut in German farm support prices. UK farmers, in contrast, faced a weakening Sterling and should have received higher support prices. In both cases, the discretion of their respective national Governments over the timing of changes green currency exchange rates prevented farmers from experiencing the

---

4   See Strak (1982) for a definition and analysis of how the concept of effective protection can be used to measure value-added processes in agriculture.

5   The reader is advised that the agrimonetary system of the European Union is an extremely complex subject. For the interested reader the exposition here should be supplemented by reference to specialists in the area esepacially those working with or for trade associations representing the food industry such as the FDF or, in Europe, the CIAA.

full costs or benefits of exchange rate fluctuations. Long term this would be expected to have significant production effects. Hence, German farmers produced more raw materials and the German food industry had more raw materials locally available to it. In due course, as the CAP adopted quotas and set-aside provisions for key commodities these production inefficiencies were fixed in the food industry's production/processing environment across Europe.

A further complication in the history of the agrimonetary system was the introduction of the "switchover" system in 1984 which "switched over" the effect of a strong currency in the system to the weaker currencies e.g. instead of a German revaluation and farm support price reduction, all weak currencies were devalued and farm support prices rose in member state currencies. The gap between the ECU at market rates and the ECU used in farm price calculations grew to around 20% (which is a measure of the extra incentive given to German farmers). Hence, the CAP budget and EU consumers and food manufacturers, faced farm product prices that were c. 20% higher than the use of market exchange rates would have produced.

The advent of the Single Market meant that all customs barriers at member state frontiers had to be abolished. hence, the "common market" in agricultural products was to be extended to all products in the new European Single Market. Without customs barriers MCAs could not be operated. With this in mind, a new system was introduced in January 1993 and the narrow band (hard currency) ERM members at that time fixed their green rates at their central ERM rates. The switchover gap was consolidated in the new system. The new system also required all currencies, including the UK, to automatically link their market exchange rates to their green rates and a complex system of revaluation/devaluation was introduced to facilitate this "tracking". The automatic element of this new system was important because it effectively removed the discretion of national Governments from the system. This new system, without MCAs, and with automatic revaluations/devaluations lasted until September 1993 when the narrow band currencies and the ERM came under renewed pressure from the foreign exchange markets. Under political pressure from the strong currency countries keen to avoid a revaluation that would have reduced farm support prices, the system was frozen. Only in December 1993 was a revised system introduced (the mini-switchover) which was scheduled to automatically expire by January 1995. This went some way to meet Germany's demands. New proposals to abolish switchover came from the Commission in the autumn of 1994 and political agreement on a less transparent system, was reached in December 1994 - to take effect in February 1995. Further currency instability in March 1995 and the lack of transparency in the revised system led to uncertainty and large disparities between green rates and market rates without, of course, any compensation at the border for traded food products The expected devaluations and revaluations in the new system were effectively postponed until political agreement could be reached again. European Commission proposals to limit the inflationary effects of green currency devaluations on farm support prices were due to be discussed in May 1995. These proposals were, however, subject to agreement in the Council of Ministers and to the rules agreed for limiting national aids to farming agreed in the 1994 Uruguay Round settlement.

In summary, the green currency system affects the UK food and drink industry in several ways;

- through increasing uncertainty about the cost of raw materials,
- through its inflationary impact on farm support prices,
- through its complication of trade and commercial practice, and
- through its distortionary effect on trade and production in and between Member States.

It might be considered that uncertainty about exchange rate movements is part of commercial life, but the inability to hedge against green currency movements means that the normal commercial remedy for exchange rate risk is unavailable to the food industry. Equally, the distortions caused by green currency movements have, at times, caused trade in raw material and intermediate products to follow inappropriate price signals. Currently, price gaps of 5% between Member State currencies are allowed under the latest version of the green currency system. Even this is enough to compensate for transport costs and could encourage trade distortions as raw materials move from one Member State to another to receive artificial premiums from the CAP's operation. Recent currency stability has, at times, produced price gaps larger than this and trade reports of milk, butter and other products moving from weak currency countries to stronger currency countries to take advantage of the premia are commonplace. Clearly, this is not beneficial to rational business planning in the food industry. When food manufacturing investment usually requires detailed market and location studies, a large scale financial commitment to processing and marketing capacity, and carefully considered decisions about logistics, labour availability, etc. it is difficult to avoid the conclusion that the food industry is not well served by uncertainties and distortions engendered by the green currency system. Certainly, the Single Market for raw materials and food products is seriously impaired by the current uncertainties and lack of transparency in the green currency system for CAP support prices.

Major UK Food and Drink Companies

Tables 9.1 and 9.2 display the largest companies (in terms of market capitalisation) operating in the UK food and drink industry. Table 9.1 lists the top UK based companies whilst Table 9.2 picks up the top 10 companies that are not UK owned but operating in the UK.

Table 9.1:   The Top 20 UK Food and Drink Manufacturers, 1994

	Company	Market Capital.	Sales (US$m)	Profit (US$m)	Profit Margin	Main Product
1	Unilever	31,650	43,618	3,042	6.97	Oils, dairy
2	Guinness	13,685	7,300	1,099	15.05	Spirits
3	Grand Metropolitan	12,914	12,711	986	7.76	Drinks
4	Allied Domecq	8,403	9,651	949	9.83	Wine, spirits
5	Bass	6,546	6,988	795	11.38	Brewing
6	Argyll group	4,937	8,779	566	6.45	Wholesale, retail
7	Cadbury Schweppes	4,775	5,831	652	11.18	Beverages, confectionery
8	Whitbread	4,130	3,694	366	9.92	Beer
9	Scottish & Newcastle	3,500	1,760	222	12.60	Beer
10	ABF	3,436	6,866	529	7.71	Milling, sugar
11	United Biscuits (Holdings)	2,665	5,393	183	3.39	Biscuits
12	Tate and Lyle	2,271	5,789	348	6.02	Sugar, starch
13	Northern Foods	1,968	3,207	246	7.67	Dairy, misc.
14	Harrisons and Crosfield	1,836	3,460	153	4.43	Cereals
15	Hillsdown	1,779	7,193	254	3.53	Meat & produce
16	Dalgety	1,622	7,757	188	2.42	Distribution
17	Booker	1,359	5,586	136	2.43	Wholesaling
18	Unigate	1,286	3,100	160	5.17	Dairy products
19	Greenalls Group	1,251	578	68	11.82	Beer
20	Christian Salvesen	1,188	874	116	13.27	Frozen food

Source : FT 'European 500', January 1994 and 1995, Euro PA

Note :   These figures relate to each company's last financial year - usually 1994. Market capitalisation is the average capitalisation as at end-September 1993 and 1994 Christian Salvesen figure is for 1994 year only.

The figures shown above should be read in conjunction with the notes contained in the Appendix to Chapter One.

Table 9.2:   The Top 10 Overseas Food and Drink Manufacturers Operating in the UK, 1994

	Company	Market Capital.	Sales (US$m)	Profit (US$m)	Profit Margin	Main Product
1	Coca-cola Co.	58,866	13,957	2,176	15.59	Soft drinks
2	Nestlé	32,537	44,584	3,602	8.08	Dairy, dietetics
3	PepsiCo Inc.	28,627	25,020	1,588	6.35	Soft drinks
4	Kellogg Co.	12,120	6,295	681	10.8	Cereals
5	Sara Lee Corp.	11,142	15,536	199	1.28	Cakes, misc.
6	Danone (BSN)	9,842	13,234	1,045	7.90	Dairy
7	Heinz (H J) Co	9,021	7,047	603	8.56	Misc.
8	ADM Co.	8,529	11,374	484	4.26	Milling, grains
9	Heineken	4,723	5,211	469	9.00	Beer
10	Eridania/Beghin-Say	3,539	9,609	456	4.75	Oils

Source : FT 'European 500' and 'US 100', January 1994 and 1995, Euro PA
Note :   These figures relate to each company's last financial year - usually 1994. Market capitalisation is the average capitalisation as at end-September 1993 and 1994 Christian Salvesen figure is for 1994 year only.
The figures shown above should be read in conjunction with the notes contained in the Appendix to Chapter One.

From Table 9.1, Unilever seems to be by far the largest UK based food and drink manufacturer[6].   However, Unilever is a very diversified conglomerate with operations in many sectors, especially detergents and personal products. The food part of its operations accounts for at least 50% of its turnover, incorporating oil and dairy based products (flora margarine), ice cream (Cornetto), beverages (Brooke Bond and PG tips), snacks (Pepperami) and meals (Ragù source, Batchelor's soups).

In 1993, Unilever's top nine brands had sales of almost £850 million in Britain.   Table 9.3 provides a breakdown that shows that five of Unilever's top nine brands operate in the food industry, the others are washing powder, conditioner and detergents.

Table 9.3:   Unilever's Top Brands in Britain

	1993 Sales Value (£m)
Birds Eye	237
Persil	234
Flora	129
PG Tips	123
John West	74
Comfort	57
Oxo	43
Radion	38
Domestos	36

Source : Unilever

---

6   Note Unilever is part Dutch.

Unilever has undergone a major reorganisation programme (estimated at £490 million over 1994-1996) in order to reduce costs. 80% of all Unilever's sales are branded and its portfolio of brands is impressive. However, the cost of promoting these brands, in an aggressive marketing arena[7] is extremely large. In the 1994 annual account, advertising and promotion expenditures were put at £3.34 billion. This outlay is equivalent to 11.2% of its turnover. Some financial analysts believe that they are seeing Unilever follow a *"long-term trend away from branded consumers to own-label products[8]"*. The implications of this, if true, has wide-ranging ramifications for the food industry, given that Unilever is one of the major branded companies, and a market leader.

Apart from Unilever the other major point of interest from table 9.1 is that the other four companies in the top 5, and six of the top 9 are alcoholic drinks companies. Some of these companies have high turnovers, like Grand Metropolitan, for example. If the ranking was done by turnover these companies would occupy only two of the top 5 companies. The reason why these companies have such high market capitalisation is probably because of two factors, which are interlinked.

Firstly, companies in the alcoholic drinks sector appear to have very high profit margins relative to other sectors in the food and drink industry. Part of the reason for this is that the sector is heavily branded. For example Grand Metropolitan has brands such as J&B Rare Scotch Whisky, Baileys, Smirnoff, to name but a few. Allied Domecq has brands such as Ballantines, Beefeater, Carlsberg and Tetley.

Although branding is most predominant in the alcoholic drinks sector it is an important part of almost every sector. Almost all the companies listed in Table 9.1 have their own-labels.

An interesting example of brands is provided in Table 9.2 which shows Coca-cola as the largest non-UK based company operating in the UK. This is despite the fact that Nestlé has a turnover that is three times greater. Coca-Cola is possibly the most recognised brand in the whole world. Again, if one looks at the list in Table 9.2 it is reasonably easy for the interested lay reader to associate each of the companies with certain brands.

Smaller companies do not tend to have brands which are 'household names' and consumer recognition of brands is generally associated with large amounts of advertising and marketing expenditures used to develop a brand and promoting it to the trade and consumers. With so much being spent on brands they are seen as company assets, and may

---

7   For example, Soap Wars with Proctor and Gamble.
8   See p67 of The Investors Chronicle 12 May 1995.

be listed as intangible assets in company financial accounts, along with tangible assets such as buildings and stock. Thus, the development of new brands (or the decline of established ones) can have a significant effect on the balance sheet of a company and its capitalisation.

Below are some examples of the size of these 'intangible' assets.

	Intangible assets ($m)
Grand Metropolitan	4,390
Guinness	2,095
Cadbury Schweppes	820
United Biscuits	323

Source : Annual Company accounts
Note : Exchange Rates used are US$1.50 per £

In its company report Grand Metropolitan had fixed assets of around US$4 billion in 1993. Intangible assets, as can be seen in Table 9.3, amounted to almost US$4.4 billion. It should be noted, however, that many companies do not list brands as intangible assets. Brands that are acquired as part of a take-over or merger are usually valued as goodwill and are written off in the accounts. Brands developed from scratch by a company may not even be mentioned.

Table 9.3 does not aim to provide a definitive financial value for brands but merely illustrates how important brands may be in the valuation and operations of some large food and drink companies.

Further-Processed and Branded Products

Confectionery: Chocolate and Sugar

The total confectionery market in the UK, chocolate and sugar, was valued at around £4.35 billion in 1993. Chocolate confectionery accounts for around 70% being valued at c.£3.0 billion. The sugar confectionery market is worth c.£1.35 billion.

Since 1980 the value of sales of both types of confectionery have risen, though the growth in chocolate confectionery has been far greater than that for sugar. In 1980 the sugar confectionery market was valued at around £600 million. By 1993 the market was worth £1.35 billion, a rise of 100% in 13 years, approximately 5.5% per annum. The chocolate confectionery market has risen from around £1.2 billion in 1980 to £3.0 billion in 1993. This is almost a 150% rise in 13 years which corresponds to an annual increase of around 7%. Figure 9.1 illustrates these trends.

Figure 9.1:   Total Confectionery; Annual Market Value in the UK (£ million)

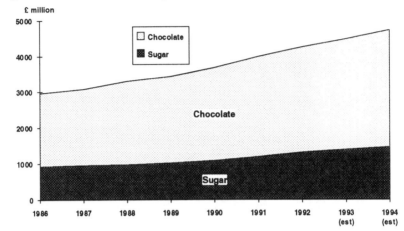

Source : Trebor Bassett - Review of the UK Sweets Market 1993

The UK has amongst the highest consumption levels *per capita* of confectionery in the EU, as Figure 9.2 shows. Switzerland consumes the most confectionery per head and the most chocolate confectionery. Holland is the highest consumer per head of sugar confectionery.

Figure 9.2 :   *Per capita* Consumption in Europe and the USA - 1992

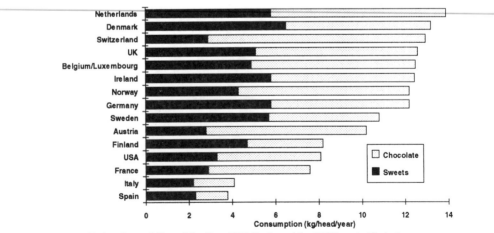

Source : Trebor Bassett 'Sweet Profits - 1993 Review of the UK Sweets Market'

Market Shares and Brands

Chocolate Confectionery

Three companies dominate the confectionery sector; Mars, Nestlé and Cadbury Schweppes. The top 10 brands are shown in Table 9.4 along with their respective companies.

Table 9.4:   The Top 10 Confectionery Brands by Value of Sales - 1993

Brand	Company
Mars	Mars
Kit-Kat	Nestlé
Twix	Mars
Snickers	Mars
Quality Street	Nestlé
Maltesers	Mars
CDM	Cadbury
Roses	Cadbury
Galaxy	Mars
Bounty	Mars

Source : Mars 'Confectionery 1993'

The chocolate confectionery market can be split into four sections; filled bars, bite size, block chocolate and assortments. Table 9.5 shows the breakdown in manufacturers sales value for 1993

Table 9.5:   Manufacturers' Sales of Chocolate Confectionery by category 1993

Category	Sales Value (£m)
Filled bars	752
Bite size	362
Block chocolate	222
Assortments	198
Total	1,534

Source : Mars 'Confectionery 1993', NMRA, GSR

Manufacturers' sales are valued at just over £1.5 billion. The total UK retail market for chocolate confectionery is valued at around £3 billion. Thus, retailers have almost a 100% profit margin on chocolate confectionery. Mars leads the Filled bars market with 43% market share and the Bite size market with 50% market share. Cadbury's leads the block chocolate (Galaxy) with 52% market share. Cadbury's and Nestlé have 37% and 36% market share respectively in the assortments sector.

Sugar Confectionery

The sugar confectionery market (or sweet market as it is sometimes termed) was worth around £1.35 billion in the UK 1993 with almost 300,000 tonnes consumed per annum. This market has been growing, in

value terms, by around 4.5% per annum in the 1990's.   Unlike the
chocolate confectionery sector, this sector is not dominated by three or
four companies.

Figure 9.3:   Market Shares in the UK Sweet Market

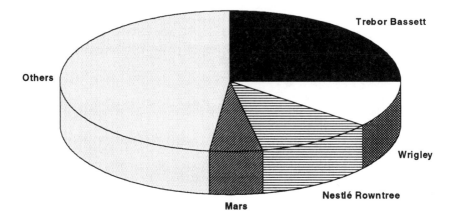

Source :   Trebor Bassett 'Sweet Fortune - 1994 Review of the UK Sweets Market'

Trebor Bassett, a Cadbury Schweppes subsidiary, has the greatest share
of the market at around 20%. Nestlé, with its Nestlé Rowntree branch,
and Wrigley vie for second place with around 10% each. Mars comes in
fourth. These four companies account for about 50% of the total sugar
confectionery market. Own-label sweets account for only around 10%
and are included in the others category.

Table 9.6 displays the top 10 sweet brands, with Nestlé having the top
brand, Fruit Pastilles. However, 4 of the top 10 are brands owned by
companies other than the top 4. The table unfortunately does not list
chewing gum. Other sources estimate that, Wrigley's Orbit Gum and
Wrigley's Extra are the two leading brands in value terms.

Table 9.6:   Top 10 Sweet Brands (in Value terms) 1993

Brand	Company
Fruit Pastilles	Nestlé
Extra-strong mints	Other
Polo Mints	Nestlé
Opal Fruits	Mars
Chewits	Other
Soft Mints	Other
Turkish Delight	Cadbury
Lockets	Mars
Halls	Other
Tunes	Mars

Source : Mars 'Confectionery 1993'

Females consume 69% of all sweets purchased. Children (0-15 years old) eat 39% of all sweets with people over 45 years old consuming 33%. With the UK population structure having an increasing number of people over 45 this may help increase brand sales. This age group tend to be more brand loyal in their purchases. With the number of females also increasing, this may also have a positive effect on sweet consumption.

Biscuits

UK biscuit production was valued at £1.6 billion in 1994 on sales of 700,000 tonnes. In the last decade, the market has grown in volume terms by 9%, less than 1% per annum, on average. Figure 9.4 shows the manufacturers' market shares (in value terms). McVities has the largest single share at 25%, though own-label products, in total, account for 28% of the market. All the manufacturers shown in Figure 9.4 produce for own-label, though it is difficult to discern how much own-label production each accounts for.

Figure 9.4: Manufacturers' Market Share of the UK Biscuit Market 1994

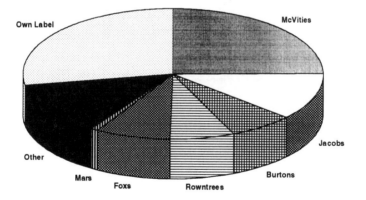

Source : McVities

Around 90,000 tonnes of biscuits were exported in 1994, while imports amounted to around 15,000 tonnes of imports.

Breakfast cereals

In 1993 the UK market for breakfast cereals was worth almost £1 billion. Ready-to-eat cereals accounted for around £900 million with the remainder made up by hot cereals.

The ready-to-eat breakfast cereal market can be broken down into several components, the largest of which is children's cereals, valued at almost £250 million in 1992. The next largest sector is corn-based cereals at £178 million and 20% of the total breakfast cereal market. Wheat biscuits account for £146 million with Weetabix, the main brand of the company bearing the same name, leading the way.

The main growth areas in the breakfast cereals market have been adult health, muesli and bran cereals. These are all linked in that they are catering for an increasingly health conscious consumer. Adult health cereals increased in volume by 43% over 1990 while Muesli had growth of 32%. Weetabix's other main brand, Alpen leads the Muesli sector. Ready-to-eat cereals are dominated by 15 brands which have 70% of the market. 10 of these belong to Kellogg's, whose main brand, Corn Flakes has 13% of the market. The brand Weetabix has around 8% of the market.

The sector has been characterised by continuous launches of new brands and new products since the beginning of the 1980's. The 1980's saw the launch of Fruit and Fibre, Start, Toppas and Crunchy Nut Cornflakes among many others. In the early 1990's Nut Feast, Corn Pops and Common Sense Oat Bran Flakes and others were launched.

Hot cereals is dominated by one brand - Ready-Brek (which Weetabix acquired in 1990). This brand has 60% of the hot cereals market, with Quaker Oats, the leading brand of the Quaker company , in second place.

Kelloggs top three brands - Corn Flakes, Crunchy Nut Corn Flakes and Frosties dominate what could be categorised the flakes market. In the Ready-to-eat cereals market as a whole Kelloggs dominates and claims to account for 50% of the market (43% of the overall breakfast cereal market). This dominance has lasted for over 50 years with rivals apparently unable to emulate their success. However, since the beginning of the 1990s competition has increased with the entrance of Cereal Partners UK (CPUK) in 1989 - a partnership between the US food company General Mills and Nestlé. Much of its operation remains the cereal brands that it purchased from Rank Hovis McDougall (RHM). These brands include Shredded Wheat. The development of Shredded Wheat Bitesize is aimed primarily at younger consumers and recorded volume growth of almost 44% in 1993. Shreddies is a similar product and remains popular despite increased competition in the children's sector.

The entry of CPUK was seen as a threat to Kelloggs dominance but so far has apparently only resulted in reducing the market share a several smaller companies. Weetabix, in particular, has see its total market share fall from 15% in 1988 to around 12% in 1993. This share might have fallen further but for the acquisition of Ready-Brek, the market leader (with 60%) of the hot cereals sector. In 1993, CPUK had a market share of 9% and was growing.

Margarine

In 1993, around 340,000 tonnes of margarine was produced in the UK with a value of c.£300 million. This represented a 2.3% fall, in volume terms, on 1992. Most of the margarine is classed as vitamised, either of a soft variety (217,900) or other than soft (29,800 tonnes). Non-vitamised margarine accounted for 91,200 tonnes. Non-vitamised margarine production increased by 9.4% in 1993 while both types of vitamised margarine fell by around 9.4% each.

Other table spreads accounted for 149,700 tonnes in 1993 a rise of almost 11%. These other table spreads are as the name suggests, all other table spreads other than margarine. St Ivel Gold is a good example of this type of spread. Though it is oil based and it is not technically margarine.

Table 9.7 below shows the oils and fats used in the production of margarine and other table spreads in 1993.

Table 9.7: Oils and Fat used in Margarine and Table Spread Production 1993

		Volume ('000 tonnes)
Vegetable Oils :	Groundnut	0.8
	Maize Germ	0.2
	Palm	41.9
	Palm Kernel	3.7
	Rapeseed	90.6
	Soya Bean	31.1
	Sunflower	101.3
	Other	0.9
Marine Oils		82.0
Animal Fats :	Butter (as butter fat equivalent)	9.1
	Other	7.9
Total		369.6

Source : MAFF
Note : Individual figures may not sum to total due to rounding

Sunflower oil is the most commonly used vegetable oil in the production of margarine and other table spreads. It accounts for c.30% of the raw materials used. Rapeseed and marine oils are the next most used oils with palm oil and soya bean oil being the other major raw materials.

Imports of margarine accounted for around 40,000 tonnes in 1993 and were valued at £31 million. This means total UK margarine supply was in the order of 380,000 tonnes in 1993. Flora is the leading margarine brand with sales of £129 million in 1993.

Infant Food

The entire baby feeding market was worth £267 million in 1993. This market has three sections, milks, meals and drinks.

Baby milks

Baby milks were worth £116.1 million in 1993. The market can be broken down into three sections:

Infant formula
This is milk commonly fed to young babies as a substitute for breast feeding. This market was worth £91.1 million in 1993, 5% less than 1992. There are only four companies manufacturing this product - their market shares are shown in Figure 9.5

Figure 9.5:   Market Shares of the UK Infant Milk Market 1993

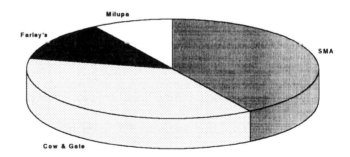

Source : FSA

Soya Milk
In 1993, this market was worth £7.1 million, 6.4% more than in 1992. This type of milk is almost all sold in pharmacies as is a nutritionally complete milk substitute for babies with cow's milk intolerance. SMA dominate this particular market with over 80% of the market.

Follow-on milk

The follow-on milks market was valued at £17.9 million in 1993, an 80% increase over 1992. Since 1991 the market has grown by over £11 million with volumes almost tripling. These milks are intended for children from 6 months to 2 years old.

Baby Meals

In 1993, baby meals accounted for £121 million, an increase of 6% on the previous year. This follows a decline in previous years. The market can again be split into three segments:

- Baby Rice
- Dry Meals
- Wet Meals

The market for baby rice is the smallest of the three, valued at £2.3 million in 1993 (9% up on 1992). Half of the sales are through pharmacies and around 40% through grocery[9] outlets (including supermarkets). Of this relatively small market, Farley's has the dominant share with 46% in 1993. Other manufacturers include Robinsons, Milupa, Boots and Cow and Gate.

The market for dry meals was worth £50.5 million in 1993, an increase of 3% on 1992. However, the number of packs fell 7% to 34 million in 1993. There were several new launches in 1993 but only Farley's volume rose significantly. By the end of 1993 Farley's had 35.5% from 32.3% in 1992 (Figure 9.6).

Figure 9.6:   Manufacturers' Market Shares of the Dry Infant Meal Market 1993

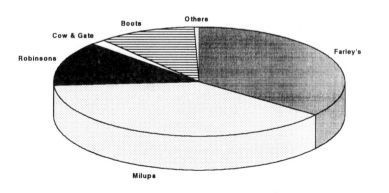

Source : FSA

9   Defined as supermarkets and grocers.

This market for wet meals was worth £70.5 million in 1993, an increase of 9% on 1992. In recent years this sector has been the main growth area of the baby feeding market, though in 1993 volume was stagnant at 174 million meals. Tinned meals have risen at the expense of meals in jars, probably due to cheaper pricing points. Heinz, who do not feature in any other sector of the infant food market lead this market with a 56.4% share. Cow and Gate are second with about half as much (26.2%).

Figure 9.7: Manufacturers' Market Shares of the Wet Infant Meal Market Segment 1993

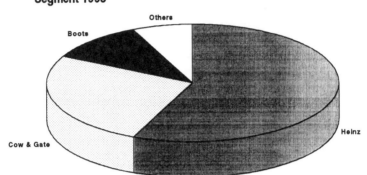

Source : FSA

Two other segments of the baby food market are relevant. In 1993 the rusks sector was valued at £8.9 million. Farley's had 77.4% of this market in 1993, with Jacobs (14.7%) and Boots own brand (7.9%). The baby drinks sector was worth £21.1 million in 1993, a fall of 10% on 1992. The fall was put down to recessionary factors. Several companies are involved in this market; Colmans, Cow and Gate, Milupa and Beecham, as well as others. Overall the baby feed market is estimated to be worth £283.2 million in 1994, this excludes baby rice and soya milk. Table 9.8 compares the 1994 estimates to 1993.

Table 9.8:   Estimates of 1994 Baby Market - relative to 1993

	1993	1994
	£ million	£ million
Baby Meals	121.10	129.80
Wet	70.50	79.57
Dry	50.50	50.23
Rusks	8.90	9.20
Baby Milks	109.00	123.80
Infant Formula	91.10	103.50
Follow-on	17.90	20.30
Baby Drinks	21.10	20.40
Total	267.20	283.2

Source : FSA

Between 1993 and 1994 the value of the baby meals market has increased almost 8% with all the gain being in wet meals. Baby milks have also increased, by 13% with advances made in both Infant Formula and Follow-on sectors. Baby Drinks have declined marginally, but overall the baby feeding market has increased. Since the end of 1993 there has been significant changes in industry structure with the acquisition of two leading brands by two top manufacturers. Heinz has purchased the Farley's brand (the market leader in dry meals and baby rice) from Crookes Healthcare. Cow and Gate Nutricia has purchased the Robinson's dry food brand. Overall in 1994, baby foods grew in value by 7% to £130 million, with the bulk of the increase coming from the wet meals sector. This wet meals sector is now dominated by Heinz, with other significant players being Cow and Gate's Olvarit, Boots own brand and more recently the 'Chilled Yoghurt' brands of St Ivel and Baby Danone. Within dry meals the two major players are Heinz (Farley's) and Milupa with most of the remaining market held by Boots own brand and Cow and Gate (Robinsons).

Ready-to-eat meals

Ready-to-eat meals, are usually categorised as;

- frozen, and
- chilled meal preparations

Frozen meals

In 1994 the frozen ready meals sector was valued at £541 million, an increase of 4.8% over 1993. This sector can be further broken down into traditional (British meals), International meals and healthy meals.

Traditional meals

Traditional meals were valued at £246 million in 1994 (up 0.2% on 1993) and can be broken down as shown in Table 9.9 below. Complete meals with chips have showed enormous growth in 1994 rising in value by almost 70%. In 1993, this was the smallest market and thus this growth is not reflected greatly in the total traditional food market. The two largest markets are fish and traditional meats which rose in value by 12.4% and 3.7% respectively in 1994. This growth along with that for platters (+3.7%) negates the decline in value of other sectors. The largest fall was for vegetable based traditional meals, down 28.5% but this was one of the smaller markets in 1993. Shepherds pies on the other hand, was the largest market in 1993 but declined almost 15% in 1994, losing £7 million in value.

Table 9.9:   Breakdown of Traditional Meals - 1994

	Value (£)	% change 1994 on 1993
Complete meals and chips	10.42	+68.6
Fish	50.20	+12.4
Platters	24.31	+4.0
Traditional meals	57.20	+3.7
Sliced meats	34.47	-0.5
Faggots	16.22	-9.5
Shepherds pies	48.10	-14.9
Vegetable	5.05	-28.5

Source : Birds Eye Walls - based on ABG and Neilsen data

Retailer own-label products have over 35% of the traditional market with Birds Eye Walls having 27.1%. United Biscuits (9.9%) with their Ross Young's division are also prominent with Kraft (5.7%) and Campbell (3.1%) also having a significant share.

International meals

International meals can be defined as those whose cultural origins are in other countries i.e. they are based on ethnic or foreign recipes and methods of cooking. Table 9.10 show these to be predominantly Italian (pasta, lasagne), Oriental (stir fries) and Indian (curries etc.).

Table 9.10 : Breakdown of International Frozen Meals - 1994

	Value (£)	% change 1994 on 1993
Other pasta meat	27.67	+36.0
Other pasta veg	14.78	+31.2
Other pasta fish	2.63	+26.0
Meat lasagne	55.43	+11.3
Indian authentic	12.60	+5.7
Indian mainstream	46.15	+5.4
Chinese (excl. stir fry)	13.02	+1.5
Stir fry meat and fish	33.50	-2.7
Other international	13.77	-4.5

Source : Birds Eye Walls - based on ABG and Neilsen data

In 1994 the international market grew 8.4% to £220 million. Most sectors have shown considerable growth with only the stir fry and other international frozen meals registering falls in value. Pasta (including lasagne) as a whole has increased from around £83 million to just over £100 million in 1994. Indian cuisine has also increased but by a lesser degree than pasta.

As in the traditional meals sector retailers' own-labels have the largest share of the market at 31.3%. Birds Eye Walls is in second place with 20.9% followed by United Biscuits (16.9%), Nestlé (11.3%) and Mars (5.3%).

Healthy meals

This is a smaller sector at only £75 million in 1994. However, it has shown significant growth of 11.2%. Most of these meals could be termed standard (£58 million), with platters (£14 million) and pots (£3 million) accounting for the rest. Heinz leads the healthy frozen meal market, with its Weightwatcher brand, and has over 46% of the market. Findus (Nestlé) with its lean Cuisine range has 28.3% and Bird's Eye Walls has 22.5%. Unlike the other frozen meals sectors, the retailers' own-labels account for a small proportion of the market (3.1%).

Product development has been rapid with all companies promoting new lines or revamping established brands. New recipes, such as Salmon Rosti from Findus, have been introduced to try and benefit from changes in consumer eating preferences. In Findus's case the idea has been to cater for the perceived move from red meat to fish consumption.

One particular brand, that has been successful in recent years is the Linda McCartney range from Ross Young's. Since the brand's launch in 1992 it has captured 20% of the non-meat frozen sector. This sector was worth in the region of £90 million in 1994, having being estimated to have grown 40% since 1992. As well as vegetarian dishes the range also aims to cater for meat consumers who wish to cut back on the level of meat consumed.

Chilled Ready Meals

The chilled ready meals sector was worth approximately £336 million at retail prices. The sector has grown consistently since 1989 when it was worth £175 million - a 92% rise in 5 years. Keynote estimates that the market will be valued at nearly £600 million in 1997. It is very difficult to break this market sector down into subcategories as retailers' own-labels have over 90% of the market. In 1994 Marks and Spencer accounted for £146 million or 43% of the market. Northern Foods were their main supplier. Of the remaining £190 million in the total market, Hazlewood has 17%, Noon has 13%, Food Enterprise 12% and Geest 10%. However, some of this production is also going to retailers for sale as own-label.

The branded chilled ready meals market has been expanding in recent years in absolute value and in terms of its share of the total chilled ready meals market. In 1988 it was estimated that branded products accounted for only 2%. In 1994 estimates of share are as high as 10%. The company, International Cuisine, claims to have 65% of the branded market, which was worth around £34 million in 1994. Its products encompass Indian, Italian, traditional British and other international dishes. International Cuisine was established in 1988 and is a excellent example of the utilisation of the most advanced technology to produce new products. The company has developed an aerobic pasteurisation process, capable of producing extended-life chilled ready meals for the retail grocery trade with a shelf life of production plus 17 days compared to the norm of production plus six days.

Pizza

The pizza market is estimated to be worth around £350 million in 1994. As Chapter Six noted, when discussing Mozzarella cheese production, the growth in UK-produced pizza has been an important demand factor for UK cheese producers.

Frozen pizza is valued at £200m of which mainmeal is £110m. Chilled pizza is valued at £150m.

Frozen Pizza

The frozen pizza market has increased from £139 million in 1991 to £194 million in 1994. This represents 40% growth in four years. Within this sector, mainmeal is the largest. Mainmeal is boxes of whole pizzas, i.e. the type seen in pizza restaurant. Mainmeal has been the growth area with the other sectors, pizza grills, slices and french bread declining.

In 1991 mainmeal accounted for 29% of market value or about £40 million. By 1994 it was worth 56% or £109 million. This represents 174% growth in four years. Own-label accounted for around 40% of the market in 1994. This figure is not too dissimilar to that in 1991. Ross Young's has a further 20% and has the leading brand, San Marco. San Marco was launched in 1991 to provide a 'traditional Italian' product in the market. The subsector, mainmeal, has been the growth area growing three fold over 1991-94. San Marco fits into this sector, and Ross Youngs claim to be the market brand leader having opened a new £20 million pizza factory in 1993. Mainmeal is expected to continue as the growth area though there has been a move to redefine the market with new sectors developing. One of these new sectors, snack pizzas, had sales of around £8 million in 1994. These includes products such as McCain 'Pizza Rolla' among others.

Chilled Pizza

The chilled pizza market was estimated to be worth around £150 million in 1994. The market has grown 50% since 1991. The vast majority of this market is own-label (90%+) with three main companies supplying the retailers. Geest, Northern Foods and Hazlewood each have around 30% of the market.

Pasta

The total UK pasta market was worth £323 million in 1993 and is continuing to grow. The pasta market has several sectors; fresh, dried, canned meals, sauces and ready to eat meals (fresh, chilled and ambient).

Nearly all non-fresh pasta originates from Italy, with much processed and packed in Italy. Buitoni the leading dry pasta brand is all packed in Italy. Fresh pasta, with a limited shelf life, is produced in the UK. With dried pasta being the main growth area - pasta imports from Italy will increase.

The fresh pasta market was estimated to be worth £24 million in 1994, up from £19 million in 1993. Most growth is in the filled variety rather than the unfilled variety. Own-label accounts for around 60% of all sales. UK companies that have developed a range of fresh pasta for the chilled shelf space in supermarkets include The Pasta Company (Geest) and Pasta Reale.

Dried pasta has seen major growth over the last decade with sales increasing four-fold to £110 million in 1993. Spaghetti is traditionally the leading type of dried pasta but is being replaced by pasta shapes. In 1989 29.5% of sales were pasta shaped, today this figure is over 40%. Own-label accounts for around 65% of the market. Nestlé (Buitoni was purchased in 1988) has the largest branded presence with 7% followed by JA Sharwood and Co. on 6%. Canned pasta meals, principally macaroni cheese, spaghetti and ravioli, were valued in the region of £96 million in 1993. Own-label takes 29% of this sector.

Another sector linked frequently linked with pasta is wet cooking sauces. In 1993 this market was worth just over £202 million. By 1994 it was estimated to be worth £239 million, a rise of 19%. The sales value of these sauces has risen by at least 19% since the late 1980's becoming a major growth area.

Master Foods, with their Dolmio and Uncle Ben's brands, lead the market. Master Foods estimate their market share to be 28.8% in 1994.

The same source estimates Brooke Bond (Ragu and Chicken Tonight) to have 21.8% of the market. However, Brooke Bond's share increased dramatically in 1994, from 13.5% in 1993. Home Pride (with the Homepride label) have just under 20% but their share has been gradually falling since 1990 when they had 26.7% and led the market. Own-label has 13.9% of the market in 1994 down from 15.1% in 1993.

Most sauces are Italian (43%) with Indian accounting for 22% of the market. There seems to have been a gradual move to Indian sauces in the early 1990's. In value terms Indian sauces have been growing by almost 25% per annum since 1990. In comparison, Italian sauces have increased by almost 16% since 1990. The dry cooking sauces market was valued at around £70 million in 1994, representing 2% growth over 1993. Most products are cook-in sauces (71%) the rest pour over sauces. Of the cook in sauces, casserole sauces account for a third with chicken having 15%, followed by Italian (12%), chilli (11%) and fish (10%). The market is led by Colmans (38%) and Crosse and Blackwell (17%). Own-label accounts for about 12%.

Rice

The total rice market, defined as basic and savoury, was worth around £137 million in 1994. One could also add short grain rice, but this is used primarily for rice puddings and thus is a different product to the others.

Basic

The long grain rice market was estimated to be worth £107 million in 1994 though other estimates can put the figure at closer to £130 million. Since 1990 the market has grown 41% in value. This market includes basmati, brown, parboiled long grain and non parboiled long grain. The segment is termed basic in the sense that, unlike savoury rice, nothing has been added to it. Basmati rice, the kind used in Indian curries, has been the growth area in recent years accounting for 23% of the market in 1994 as opposed to 16% in 1990. Brown rice, i.e. wholemeal long grain rice with higher fibre, accounts for 11%, down from 14% in 1990. Of white long grain rice there has been a market decline in non-parboiled from 25% in 1990 to 20% in 1994. Parboiled rice, on the other hand, has kept a constant share of around 46%. Own-label products dominate the basic rice market with around 67% in 1994. These products dominate even more in basmati and non-parboiled rice. There are only two main brands, Uncle Ben's with 22%, and Tilda with 6%.

Savoury

Savoury rice can be defined as rice plus extra ingredients such as vegetables. In 1994 the market was worth around £30 million, with growth around 3% to 4% per annum for the last five years.

In terms of volume, 46,400 tonnes was sold in the UK market in 1994, 51% by the leading brand, Batchelors. Own-label accounts for around 41%, and has grown significantly in the past few years. The other major company is Crosse and Blackwell but this company has seen their share of the market fall in recent times and now has 5%. Batchelors do most of the advertising in this sector. It spends, on average, £1.5 million per annum, promoting among others its number one brand, Batchelor's original savoury rice. Own-label are also dominant in this market.

Almost all rice is imported - with around 250,000 tonnes entering the UK in 1993. These imports were valued at around £115 million. The dominance of own-label makes it difficult to analyse what part of rice products are packaged in other countries before export, relative to rice that is imported in bulk. The rice used in savoury rice products which require additional foods to be added arrive in bulk and are generally processed in the UK.

Non-Alcoholic Beverages

Non-alcoholic beverages is a very large section of the food and drink market and includes hot beverage (tea, coffee, hot chocolate), soft drinks (including mineral water and fruit juices). In total, sales of these beverages amounted to around £7.4 billion in 1994. This section of the food market also includes some important brands.

Hot Beverages

Hot beverages includes tea, coffee and food beverages (hot chocolate and malt). In total the hot beverages market was valued at around £1.45 billion in 1994 (5.9% up on 1993). The tea market was the largest at £674 million. Coffee accounted for £657 million and food beverages £124 million. Tea sales registered a 1.1% value fall over 1993 while coffee increased by 15.6%. Figure 9.8 shows the market share of leading manufacturers in this sector. Nestlé leads the way with 23.5% of the market in 1994, with own-label a close second with 20.7%.

Figure 9.8: Manufacturer's Market Share of the Total Hot Beverage Market 1994 (%) Value

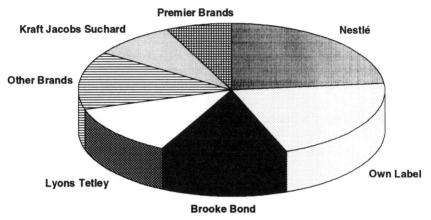

Source : Nielsen

Tea

The tea market has been declining in recent years from £682 million in 1993 to £674 million in 1993. Within this sector there are three major categories ; bags (83.6%), packet (11.8%) and instant (4.4%). Tea bags has been the growth area, but this growth rate has reduced recently. Brooke Bond remains the market leader with 26.5%, with Lyons Tetley in second with 25.7%. Own-label has grown from 16.0% in 1986 to 26.8% in 1994.

Figure 9.9: Manufacturers' Market Share of the Tea Market - 1994 (% Value)

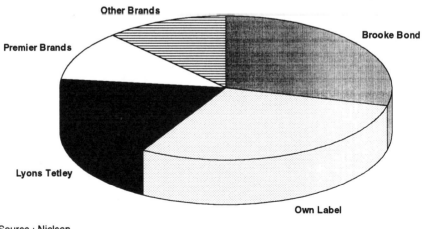

Source : Nielsen

Coffee

Total coffee sales grew strongly in 1994 recording a £89 million increase in 1994 to £657 million. Most of the coffee sold is the instant variety - £587 million in 1993 (£78 million up on 1992). Roast and ground nut coffee accounted for the remaining £70 million (£11 million up on 1993). Within the instant coffee sector Nestlé is the market leader with 57.9% in 1993. Nestlé's 'Nescafé' brand had seven of the top 10 branded lines by value. The original 'Nescafé' in 100g jar was 1st, 200g jar (2nd), 300g jar (4th) and 50g jar (7th). As well as the original 'Nescafé Gold Blend' (100g-3rd and 200g-5th) and 'Nescafé decaffeinated' (100g-9th) were also prominent. Kraft Jacobs Suchard occupied second place with 20.2% of the instant coffee market % (down from 21.1% in 1993) with its two brands, 'Kenco' and 'Maxwell House'. Brooke Bond has 2.9% with its 'Red Mountain Brand'. Own-label accounts for 15.8% of the market (up from 14.4% in 1993).

The roast and ground coffee market grew 18.6% in 1994 and is led by own-label products. Own-label accounted for 39.5% (37.3% in 1993), with Lyons Tetley's on 17% (down from 18.9% in 1993) and Sara Lee (13.1%) and Kraft Jacobs Suchard (12.3%).

Food Beverages
Food beverage sales had only slight growth in 1994 following a rise of 5.8% in 1993. In 1994 sales value was £124 million.

Figure 9.10: Food Beverages by Sector 1993 (% Value)

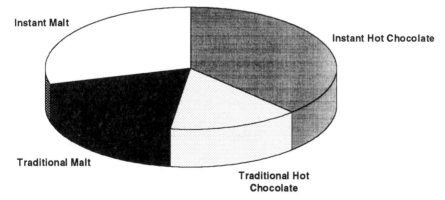

Source : Nielsen

In 1995, Lyons Tetley was sold by its parent Allied Domecq as part of a move to focus on spirits rather than food. The tea section of Lyon's Tetley was sold to a company called Tato, the coffee operations to General Foods, a large US food company.

Soft Drinks

The total European soft drinks market was just under 70 billion litres in 1993. Germany is the largest European market in terms of consumption per head and total consumption. Belgium is very close to the German *per capita* consumption.

Table 9.11: European Consumption of Soft Drinks (litres/head) 1990

	Population (million)	Consumption (litres/head)	Consumption (billion litres)
Germany	80.19	208	16.68
France	59.05	178	10.51
Italy	57.57	156	8.98
UK	57.10	147	8.39
Spain	40.52	134	5.43
Belgium	10.01	200	2.00
Netherlands	15.13	126	1.91
Rest of EU*			
Total EU*			**53.90**

Source : BSDA

The UK ranked 4th in 1990, in terms of total market size (see Table 9.11). Our *per capita* consumption level is significantly lower than that of France and Germany. The total UK market for soft drinks, which includes fruit juices and mineral water, as well as carbonates and dilutables was just over 9 billion litres in 1994, and was valued at just under £6 billion.

Figure 9.11 illustrates how consumption, in total and *per capita*, has grown over the last decade. *Per capita* consumption has risen almost 50% between 1984 and 1994, to reach 157 litres per person in 1994. Of all other beverages only tea has a higher *per capita* consumption rate of all beverages.

Figure 9.11: UK Consumption of Soft Drinks 1984-1994

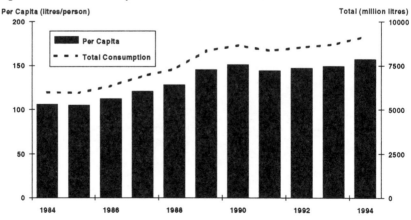

Source : Zenith International, 'The 1995 Sucralose Soft Drinks Report'

Within soft drinks there are five main categories; carbonates, dilutables, fruit juice, fruit drinks and bottled water. The breakdown in consumption is shown in Figure 9.12.

Figure 9.12: Breakdown on UK Soft Drinks Consumption 1984 and 1994

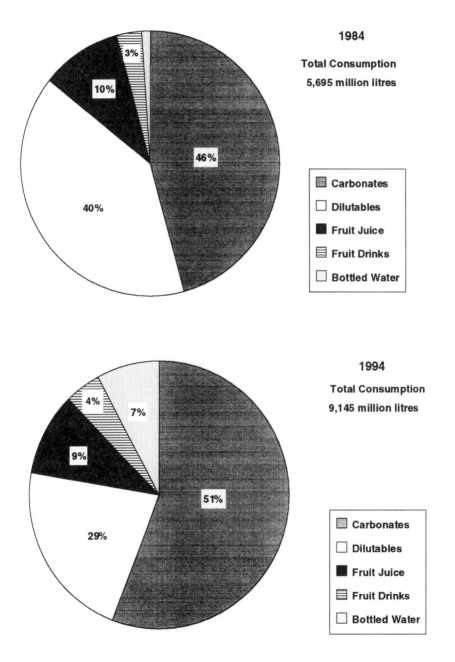

1984

Total Consumption

5,695 million litres

1994

Total Consumption

9,145 million litres

Source : Zenith International, 'The 1995 Sucralose Soft Drinks Report'

The market is dominated by carbonates which accounted for over 50% in 1994. However, the emergence of bottled water has been the major change of the last decade. Figure 9.12 shows changes in shares of the market between 1984 and 1994.

Carbonates

The carbonate market is worth some £3.5 billion (at retail prices) in 1994, with over 4.6 billion litres sold. Cola leads the market with almost 50% followed by Lemonade (23%) and orange (8%). Coca-Cola Schweppes is the leading company with the brands Coca-Cola (1st) and Schweppes (3rd). Wedged between these two brands is Pepsi-Cola. The carbonate market (Figure 9.13) has been one of the major growth areas in soft drinks. Consumption has risen every year since 1984 bar 1991.

Figure 9.13: Consumption of Carbonates 1989-1994

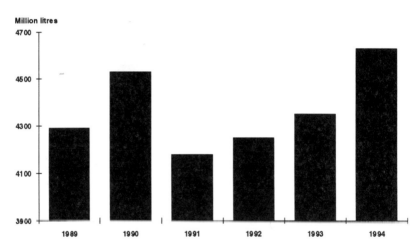

Source : Zenith International, 'The 1995 Sucralose Soft Drinks Report'

In 1994 the cola wars, traditionally Coca-Cola against Pepsi-Co, was expanded to include several own-label entrants. The UK retailer, Sainsburys, produced their Classic Cola which sells at a discount to the two major brands. Safeway followed suit with its Select Cola. With the benefit of retail outlets across the country these brands, present a real challenge to Coca-Cola and Pepsi-Cola. Virgin cola was also launched in 1994 by the Virgin group. The Cott Corporation - a Canadian company supplying cola to retailers has had a significant impact on the cola market.

Fruit Juices

UK fruit juice consumption has started to recover from a decline in the early 1990's. However 1994's consumption of 805 million litres is still lower than the 830 million litres consumed in 1989. Orange juice is by far the most popular flavour with over three-quarters of the market. Most fruit juices are of the long life variety (77%) as opposed to fresh or chilled, being sold predominantly in 1 litre cartons (68%). In this market retailer's own-label products have 60% against 40% for branded products. This is partly due to the difficulty manufacturers have had in establishing brand and product differentiation.

Fruit Drinks

Fruit drinks are still drinks which do not have 100% fruit content. Squashes and cordials are major parts of this sector. In recent years (1991-1994) consumption has been relatively static at around 360 million litres, with a value of around £250 million in 1994. Half of the market is made up of products which have 5-25% fruit juice content. Those products with a fruit content less than 5% accounted for 27%, with the remaining 23% made up of drinks with 25 to 99% fruit juice content.

Unlike fruit juices the preferred packaging is a small carton (50%), i.e. less than 1 litre. A quarter of sales is in 1 litre cartons, and a further 20% in plastic cups. As far as flavours are concerned, orange accounts for 30% and blackcurrant 20%. Blended drinks, i.e. a mixture of two or more flavours account for a further 37%. Branded fruit drinks account for 75% of the market with own-label penetration of around 25%.

Dilutables

This sector of soft drinks is second only to carbonates, with sales of 2.64 billion litres. Sales in value terms are low relative to volume, £800 million in 1994, as dilutables are sold in concentrated form.

Sales have been relatively static over the past five years at around 2.6 billion litres, though this greater than the consumption levels of the 1980's. Orange (50%) is the dominant flavour followed by blends (25%) and lemon and blackcurrant (10% each). 39% of dilutables are of a low sugar variety with a further 58% having a 'regular' sugar content. Low sugar dilutables are not new, the main change is the increased prominence of no-sugar varieties. Within the dilutables sector, Robinson is by far the dominant UK manufacturer.

Bottled Water

Bottled water, most of which is mineral water (67%) has been the growth
area in soft drink consumption in the 1990's. Consumption *per capita* has
almost doubled from 1989 to 1994 with almost 12 litres *per capita* being
consumed in 1994. This *per capita* consumption equates to almost 700
million litres with a retail value of £350 million in 1994. The majority of
bottled water is still (62%) rather than sparkling (38%). Originally most
supplies came from abroad, especially France. These imports have
declined, however, from 60% in the mid-1980's to 30% in 1994. The
leading brand, Evian, is French though domestic suppliers have
increased production substantially. According to Datamonitor, the Top
20 companies operating in Europe sold approximately 22 billion litres of
soft drinks in 1992 (Table 9.12).

Table 9.12:   Europe's Top 20 Soft Drinks Companies 1992

	Group	Million Litres
1	Coca-Cola	10,000
2	Nestlé	4,300
3	BSN	3,000
4	Pepsi-Cola	2,100
5	Cadbury Beverages Europe	1,500
6	San Pelligrino	1,200
7	Hero	1,130
8	San Benedetto	1,090
9	Crippa e Berger	760
10	Spadel	610
11	Castel	605
12	Nordetränke	600
13	Italfin '80	590
14	Wesergold	580
15	Gerolsteiner	550
16	Überkingen	545
17	La Casera	525
18	Stute	520
19	Procordia	480
20	Dittmeyer	460

Source : Datamonitor

The top five UK bottled water brands in 1994 were Evian, Volvic,
Highland Spring, Buxton, and Strathclyde. Presumably, the growth in
demand for bottle water has been driven by the general interest in more
natural products. Apart from the occasional media scares about the
quality of tap water (which are usually local issues) it is difficult to see
why bottled water consumption in the UK has increased so rapidly.

Industry Structure and Performance

The top 5 companies operating in the soft drinks sector, in terms of volume, are shown in Table 9.13

Table 9.13: Sales (Volume) of Major Soft Drink Companies

	UK Sales 1994 (Million litres)
Coca-Cola & Schweppes Beverages (CCSB)	1,800
Britvic	900
Barraclough	300
Carters	300
Wells	250
Total	3,550

Source : Zenith International 'The 1995 Sucralose Soft Drinks Report'

These top 5 companies accounted for 3.55 billion litres, or approximately 40% of all UK sales. Figure 9.14 below shows the concentration ratio for gross output to be around 55%. However, the concentration ratio is calculated by the share the top 5 UK companies have of the total value of output of all the UK companies. Also, the total of each companies total turnover will be used in the calculation of concentration ratios not just that turnover attributable to soft drinks.

Figure 9.14 : 5 Firm Concentration Ratios - Soft Drinks

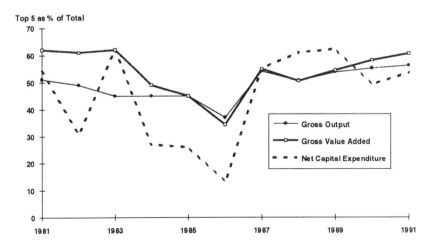

Source : CSO Business Monitor PA1002, selected years

Alcoholic Drinks

Overview of Demand

The alcoholic drinks sector is a key part of the UK food and drink industry. Whilst its utilisation of raw materials is relatively modest, the value-added in the distilling and brewing processes is huge. The indirect expenditures associated with bottling, distribution and marketing alcoholic drinks is also large. The alcoholic drinks sector also contains many examples of major brands. Table 9.14 makes international comparisons of alcohol consumption. Surprisingly all the top countries are European. The top four with regards to *per capita* consumption of all alcohol are west European, with Luxembourg leading the way. Table 9.14 gives information for beer and spirits but not for wine - this explains why Luxembourg, France and Portugal, three largest wine drinkers, top the total alcohol *per capita* consumption list. The UK is also shown for comparative purposes and is ranked high in *per capita* beer consumption (10th) but relatively low in terms of spirit consumption (22nd).

Table 9.14 : International Comparisons of Per capita Alcohol Consumption 1991

Beer (Litres)		Spirits (LPA*)		Total Alcohol (LPA*)	
Germany	142.7	Poland	4.50	Luxembourg	12.3
Czechoslov.	135.0	Hungary	3.43	France	11.9
Denmark	125.9	Cyprus	3.30	Portugal	11.6
Austria	123.7	Czechoslov.	2.80	Germany	10.9
Eire	123.0	Bulgaria	2.70	Switz.	10.7
Luxembourg	116.1	Germany	2.70	Hungary	10.5
Belgium	111.3	Spain	2.70	Spain	10.4
UK	106.2	UK	1.61	UK	7.4

* LPA = Litres of Pure Alcohol
Source : World Drink Trends 1993 edition

Figures 9.15 and 9.16 shows real and nominal consumer expenditure on alcoholic drinks, by category, going back to 1970. Figure 9.15 indicates that in nominal terms consumer expenditure on all types of alcoholic drinks has been rising since 1970. This is especially true of beer, from just over £1.3 billion in 1970 to £13.5 billion in 1993.

However this picture is distorted by the changes in relative prices that have occurred. Figure 9.16, consumer expenditure in constant 1990 prices, shows the complete story. Beer expenditure has been relatively flat and in fact shows a small decline. Higher nominal sales values have also been a feature of the other three markets; spirits, wine and cider. In the case of spirits, real expenditure has been fairly constant at around £4 billion, especially since 1980. Only wine sales show real increases year on year.

Figure 9.15:   Nominal Consumer Expenditure on Alcoholic Drinks -1970-1993

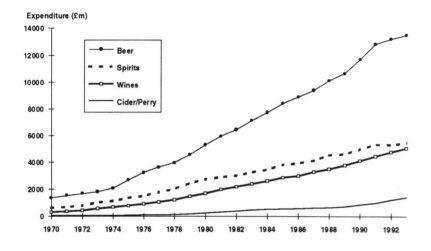

Source : HM Customs & Excise

Figure 9.16: Real Consumer Expenditure on Alcoholic Drinks
1970-1993 (1990 prices)

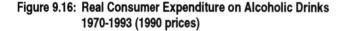

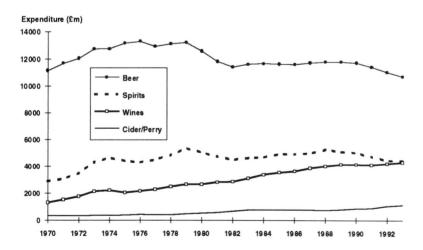

Source : HM Customs & Excise

Beer

Figure 9.17 shows that beer consumption has fallen by just over 10% between 1980 and 1993. However, more than half this fall was between 1980 and 1982. Since 1983 beer consumption has fallen 4.8% or around 0.4% per annum. Falls in beer consumption have occurred at times of economic recession i.e. 1979-81 and 1989-92, and it is likely that recession was the cause of the most recent fall. However, in periods of economic prosperity previous falls were not reversed, leaving a significant downward trend over the last two decades.

Figure 9.17: Volume of Beer Consumption 1980-1993

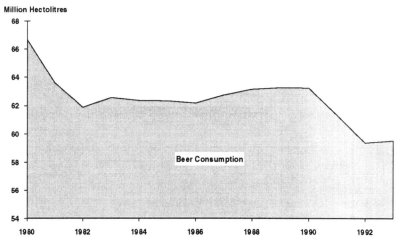

Source : HM Customs & Excise

Spirits

When analysing spirit statistics its has to be borne in mind the difference between volumes in pure alcohol (PA) and volumes in 40% proof (or Alcohol by Volume -ABV). Retail sales are at 40% ABV whereas production figures tend to be in Litres of Pure Alcohol (LPA). 1 LPA = 2.5 litres @ 40% ABV. Note also that figures are often expressed in hectolitres (HL) which equals 100 litres.

It is possible to break down the spirits market into five main segments; Whisky, Cognac/Brandy, Dark Rum, White Sprits and Flavoured Spirits. In terms of UK sales, whisky is the largest market with almost one million hectolitres (@ 40% ABV) sold in 1993. Since 1986 sales have been declining constantly in volume terms but in 1993 this trend was reversed. White spirit (Vodka, Gin) sales, on the other hand, have been much more stable since the mid-1980's, with between 750 and 800 thousand hectolitres (@ 40% ABV) being sold.

Cognac/Brandy and Dark Rum sales have also been relatively constant though both have shown a slight downward trend. Sales of flavoured spirits have both increased and decreased between 1986 and 1993. From 1986 to 1989 sales rose by 80,000 hectolitres (41% in 3 years). Since then, sales have fallen, levelling out at around 220,000 hectolitres in 1993.

Figure 9.18: UK Spirits Sales - ('000 hectolitres @ 40% ABV) 1986-93

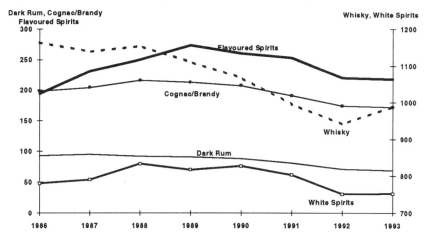

Source : HM Customs & Excise
Note :   White Spirits = Gin, Geneva, Vodka, Tequila and White Rum. Flavoured Spirits = Liqueurs, Anis, Ouzo, Calvados, Fruit Brandy, Cocktails and Aperitifs

Figure 9.19 shows that real consumption on spirits rose from a low in 1982 to a peak in 1988. Since 1988 though, the trend has been downwards with real expenditure down over 16% by 1993.

Figure 9.19: Consumer Expenditure on Spirits (£m)

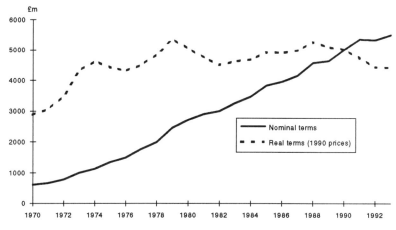

* 1990 prices
Source : CSO, Euro PA

Nominal expenditure has increased every year, with the exception of 1992, rising over 100% between 1980 and 1993. With real expenditure down 12% in the same period, this only serves to highlight the increase in prices that must have occurred.

Wine

The trends in consumer expenditure for wine are shown in Figure 9.20. Both real and nominal expenditure increased in the thirteen year period illustrated. Real expenditure growth of 62% over the period equates to almost 4% growth per annum. This is in contrast to beer and spirits which have seen declines in real expenditure.

Figure 9.20: Consumer Expenditure on Wine (£m) 1990 prices

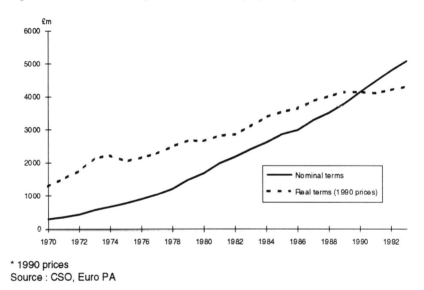

* 1990 prices
Source : CSO, Euro PA

Sales of wine can be split into two types - those of fresh grapes and those that are man-made. Figure 9.21 shows the UK sales of wines of fresh grapes. Still light wines dominate sales reaching 5.7 million hectolitres (570 million litres). This is 80% of the total fresh grape wine sales. Between 1990 and 1993 sales of still white wine increased by 16%, while all other categories saw falls, especially sparkling wines (31%).

Figure 9.21: UK Sales of Wines of Fresh Grapes ('000 hectolitres)

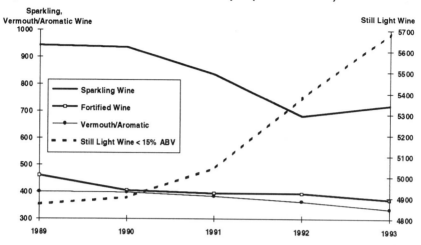

Note : Sparkling wine = Champagne etc. ; Fortified wines = Sherry, Port, Madeira etc.
Source : HM Customs & Excise

UK sales of made wine can be split in to two sectors, still white wines and reduced alcohol. Still white wine sales are very stable at 500,000 hectolitres. Reduced alcohol wine, on the other hand, is growing rapidly rising from 74,000 hectolitres in 1989 to 461,000 hectolitres in 1993. This is a 520% increase in five years - 44% per annum.

Trade in Alcoholic Drinks

Figure 9.22 illustrates the UK balance of trade in alcoholic drinks from 1980 to 1992. The balance has always been positive. From 1980 to 1986 the balance was actually falling, but since 1987 the balance has risen considerably from under £400 million in 1987 to almost £1 billion in 1993.

Figure 9.22: UK Balance of Trade in Alcoholic Drinks - 1980-1993

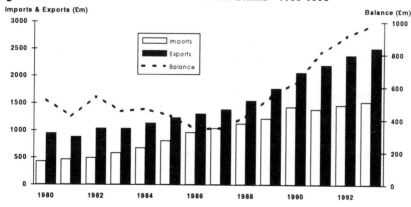

Source : CSO, HM Customs & Excise

However, this positive balance of trade in alcoholic drinks, masks various trends. Table 9.15 shows that in 1993 it was only the spirits sector that had a positive balance of trade, with over £2 billion surplus. Wine imports, primarily from France, Spain and Germany accounted for over £800 million and reduced the overall alcohol trade balance to around £1 billion.

Table 9.15: UK Balance of Trade in Alcoholic Drinks - 1993 by Category

	Imports (£m)		Exports (£m)		Balance (£m)
	Intra-EU	Extra-EU	Intra-EU	Extra-EU	
Beer	230	23	47	76	-130
Spirits	158	68	840	1505	2119
Wines	833	184	11	25	-981
Cider/Perry	32	4	10	6	-20
Total	1253	279	908	1612	988

Source : CSO Business Monitors MM20 & MQ20

Beer import sources are shown in Figure 9.23. Eire is the primary source accounting for 43% of the total, with Germany accounting for 26%. Total imports rose from 1989 to 1992 but showed a fall in 1993 that left them close to 1989 levels.

Figure 9.23: Beer Imports 1989-93

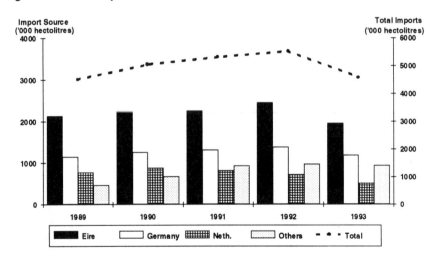

Source Trade Statistics

Beer exports, as shown in Figure 9.24 are increasing steadily reaching 2 million hectolitres in 1993. The USA is the main destination, along with Eire, though Russia is becoming a large export market.

Figure 9.24: Beer Exports 1989-93

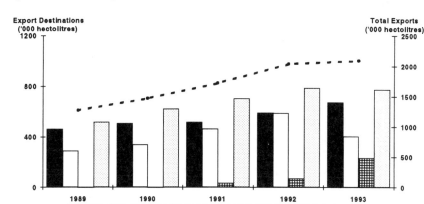

Source : Trade Statistics

In 1993 there was 2.1 million hectolitres of beer exported, imports were almost 4.6 million hectolitres, leaving a deficit of 2.5 million hectolitres valued at £130 million. UK imports of wine follow the trends in Figure 9.21 which shows the consumption of wine. This is because domestic production is mainly made wines (from imported grape must) not of fresh grapes. Most still white wine and sparkling wines imports are from France, while Italy supplies most of the vermouth/aromatic wines and Spain the fortified wine (in particular, sherry). Both imports and exports have increased since the mid-1980s, though imports have risen most, leaving a 55,000 hectolitre deficit in 1993 worth £20 million.

Figure 9.25: Trade in Cider/Perry 1986-1993

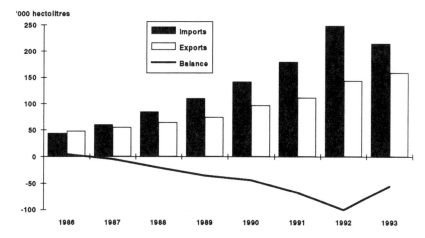

Source :Foreign Trade Statistics

In 1993 45% of cider/perry imports were from Belgium/Luxembourg.
Eire was a source of 27% of imports who incidentally received 55% of our
exports. Netherlands and Germany accounted for almost all the rest of
imports.

Spirits[10]

Trade in spirit is particularly important as over 70% of domestic spirit
production is exported. This is the highest level of exports for any of the
major sectors in the UK food and drink industry.

A breakdown of spirit imports from 1986 to 1993 is shown in Figure 9.26.
Rum used to be the largest import, in terms of volume, but the level has
been falling since 1990. Cognac/Brandy imports are the now the highest.
but these imports have varied considerably since 1986. In 1992 imports
were only 108,000 hectolitres. In 1993 the level was 271,000 hectolitres,
an increase of 150%.

Figure 9.26: UK Spirit Imports 1986-93 @ 40% Alcohol by volume (ABV)

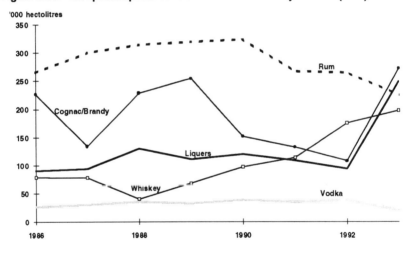

Source : Trade Statistics

Imports of liqueurs has been rising though it two has shown a large
increase between 1992 and 1993 of 160% to 249,000 hectolitres in 1993.
Vodka imports have been relatively stable by comparison reaching a high
of 39,000 hectolitres in 1992 (same in 1990). However, in 1993 imports
were under 21,000 hectolitres - a fall of almost 50%. Since 1988 whisk(e)y
imports have been on an constant upward trend rising almost 400% by

---

10   All figures @ 40% ABV

1993. UK exports of spirits are difficult to illustrate, as Figure 9.27 shows. This is due to whisky exports being ten times higher than gin exports which in turn are five times higher than the remaining categories. Whisky exports are usually around 5.9 million hectolitres. Exports since 1986 have varied from a high of just of 6 hectolitres to under 5.8 million hectolitres. There also seems to be no definite trend. Gin exports are also steady over the period 1986-93 at around 600,000 hectolitres, but since a 1988 peak of 619,000 hectolitres exports have fallen to 567,000 hectolitres in 1993. In 1994, preliminary figures indicate exports to be 668,000 hectolitres, up 17.8% on 1993 at the highest level since 1988.

All the other spirit exports, though small in comparison to whisky and gin, have been increasing consistently. Liqueurs rose from 79,000 hectolitres in 1986 to 135,000 hectolitres in 1993.

The increase in vodka and rum exports took place between 1992 and 1993. Beforehand vodka exports were around 30-40,000 hectolitres and rum 50-60,000 hectolitres. By 1993 vodka exports were 118,000 hectolitres (200+% up on 1992) and rum was 131,000 hectolitres (140% up). Preliminary figures for 1994 show that vodka exports have reached in the region of 180,000 hectolitres a rise of 52.5% over 1993. Clearly vodka sales are a major growth area.

Figure 9.27: UK Spirit Exports 1986-93 (@ 40% ABV)

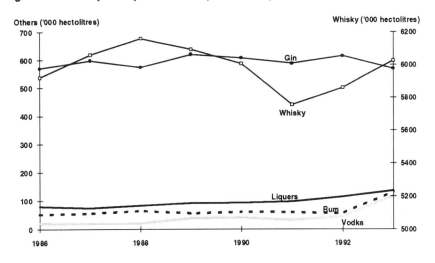

Source : Trade Statistics

Figures 9.28 shows how trade balances for spirits (by volume) have changed since 1986. Note the whisk(e)y balance has been divided by

1000 to enable it to fit on the same scale as the rest. From Figure 9.28 is seems that the balance for whisk(e)y and gin are relatively constant. The cognac/brandy balance (almost identical to imports as there are hardly any exports) is consistently negative as is the rum balance. In rum's case fall in the balance in 1993 seems to be part of a trend as imports have fallen since 1990 and exports have increased (albeit only in 1993). Vodka now have a positive balance where as in 1986 it was almost zero. Liqueurs seem to have gone the other way with a growing negative balance.

Figure 9.28: Balance of Spirit Trade 1986-1993 by volume @40% ABV

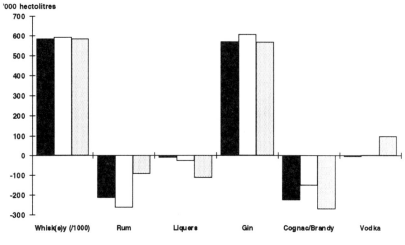

Source : Trade Statistics

Production of Alcoholic Drinks

Unlike many of the further-processed goods considered in this chapter, the production of alcoholic drinks differs greatly from UK consumption. This is explained by the high levels of exports in the spirits sector and imports in the wine and beer sectors.

Beer

Figure 9.29 illustrates the decline in both production and consumption in the 1980's and early 1990's. Production has fallen from just under 65 million hectolitres in 1980 to 57 million hectolitres in 1993.   This represents a 12% decline or approximately 1% per annum. Consumption has also fallen by a similar amount over the same period. However, between 1986 and 1990 in a period of relative prosperity, consumption did manage to rise whereas production levels remain stable. Net imports increased from 1980 through to 1990 where it reached a peak of 3.6

million hectolitres. By 1993 the balance had fallen to 2.5 million hectolitres, costing £130 million.

Figure 9.29: Beer Production and Consumption

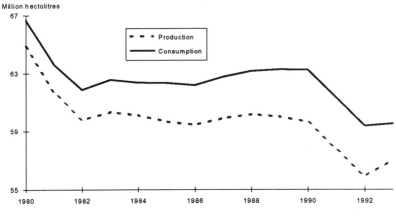

Source : HM Customs and Excise

Spirits[11]

UK spirits production is dominated by whisky. In 1993 Scotch whisky accounted for over 3.52 million hectolitres of pure alcohol (HLPA)[12], or around 90% of the total spirit production of 3.86 HLPA. Figure 9.30 shows the trend in the production of whisky from 1980 to 1993. It also shows that the dominant share that whisky has in the spirit market has been present throughout the 1980-1993 period.

Figure 9.30: Scotch Whisky Production (HLPA) 1980-1993

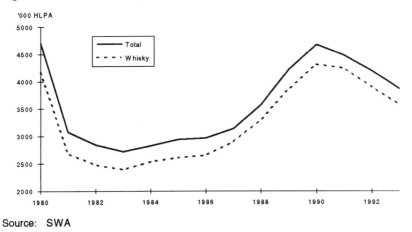

Source: SWA

---

[11] All figures in pure alcohol
[12] 1 litres of HLPA = 2.5 litres of alcohol @ 40% ABV.

In 1993, 60% of whisky production was grain whisky, the other 40% being malt whisky. This proportion has remained relatively stable over the 1980-1993 period. Figure 9.31 shows the trend since 1980 of the production of gin and vodka. Whisky production, and for that matter consumption, has tended to move with the level of economic prosperity, falling in the early 1980's and 1990's during times of recession and rising in the mid-1980's in a period of relative economic growth. Gin and Vodka production, although at lower levels than whisky output, has not followed this trend. Gin has declined from 1980 when it stood at over 425,000 HLPA. Since 1984 production has fluctuated from over 375,000 HLPA (1992) to below 320 HLPA (1991). The change between 1991 and 1992 was around 17%. Vodka production, on the other hand, has increased greatly, especially since 1991. The growth from 1982 to 1993 has been 46% or 3.5% per annum.. This has coincided with increased exports, primarily to EU countries.

Figure 9.31: Gin and Vodka Production 1980-1993 (HLPA)

Source : Gin and Vodka Association

Wine

Wine production in the UK can be split into two types; wine made from grapes grown in the UK and wine produced in the UK from imported grape must. The latter type can be referred to as made wine. In the trade, made wine is referred to as British wine while wine from UK grown grapes are labelled English. In 1992 MAFF estimated that 26,400 hectolitres of wine was made from UK grapes, though production has been as low as 4,100 hectolitres (1988).

Made wine accounts for a greater proportion of the wine produced in the UK. Estimates for 1992 are in the order of 850,000 hectolitres. Though it may be difficult to discern the exact level there has been a clear increase in production of 'British' wine. In 1984, the level of production was just under 500,000 hectolitres. This means a 70% increase in output between 1984 and 1992. Unlike 'English' wines these wines do not suffer from the vagaries of British climate. Must is imported mainly from the EU.

In 1992 UK consumption of wine was 7.7 million hectolitres so total UK production accounted for around 11%.

Industry Structure and Company Performance

The alcoholic drinks industry is usually split into three different sectors: brewing, spirits and wines. Of these three groups brewing is the least concentrated. Figure 9.32 shows that the gross value output of the top five firms was around 50% in 1991, which is down from a high of 60% in 1981. Gross value-added has fallen by even more from 60% in 1981 to around 45% in 1991.

Figure 9.32: 5 Firm Concentration Ratios - Brewing

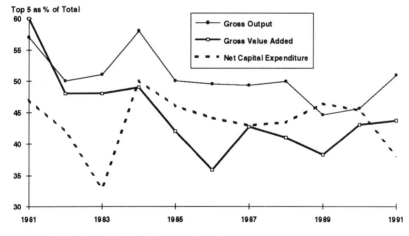

Source : CSO Business Monitor PA1002, selected years

Figure 9.33 displays the concentration ratios for the spirits sector. This sector has also declining shares for the top five companies. Of interest is the fact that gross value-added ratio is higher than the gross output ratio.

Figure 9.33: 5 Firm Concentration Ratios - Spirits

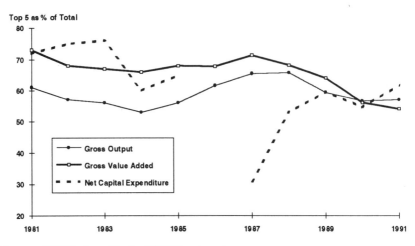

Source : CSO Business Monitor PA1002, selected years

The UK's five firm concentration ratios for wine production are extremely high. Little wine is produced domestically (relative to total consumption) and there is one large producer (Denby) that has 20-25% of English (grape) wine output. In 1991 the gross output and the gross value-added stood at around 95%.

Figure 9.21 : 5 Firm Concentration Ratios - Wine

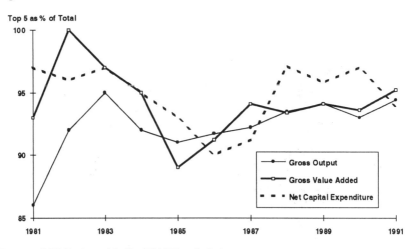

Source : CSO Business Monitor PA1002, selected years

Table 9.16 lists only 6 companies, two of them subsidiaries of Allied Domecq.

Table 9.16: Summary of Average UK Drinks Company Results
3 year average - years shown)

Company	Turnover £m	Profit £m	Profit/ Sales(%)	ROCE (%)	Current Ratio	Debt Ratio	Years
Grand Metropolitan plc	8,260.33	663.67	8.14	9.30	1.45	0.61	91/92-92/93
Bass	4,403.00	511.00	11.60	10.23	1.35	0.43	90/91-93/94
Guinness	4,364.33	799.00	18.31	14.25	1.49	0.53	91/92-92/93
Whitbread	2,299.00	176.67	7.63	6.72	0.76	0.31	91/92-93/94
Scottish & Newcastle	1,587.00	204.67	12.90	11.40	0.66	0.44	91/92-93/94
The Hiram Walker Group (Allied Domecq)	840.67	78.33	9.36	9.19	1.00	0.56	91/92-92/93
Carlsberg-Tetley (Allied Domecq)	205.25	47.69	25.80	14.04	1.17	0.56	89/90-91/92
Average weighted by turnover		**547.63**	**11.34**	**10.39**	**1.29**	**0.51**	
Straight average		**354.43**	**13.03**	**10.73**	**1.13**	**0.49**	
Total Turnover	**21,960**						

Source : Kompass, Euro PA
Note : The figures should be read in conjunction with the notes contained in the Appendix to
Chapter One
International Distillers and Vintners (IDV) is Grand Metropolitan's drinks subsidiary.
In 1993 IDV accounted for 42% of group turnover.
Greenalls Group excluded as primarily pub retailing rather than manufacturing

- The turnover of each of the companies in Table 9.16 is extremely large, with the top 3 in the list having turnovers in excess of £4 billion each.

- The profit margin for this sector is also higher than for any other sector, with a straight (arithmetic) average of over 13%.

- This average figure is possibly reduced by the fact only £3.5 million of Grand Metropolitan's turnover is in drinks. The remainder is in food, which generally has a lower profit margin.

- Returns on capital are low, probably due to the enormous amount of capital investment required.

- The debt ratios of all the companies are low in comparison with other food sectors.

Scottish and Newcastle agreed to buy another brewer[13], Courage, from the Australian group, Fosters, for £425 million in May 1995. This deal which gives S&N the Courage, John Smiths, Websters, Beamish and Hofmeister brands, among others, will make S&N the market leader in beer with 25%. The traditional leader is Bass with around 23%.

Concluding Comments

The further-processed and branded goods sector of the UK food industry contains, perhaps, what the lay reader would expect to see in a modern food industry - many examples of food products, branded and own-label, that are produced from a combination of raw materials and intermediate products. For the analyst though, the diversity and dynamics of the further-processed and branded goods sector is frustrating. Data sources are either non-existent, difficult to define, or impossible to verify from trade or public sources. The definition problem is compounded by the growth in the range of types of products, and new product introductions over time. The drinks sector is more stable and definitions and product types are easier to follow through the years, but the economic issues thrown up by the prevalence of major food and drinks brands are not dealt with in this chapter.

A key impression taken from this review of the further-processed sector is that there are many examples of dynamic, innovative companies in the UK food industry that are able to identify new market opportunities, adopt technical innovations and successfully market new food products. Indeed, the trade literature, and some empirical evidence, suggests that it is often smaller companies that advance the application of new technology or spot new market opportunities. Equally, however, there is the impression that successful small companies do not easily attain large company status i.e. small and medium sized companies with product and brand portfolios that are growing, or fit into another (larger) company's product portfolio, are acquired. Some of the largest food companies or conglomerates have attained this status by a process of merger and acquisition over the years. In a European and global context the building up of branded product markets has put several UK food and drink companies into the premier league. Their size and scale of operation in sourcing, production and marketing is very significant in absolute and relative terms. The alcoholics drink companies are a special case but the relative decline of UK spirits consumption has emphasised the competitive nature of the domestic market for them and the need to

---

[13] At the present time it is not known whether the bid will be referred to the Monopolies and Mergers Commission.

expand export markets. Of course, many UK spirits companies have a diversified portfolio of alcoholics drinks as part of their strategy. However, their dependence on brands when the own-label and "look-a-like" aspects of the food and drink market are obviously going to be a source of continuing competitive action in the 1990's makes them vulnerable and may force further restructuring. This last point provides the final comment here. Own-label production and retailer relationships are very important for many food processors in the further-processed goods sector. There are several examples in this chapter of very large own-label market shares in rapidly growing product areas. Strategically, this suggests that the further-processed goods sector will be of major interest to commercial operators and analysts in the food and drink industry in the years ahead.

References

Birds Eye Walls (1994). *Frozen Food Fact File*, Walton-on-Thames, KT12 1NT

CSO (selected years), *Business Monitor PA1002 Summary Volume*, HMSO, London.

CSO (1995). *Annual Abstract of Statistics*, HMSO, London.

EuroFood & Drink, (August 1994). Feature on International Cuisine Prepared for Ready Meals Growth, p 17, Dame Publishing Ltd, London.

European Commission (1994). *Official Journal L136 31 May 1994*, p5, Brussels.

Farleys (1994). *Market Report 1994*, Mint Bridge Road, Kendal, LA9 6NL.

Financial Times (1994 & 1995). *FT-500*, Number One, Southwark Bridge, London, SE1 9HL

Mars (1994). *Confectionery 1993*, Dundee Road, Slough, SL1 4JX

Master Foods (1995). *Wet Cooking Sauces - Market Report 1995*, Hansa Road, King's Lynn, Norfolk, PE30 4JE.

Nestlé (1994 & 1995). *The Hot Beverages Report*, Park Lane, Croyden, CR9 1NR.

The Brewers' Society (1993). *Statistical Handbook*, Brewing Publications Ltd, London.

Trebor Bassett (1995). *Sweet Fortune - 1995 Review of the Sweet Market*, Hertford Place, Denham Way, Maple Cross, Hertfordshire, WD3 2XB.

Zenith International (1995). *The 1995 Sucralose Soft Drinks Report - UK Market Review*, Splash of Paint Ltd, London.

Chapter 10: The Future of the Food and Drink Industry

Wyn Morgan and John Strak[1]

Introduction

The preceding chapters of this book have only occasionally made comment about the future. Most of what has been presented has been concerned with data that is recent but still historical. In all this detail it is possible for the reader and analyst to lose sight of the strategic pressures on the food industry which will drive it forward in the next decade. So, at the end of the foregoing nine chapters covering the overview and sectoral analysis of the UK food and drink industry it is appropriate to consider; what the future may hold, what questions are answered in this book or left unanswered and what research and analysis should be suggested next. These ideas and suggestions for future research are presented in this final chapter using references from the previous chapters to support the case for further work.

Significantly, the way in which consumers and industries change over time and the future shape and structure of industrial sectors has been the subject of much analysis in the 1990's. Strategic analysis of this type is prevalent, perhaps, because the technological opportunities now available to industrialists can so radically affect the investment and labour/capital ratio in manufacturing. Increased unemployment and increased leisure time for enforced- and voluntarily-retired workers also drives the research interest in strategic aspects of consumer/company behaviour. Speculation about changes in the international trade environment and the comparative advantage of newly industrialised countries has also encouraged this analysis of the future. General references abound[2] although for the food industry specifically there are fewer references. The EC's FAST II programme included a research project to consider the European food industry. The studies that formed this research were published in Traill (1989) and some of the conclusions

1   Dr Wyn Morgan is a lecturer in Economics in the Department of Economics at Nottingham University; Dr John Strak is Principal at Euro PA & Associates, Cambs.

2   See Wood (1995) for an extensive review of publications dealing with changing comparative advantage in world economies, also Wood (1995) for specific calculations on the impact of large newly industrialised countries. Also Chapter 10 in "State of the World 1993", Earthscan, 1993.

there are relevant to the UK food and drink industry. The following pages will present a modest attempt to summarise the important elements of the future environment for the UK food and drink industry using five "dimensions of change" and the conceptual framework of a "food industry web".

The Dimensions of Change

There are several possible dimensions to a discussion of the future environment for the food industry. Five dimensions are identified and discussed here:

1. The consumer dimension, e.g. in what ways have consumers changed and how will they change in the future and so affect the demand for food and drink products?

2. The product or technological dimension, e.g. what new products/purchasing options or packaging opportunities will there be for the food industry in the future?

3. A market position dimension, e.g. how will market power and structural changes in the different parts of the agriculture/food processing and distribution/retailer chain affect the food industry nationally, regionally and globally?

4. The geographical dimension, e.g. what changes will we see in the food and drink industry's raw material supplies, and its consumer demand in food markets in the Pacific Rim and Far East, South America, Africa, Western and Eastern Europe, and Australia. What will a global food industry look like?

5. An institutional dimension, e.g. what will be the effect on the food industry of current and forecast changes in national and international policies on farming, food, the environment, competition policy and health and nutrition?

Each of these dimensions is discussed in more detail in the remainder of this chapter. Firstly, these dimensions are brought together in a conceptualisation of the "food industry web".

The Food Industry Web

The term "food chain" with which this book began, and which is often used to describe the food industry's activities from farmer through processor and distributor to retailer, may need significant modification if it is to be useful in the future. Now and in the future, food industry activities may perhaps be better understood as a "web" not a chain. This concept of a "food industry web" has connections and linkages stretching across international boundaries and backwards and forwards between the different dimensions of the whole system.

The five dimensions of change noted above are captured in this web and the concept is illustrated in Figure 10.1 below.

Figure 10.1: The Food Industry Web

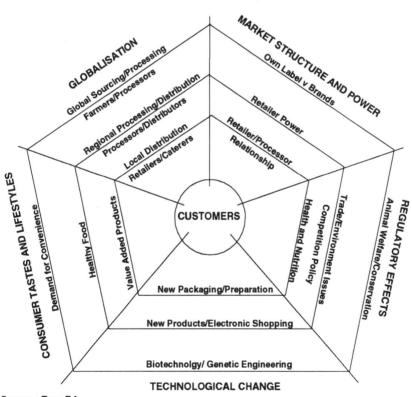

Source : Euro PA

The First Dimension

Already we have seen changes in the way in which consumers live and work which directly affect the UK food and drink industry.

Figures 1.3 and 1.4 in Chapter One illustrated two key trends in the UK, the numbers of working women and numbers of meals taken outside the home. The impact of these trends is reinforced by the increasing leisure time available to the population, voluntarily or through redundancy, and by the increasing proportion of elderly people who still have real purchasing power. All these are important drivers of the demand for the attributes of increased preparation and "convenience" in foods. Consumers have also become more concerned about health and nutrition and the recognition of "healthy" foods and health issues is another important influence on the food industry. This last aspect of demand is underlined by Dodd *et al* (1994) in their consideration of the impact of media coverage on health issues; also Darrall (1992) and Wheelocke (1992). See also Euro Analysis (1992) for a review of health and nutrition policies. The UK food industry has reacted positively to these changes and there is hardly a part of the supermarket or catering industry that has not seen new and increasing amounts of food products that try to satisfy these new demands in the last decade.

Changing consumer tastes have allowed and encouraged producers of branded and own-label products to increase the range of goods (product proliferation and segmentation). This has two key facets. First, as suggested by Lancaster (1966) processors are responding to consumers' demand for differing product characteristics. Consumers are not homogeneous in their wants and the ability of processors to alter the "bundle" of characteristics in their products improves consumers' welfare. Hence, for example, the market for baked beans now includes varieties that are; traditional, low-sugar, flavoured, childrens, etc. and this caters for different tastes in the marketplace. As Chapter Two noted, product proliferation can also be used to protect a food manufacturer's position by acting as a barrier to entry. New technology and food product development can aid the process of satisfying consumer demands or constructing barriers to entry. A guide to this area is given in Martin (1994). Thus these points show how the dimensions of the food web are linked - consumer demand with market power with technological change.

Changes in consumer lifestyle and demand will not be reversed in the future. Whatever the problems that unemployment and increased job uncertainty bring, it is difficult to believe that the modern generation will go back to the preparation times and practices for food that a previous generation accepted without question. Indeed, it is not clear that the latent knowledge is there in many western developed economies to allow people to revert to historical behaviour patterns in meal preparation. People now depend on the food industry to provide them with a meal (outside <u>and</u> inside the home) rather than just the raw materials for cooking a meal.

The important conclusion that comes from these observations about consumer demand and lifestyles is that market research and developments in economic theory will have to keep up with the changes that drive consumer demand.   Relevant commercial and academic research will need to be able to incorporate the relative sophistication of modern consumers and, effectively, be able to mirror the food industry's efforts in meeting those demands in the marketplace for its products. It is interesting that the most comprehensive market data and information on consumers' purchasing behaviour now resides with food retailers. But this is the area that is least well represented in the published literature. Retailers' access to data generated by electronic scanning and bar coding systems provides an opportunity for modelling and predicting consumer change and the food industry's derived demand that has not been seen before. This electronic data must raise specific questions about the relevance and cost of traditional food surveys such as the NFS and conventional market research analysis and general questions about business information in the food chain, see EuroAnalysis (1992).

The Second Dimension

The second area for future development in the food industry is that concerned with technological change.

New technology affects the food industry in many ways[3]. For example;

- via new ways of producing raw material, e.g. genetics and "designer genotypes"

- through new products that combine ingredients in new or novel ways

- through new preparation or packaging techniques, e.g. the microwave or tetrapaks

- through allowing consumers a chance to express their purchasing behaviour more fully, e.g. through supermarket shopping or "electronic" shopping from home[4].

---

3   Traill (1988) and Goldberg (1991)

In summary, all of these points are allowing processors, distributors and retailers the chance to satisfy consumer demands for novelty, freshness, timeliness, and convenience, etc. The future food industry will continue to change to the extent that new technology continues to enable and facilitate this service process. A simple example of this is shown in Figure 10.2 which illustrates the growth in ownership of microwaves in UK households - from 18% in 1985 to 64% in 1993. The availability of this technology in the home opened up the possibility of a new range of preparation and packaging issues for the food industry with consequent effects on chilled distribution services, chilled shelf space in retailers, and competitor products in the canning and dehydrated areas.

Figure 10.2 : The Proportion of UK Households with Microwaves

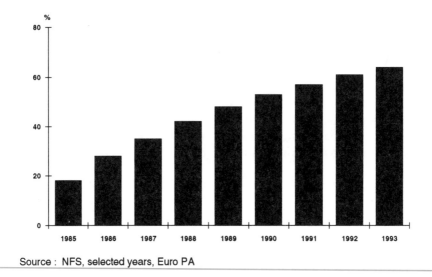

Source : NFS, selected years, Euro PA

A future example of consumer-driven technological change may be the growth in the use of the Internet by the population. The growth rates and rapid assimilation of electronic media symbolised by Internet usage are phenomenal. In June 1994, the number of internet users was estimated at 20 million. By the beginning of 1995 a survey reported that the number of users world-wide was around 50 million. Current estimates are that the number of users is growing by c. 14% per month. This is equivalent to an annual growth rate of c. 350%. An additional feature of the modern home will be the personal computer, modem and

---

4   The question arises whether this aspect of technology change should be dealt with here, on the costs side, or in the previous consumer dimension, on the demand side. "Technically proficient" consumers could be seen as an important potential segment of the food industry's customer base.....in the way that direct banking and insurance services have developed in the UK.

fibre optic cable. There are currently an estimated 1 million PCs in UK households - about 5% of all households. Figure 10.3 illustrates the age distribution of the users of the Internet.

Figure 10.3: The Age Profile of Internet Users

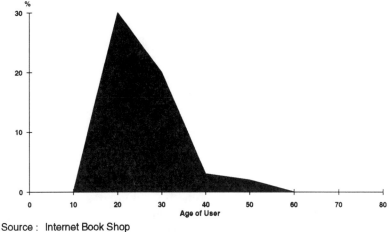

Source : Internet Book Shop
Note : Survey used age bands of five years i.e. 15-20 years, 20 to 25 years etc.

The Internet population is concentrated in an age band of 10 to 40 years, with most users being in their 20's. Through the Internet, or "virtual reality" shopping, will a new generation of consumers want to make their food purchases electronically? The establishment of fibre optic cables (the information superhighway) will allow low cost high definition video pictures to arrive in the home. This would allow consumers and retailers (distributors) to access those computer literate individuals who want to make their food purchases electronically. In the same way that electronic banking and direct line insurance services have grown, there may be a lesson for the food industry. In the United States, researchers in California[5] have developed the "virtual mall" where the consumer sits at home and "goes shopping" via his or her PC and modem. This may have a fundamental impact upon the presentation/packaging of food - for example, would product packaging in the "virtual mall" have to be carried through to home delivery? Would this type of shopping re-establish the processor/wholesaler as a major source of contact with the consumer rather than the final retail store? Wholesalers could develop this concept for their business customers e.g. the UK's cash and carry sector, or retailers/mail order outlets may wish to develop it as an additional service for existing customers.

---

5   Report on ABC TV News, USA, April 1995.

Thus, it is not simply that consumers are more aware of technology, it may be the case that technology shapes their patterns of consumption and has a direct impact on the food and drink industry's packaging and distribution decisions. Whilst not all will choose to shop this way (indeed it will be a minority for many years) such a creeping change in habits and technical proficiency will need a response from retailers and processors. Interesting questions are; will an established UK retailer or wholesaler create a virtual shopping mall leaving the collection and distribution of the physical product to another (computer driven) distribution functionary, or will this "virtual shopping" concept be one that is first taken up by a new entrant to the market?

The Third Dimension

The third area of discussion for the future environment of the food and drink industry is one that is very much with us today: the growth in the market power of the retailers which is symbolised by the rise and rise of own-label (sometimes referred to as private label). Figure 10.4 summaries the growth of own-label products in the UK. Almost every chapter in the book has made reference to this phenomenon. The UK food industry has been a pioneer in this area and, of course, the practice has been supported and encouraged by the multiple retailers in the UK.

Whilst the formal analysis is not clear, or does not exist, the rise of own-label brands is likely to have been a significant factor in strengthening the hand of the retailers in the late 1980's and early 1990's. This has two important consequences. First, the role of advertising and marketing has and will become increasingly important for the retailer as opposed to the "own-label" processor. It may also encourage larger marketing and advertising expenditures from existing major brands as a countervailing effect. This has implications for costs and prices for the consumer. Second, whilst it reduces the "power" of the big brands it does provide opportunities for other (small?) manufacturers in the sector. This, the retailers claim, is pro-competitive and it appears to be so. The Cott cola[6] example is the obvious one to quote, but there are many other situations where food processors access national markets which might otherwise be denied to them because of the market power of brands. But retailers will also have significant market power over manufacturers and suppliers and it remains an open question as to what the balance of power will be and how it will be operated. This raises competition policy issues and, as demonstrated by the recent debate on "look-a-likes" in the UK, issues on

---

6   See Harvard Business School 1993 and 1994.

the ownership of intellectual property in product packaging and labelling. These questions were noted in Chapter Two but are far from resolved.

One consequence of the growth in own-label is the emphasis it puts on supplier/retailer relationships in the food industry. In the UK an important aspect of the food manufacturing/food retailer relationship in the UK is the quality and production assurance conditions that food manufacturers have had to meet to satisfy retailers' demands. In certain cases, these extend right down to the farm level through the operation of the "due diligence" provisions of the UK Food Safety Act (1990).

These conditions produce a very disciplined relationship which has its own problems and opportunities. One opportunity is to develop the relationship in such a way that investment in new processing and distribution facilities by food processors is better rewarded. It is important to see that own-label is not just a threat to the food industry it is also an opportunity. Again, the example of the Cott Corporation and its assault on the Coca-Cola and Pepsi-Cola brands shows that new relationships and retail alliances are possible between retailers and food companies that can provide opportunities for food companies. Strategic alliances and partnerships are another example of the same type of phenomenon. Across sectors and regions companies may try to co-operate and combine in the future rather than accept aggressive marketing or acquisition strategies as the only ways to expand[7].

Figure 10.4 : The Growth of Own-label Share of UK Trade for all Products 1977-94

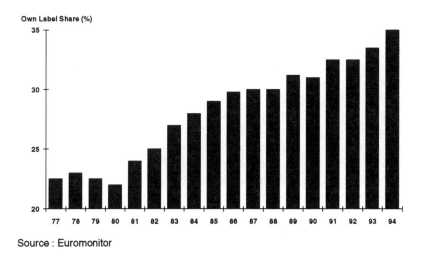

Own Label Share (%)

Source : Euromonitor

---

7   See Hughes (1994) and Chapter 10 in Porter (1986)

The Fourth Dimension

The fourth dimension is exemplified by the term "globalisation". The food industry is able to take advantage of new or existing raw material supplies in different parts of the world and also transport and sell the final food product to global consumers in a way that only 10 or 15 years ago would have seemed like science fiction. On the supply side, changes in trade regulations and the development of new sources of production allows the food industry to consider the location and size of its processing operations in a new light. The continuing reference to the Uruguay Round Agreement on agriculture throughout this book is relevant to this point and provides another link between the dimensions of the food web. On the demand side, consumers in Berlin, Beijing, London and New York are increasingly seen by the food industry as being uniformly accessible **and** having a similar set of tastes and demands. Partly this is due to the way the media and advertising have extended their influence internationally, partly it is due to the growth of mass tourism whereby new tastes and experiences discovered abroad are pursued on return, and partly it is due to the transfer of cultures and systems that is a spin off from international manufacturing investment.

The future environment for industry, therefore, is an international one[8]. That means the UK food and drink industry will increasingly have to deal with different cultures and the logistics of world-wide sourcing and distribution of the final product. The global markets in shipping/air transport also become important to the opportunities that can be realised. And the local markets for distribution of product at wholesale and retail level are also critical. For processors/retailers to prosper in final markets outside the UK these local distribution services must be predictable and/or competitive. Because distribution markets and final consumers do not change quite as fast as the economic theorists, advertisers and marketeers may wish, the UK food and drink industry will have to be ready to deal with the discontinuities and difficulties of bringing people and products together from different backgrounds and histories. Food and drink products are a fundamental element in consumers' purchasing patterns so the food industry cannot wait for another sector to deal with these potential problems. All this suggests a major and active role for the UK food and drink industry if it wishes to build and develop a presence in world markets. It also suggests another link in the food web - between global activities in sourcing and final markets and the market power/competition policy aspects of large companies controlling processing, distribution and retailing.

---

8   See Ohmae (1994)

The Fifth Dimension

The last area of consideration for the future environment of the food industry is one that which deals with institutional change. External change of this type is often exemplified by reference to "regulatory effects". Governments interfere with the food and drink industry. This is a fact of modern economic life. In the future, the likelihood is that Governments, and multilateral organisations, will interfere with the industry's interests even more[9].

The trade liberalisation seen in the Uruguay Round of the GATT should bring about an improved situation for the food industry in aggregate. However, the precise effects resulting from the implementation of the GATT are not yet clear. It could well be that specific parts of the food industry, in the EU for example, could face difficult decisions about their sourcing and investment in the medium term. The GATT may yet make many existing players in the European food industry reconsider their location and distribution strategies. Meanwhile, the UK food industry has to deal with the inefficiencies and distortions that arise from the regimes of the CAP on a day-to-day basis.

Further institutional pressures on the future of the food industry will come from;

- new trade, investment and economic policies in the CEECs e.g. the Europe Association agreements and the application to join the EU by various CEECs

- environmental policies being discussed in international bodies e.g. the Committee on International Trade and the Environment in the WTO, and environmental policies being discussed and implemented in national and regional bodies e.g. by the Environmental Protection Agency in the US and through the various Directives and Regulations of the EU[10]

- the likely change to transport costs and transport functions arising from revised transport policies in the western world and, linked with the previous point, the effect of new recycling laws on plant location and packaging decisions.

- the possibility that FAO recommendations, Governments or private insurers will combine together to regulate or place incentives on improved health and nutrition e.g. through dietary guidelines or increased insurance costs.

---

9   See Manser *et al* (1994) and Sun *et al* (1995) and Vietor (1994).

10   Esty (1994)

- the recognition by national governments that competition policy has an increasing part to play in international trade. Hence, for example, the structure of the food industry will not be allowed to proceed unchecked to a position where a small number of large players control the market[11].

In the field of international trade the food industry might be affected by the fashion to reconsider the benefits of comparative advantage. The writings of Goldsmith (1994) and Lang *et al* (1993) do not suggest smooth passage for the next round of trade liberalisation in the WTO.

Summary

The future UK food and drink industry will contain;

- new products and services that reflect the changing pattern of consumption and consumer tastes, especially those that emphasise value-added in food products

- raw material and production and distribution facilities that allow food companies to operate on a global scale and that will reflect the myriad of regulatory changes

- producer/retailer relationships, and marketing budgets, that enable food companies to react to the growth in market power of food retailers and the competition from and new opportunities in the own-label product area

- information technology which offers food companies the chance to significantly improve their contact and understanding of customers and to gain cost efficiencies in distribution.

This last simplified summary of what will be does of course, require a caveat. None of these elements will be obtained without a degree of uncertainty and risk, research and investment and regulatory interference. The importance of the '3Rs' "risk, research and regulation", may be an appropriate final comment for this book for an industry that wishes to remain up-to-date and relevant to the final consumer in the future.

---

11   See for example, various authors who have written for the Institute for International Economics on this subject.

References

Collins, N.R. and Preston, L.E.(1965). Price Cost Margins and Industry Structure. *Review of Economics and Statistics* 47 (2) pp 182-9.

Darrall, Jan (1992). The Response of the Food Chain to Healthy Eating. *British Food Journal* Vol 94 No 4. pp7-11.

Dodd, T.H. and Morse, S.(1994). The impact of media stories concerning health issues on food product sales: Management planning responses. *Journal of Consumer Marketing* 11(2) pp 17-24

Euro Analysis (1992) unpublished report R49, *Business Information in the Food Chain*, Euro PA & Associates, 11 Church St, Northborough, Cambs.

Esty Daniel C, (1994). *Greening the GATT - Trade, Environment and the Future*, Institute for International Economics, Washington, USA.

Goldberg, Ray A. (1991). *'The Role of New Technologies in Changing the Global Food System.'* Paper given at the Second Ceres Conference.

Goldsmith, J. (1993). *The Trap*. Macmillan, London

Harvard Business School (1994). *Cott Corporation: The European Entry*, Harvard Business School Publishing, Boston, Massachussetts, USA.

Harvard Business School (1993). *Cott Corporation: Private Label in the 1990s*, Harvard Business School Publishing, Boston, Massachussetts, USA

Hughes, D. (1994). *Breaking with Tradition: Building Partnerships and Alliances in the European Food Industry*. Wye College Press, Ashford, Kent.

Lancaster, K. (1966) A New Approach to Consumer Demand. *Journal of Political Economy*, Volume 74 (2).

Lang, T and Hines, C. (1993) *The New Protectionism: Protecting the future against free trade*. Earthscan, London.

Manser, W.A.P. (1994). *Control from Brussels*. E.I.U./Addison-Wesley

Martin, S. (1994). *Industrial Economics: Economic Analysis and Public Policy* 2nd Edition, Macmillan.

Ohmae, K. (1994). *The Borderless World*. Harper Collins London.

Porter, Michael E. (Ed) (1986). *Competition in Global Industries*. Harvard Business School Press, Boston.

Strickland, A.D. and Weiss, L.W. (1976). Advertising, Concentration and Price Cost Margins. *Journal of Political Economy*, 84(5) pp 1109-21

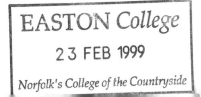

Sun, J.M. and Pelkmans, J. (1995). Regulating Competition in the Single Market. *Journal of Common Market Studies* 33(1) pp 67-87

Traill, B. (Ed) (1989). *Prospects for the European Food System.* A report from FAST programme of the Commission of the European Communities. Elsevier Applied Science.

Traill, B (1988). *"Technology and Food"* Occasional Paper 215, FAST, EC.

Vietor, R. (1994). *Contrived Competition: Regulation and Deregulation in America.* Belknap/Harvard University Press, Cambridge, Massachusetts, USA

Wheelock, V. (1992). Healthy Eating: The Food Issue of the 1990's. *British Food Journal* Vol 94 No 2. pp3-8

Index

Index of Companies